✳ **HAESE & HARRIS PUBLIC**

C000124566

EXAM PREPARATION & PRACTICE GUIDE

Mathematics
for the international student
Mathematics HL (Core)
Also suitable for HL & SL combined classes

Paul Urban

John Owen

David Martin

Robert Haese

Sandra Haese

Mark Bruce

International Baccalaureate
Diploma Programme

David Martin
Paul Urban
Robert Haese
Sandra Haese
Tom van Dulken

 Haese & Harris Publications

MATHEMATICS FOR THE INTERNATIONAL STUDENT
International Baccalaureate Mathematics HL (Core) Course
EXAM PREPARATION & PRACTICE GUIDE

David Martin   B.A., B.Sc., M.A., M.Ed.Admin.
Paul Urban   B.Sc.(Hons), B.Ec.
Robert Haese   B.Sc.
Sandra Haese   B.Sc.
Tom van Dulken   B.Sc.(Hons), Ph.D.

Haese & Harris Publications
3 Frank Collopy Court, Adelaide Airport, SA 5950, AUSTRALIA
Telephone: +61 8 8355 9444, Fax: + 61 8 8355 9471
Email: info@haeseandharris.com.au
Web: www.haeseandharris.com.au

National Library of Australia Card Number & ISBN 1 876543 93 0

© Haese & Harris Publications 2006

Published by Raksar Nominees Pty Ltd
3 Frank Collopy Court, Adelaide Airport, SA 5950, AUSTRALIA

First Edition   2006

Artwork by Piotr Poturaj and David Purton
Cover design by Piotr Poturaj
Computer software by David Purton

Typeset in Australia by Susan Haese (Raksar Nominees). Typeset in Times Roman 9/10

The Guide has been developed independently of the International Baccalaureate Organization (IBO). The Guide is in no way connected with, or endorsed by, the IBO.

This book is copyright. Except as permitted by the Copyright Act (any fair dealing for the purposes of private study, research, criticism or review), no part of this publication may be reproduced, stored in a retrieval system, or transmitted in any form or by any means, electronic, mechanical, photocopying, recording or otherwise, without the prior permission of the publisher. Enquiries to be made to Haese & Harris Publications.

Copying for educational purposes: Where copies of part or the whole of the book are made under Part VB of the Copyright Act, the law requires that the educational institution or the body that administers it, has given a remuneration notice to Copyright Agency Limited (CAL). For information, contact the Copyright Agency Limited.

Acknowledgements: While every attempt has been made to trace and acknowledge copyright, the authors and publishers apologise for any accidental infringement where copyright has proved untraceable. They would be pleased to come to a suitable agreement with the rightful owner.

The authors and publishers would like to thank all those teachers who have read the proofs of this book and offered advice and encouragement.

Special thanks to John Bush for his detailed advice and criticism in the early stages of planning the Exam Preparation & Practice Guides. Others who offered to read and comment on the proofs include: Irene Owen, Jane Kerr, Paula Waldman, Genny Green, Margie Karbassioun, Susan Cox, Andrew Spray, Mark Banner-Martin, Brendan Watson, Jeff Jones, Wallis Green, Andrzej Cichy, Peter Blythe, Robert Sloan, Mark Willis, Edward Kemp, Peter Joseph, Jim Napolitano, Sonja Bartholomew, Myrricia Holmann, Rema George, Peter Hamer-Hodges. To anyone we may have missed, we offer our apologies.

The publishers wish to make it clear that acknowledging these teachers does not imply any endorsement of this book by any of them, and all responsibility for the content rests with the authors and publishers.

FOREWORD

This Guide aims to support your preparation for the Mathematics HL final examinations. It should be used in conjunction with other material suggested by your teacher. Sample or past examination papers are invaluable aids.

- While using this Guide, ensure that you frequently refer to your information booklet. It is essential that you become familiar with the layout and content of the booklet.

This Guide covers all seven topics in the syllabus. Each Topic is preceded by a short section which highlights the important concepts. These are intended to complement your textbook and information booklet. When a formula can be found in the information booklet, it may not be repeated in this Guide. Following each introductory section is a set of "skill-builder questions" which can be used as a warm-up and should remind you of the fundamental skills required for the topic.

The best way to consolidate your mathematical understanding is by being active.

- This includes summarising the topics in an effective way and attempting questions.

This Guide provides fifteen sets of examination practice questions. Each covers most of the course topics and includes some shorter, Paper 1 type questions and some longer, Paper 2 type questions. Full solutions are provided but it is suggested that you work through a full set before checking the solutions.

Try to complete the sets under examination conditions. Getting into good habits will reduce pressure during the examination.

- It is important that you persevere with a question, but sometimes it is a good strategy to move on to other questions and return later to ones you have found challenging. Time management is very important during the examination and too much time spent on a difficult question may mean that you do not leave yourself sufficient time to complete other questions.

- Use a pen rather than a pencil, except for graphs and diagrams.

- If you make a mistake draw a single line through the work you want to replace. Do not cross out work until you have replaced it with something you consider better.

- Set out your work clearly with full explanations. Do not take shortcuts.

- Diagrams and graphs should be sufficiently large, well labelled and clearly drawn.

- Remember to leave answers correct to three significant figures unless an exact answer is more appropriate or a different level of accuracy is requested in the question.

Get used to reading the questions carefully.

- Check for key words. If the word "hence" appears, then you must use the result you have just obtained. "Hence, or otherwise" means that you can use any method you like, although it is likely that the best method uses the previous result.

- Rushing into a question may mean that you miss subtle points. Underlining key words may help.

- Often questions in the examination are set so that, even if you cannot get through one part, the question can still be picked up in a later part.

After completing a practice set, identify areas of weakness.

- Return to your notes or textbook and review the topic.

- Ask your teacher or a friend for help if further explanation is needed.

- Summarise each topic. Summaries that you make yourself are the most valuable.

- Test yourself, or work with someone else to help improve your knowledge of a topic.

- If you have had difficulty with a question, try it again later. Do not just assume that you know how to do it once you have read the solution. It is important that you work on weaker areas, but do not neglect the other areas.

In addition to the information booklet, your graphics display calculator is an essential aid.

- Make sure you are familiar with the model you will be using.

- In trigonometry questions remember to check whether the gdc should be in degrees or radians.

- Become familiar with common error messages and how to respond to them.

- Important features of graphs may be revealed by zooming in or out.

- Asymptotic behaviour is not always clear on a gdc screen; don't just rely on appearances. As with all aspects of the gdc, reflect on the reasonableness of the results.

- Are your batteries fresh?

We hope this guide will help you structure your revision program effectively. Remember that good examination techniques will come from good examination preparation.

We welcome your feedback:

web: http://haeseandharris.com.au

email: info@haeseandharris.com.au

TABLE OF CONTENTS

Number of practice questions

Topic 1	**ALGEBRA**	**5**	
	Important concepts	5	
	Skill builder questions	5	*15*
Topic 2	**FUNCTIONS AND EQUATIONS**	**6**	
	Important concepts	6	
	Skill builder questions	7	*15*
Topic 3	**CIRCULAR FUNCTIONS AND TRIGONOMETRY**	**8**	
	Important concepts	8	
	Skill builder questions	8	*15*
Topic 4	**MATRICES**	**9**	
	Important concepts	9	
	Skill builder questions	9	*15*
Topic 5	**VECTORS**	**10**	
	Important concepts	10	
	Skill builder questions	11	*15*
Topic 6	**STATISTICS AND PROBABILITY**	**12**	
	Important concepts	12	
	Skill builder questions	14	*16*
Topic 7	**CALCULUS**	**15**	
	Important concepts	15	
	Skill builder questions	15	*30*
EXAMINATION PRACTICE SETS		**16**	
	Examination practice set 1	16	26
	Examination practice set 2	17	26
	Examination practice set 3	19	26
	Examination practice set 4	20	26
	Examination practice set 5	21	26
	Examination practice set 6	22	26
	Examination practice set 7	23	*26*
	Examination practice set 8	24	*26*
	Examination practice set 9	25	*26*
	Examination practice set 10	26	*26*
	Examination practice set 11	27	*26*
	Examination practice set 12	28	*26*
	Examination practice set 13	29	*26*
	Examination practice set 14	30	*26*
	Examination practice set 15	31	*26*
	Total questions		*511*
SOLUTIONS TO SKILL BUILDER QUESTIONS		**33**	
	Solutions to Topic 1	33	
	Solutions to Topic 2	33	
	Solutions to Topic 3	35	
	Solutions to Topic 4	36	
	Solutions to Topic 5	37	
	Solutions to Topic 6	39	
	Solutions to Topic 7	40	
SOLUTIONS TO EXAM PRACTICE SETS		**43**	
	Solutions to exam practice set 1	43	
	Solutions to exam practice set 2	47	
	Solutions to exam practice set 3	51	
	Solutions to exam practice set 4	54	
	Solutions to exam practice set 5	58	
	Solutions to exam practice set 6	62	
	Solutions to exam practice set 7	66	
	Solutions to exam practice set 8	69	
	Solutions to exam practice set 9	73	
	Solutions to exam practice set 10	77	
	Solutions to exam practice set 11	81	
	Solutions to exam practice set 12	84	
	Solutions to exam practice set 13	87	
	Solutions to exam practice set 14	91	
	Solutions to exam practice set 15	94	

IMPORTANT CONCEPTS

ARITHMETIC AND GEOMETRIC SEQUENCES AND SERIES

To establish that a sequence is **arithmetic**, show that there is a common difference, i.e., there is a constant d such that $d = u_{n+1} - u_n$ for all $n \in \mathbb{Z}^+$.

To determine that a sequence is **geometric**, show that there is a common ratio,

i.e., there is a constant r such that $r = \dfrac{u_{n+1}}{u_n}$ for all $n \in \mathbb{Z}$.

If an expression for the sum of a sequence is given and you need to find the sequence, two approaches are

- For arithmetic sequences use $u_n = S_n - S_{n-1}$.

  For geometric sequences use $u_n = \dfrac{S_n}{S_{n-1}}$.

- Alternatively for all types of sequences, $u_1 = S_1$.
  Then find u_2 by using $u_1 + u_2 = S_2$.
  The respective common difference or common ratio can then be determined.

For compound interest problems, the first term is the initial amount invested.

If the interest rate is $i\%$ per time period, then the common ratio is $1 + \frac{i}{100}$. The number of compounding periods is n.

For example,

if \$8000 is invested at 7% per annum, compounding monthly for 5 years, then $u_1 = 8000$, $r = 1.07$ and $n = 60$.

EXPONENTS AND LOGARITHMS

Exponential functions and logarithmic functions are inverse functions of each other.

The graph of $y = \log_a x$ is the reflection in the line $y = x$ of the graph of $y = a^x$.

Laws of exponents and logarithms

Exponents	Logarithms
$a^x \times a^y = a^{x+y}$	$\log_a xy = \log_a x + \log_a y$
$a^x \div a^y = a^{x-y}$	$\log_a \left(\dfrac{x}{y} \right) = \log_a x - \log_a y$
$(a^x)^y = a^{xy}$	$\log_a x^y = y \log_a x$
$a^0 = 1$	$\log_a 1 = 0$
$a^1 = a$	$\log_a a = 1$

COUNTING AND THE BINOMIAL THEOREM

Remember that the formula $\binom{n}{r}$ is used when selecting r objects from n different objects without replacement.

Note that $\binom{n}{r} = \binom{n}{n-r}$, $\binom{n}{0} = \binom{n}{n} = 1$ and $\binom{n}{1} = \binom{n}{n-1} = n$

PROOF BY MATHEMATICAL INDUCTION

Ensure that the proposition is stated clearly.

Make it clear that, in the second step, you are only showing that $P(k+1)$ is true if $P(k)$ is true; you are not proving that either one is true.

Clearly explain the link between the first step and second step in completing the proof.

COMPLEX NUMBERS

- $|wz| = |w| \, |z|$ and $\arg(wz) = \arg(w) + \arg(z)$

- $\left| \dfrac{w}{z} \right| = \dfrac{|w|}{|z|}$ and $\arg(\frac{w}{z}) = \arg(w) - \arg(z)$

- $|\bar{z}| = |z|$ and $\arg(\bar{z}) = -\arg(z)$

- $z\bar{z} = |z|^2$

- $\operatorname{cis} 0 = 1$, $\quad i = \operatorname{cis}\left(\frac{\pi}{2}\right) = e^{i\frac{\pi}{2}}$, $\quad -1 = \operatorname{cis} \pi = e^{i\pi}$ and
  $-i = \operatorname{cis}\left(-\frac{\pi}{2}\right) = e^{-i\frac{\pi}{2}}$.

If w is a complex, non real number such that w is a zero of a real polynomial $P(z)$, then $\bar{w}$ is also a zero and $z^2 - (w + \bar{w})z + w\bar{w}$ is a real quadratic factor of $P(z)$.

TOPIC 1 – ALGEBRA (SKILL BUILDER QUESTIONS)

1 Find the sum of the first 30 terms of the arithmetic series
$18 + 16 + 14 + \dots$

2 Find the sum of the infinite geometric series with first term 27 and fourth term 8.

3 Three numbers are consecutive terms of an arithmetic sequence. Find the numbers if the sum of the terms is 18 and the sum of their squares is 396.

4 The first term of a finite arithmetic series is 18 and the sum of the series is -210. If the common difference is -3, find the number of terms in the series.

5 Express as a single power of x: $\dfrac{x^a \sqrt{x^{3a}}}{x^{-2a}}$

6 Simplify, expressing your answer with positive indices: $\left(\dfrac{3x^{-1}}{2a^2} \right)^{-2} \left(\dfrac{4x^2}{27a^{-3}} \right)^{-1}$

7 Find x if $\quad 8^{2x-3} = 16^{2-x}$.

8 Simplify: $\quad \log_9 \frac{1}{27}$.

9 Convert $\dfrac{8}{\log_5 9}$ to an expression of the form $a \log_3 b$ where a and b are integers.

10 Express as a single logarithm: $2\ln x + \ln(x-1) - \ln(x-2)$.

11 Solve for x: $\quad \log_3 x + \log_3(x-2) = 1$.

12 Expand and simplify $(2 - ai)^3$.

13 Find the term independent of x in the expansion of $\left(x + \dfrac{1}{x} \right)^8$.

14 Write $3 - 3i\sqrt{3}$ in the form $r(\cos\theta + i\sin\theta)$.

15 Simplify $\left(\cos\left(\frac{2\pi}{3}\right) - i\sin\left(\frac{2\pi}{3}\right) \right)^{10}$ giving your answer in the form $x + iy$ where $x, y \in \mathbb{R}$.

IMPORTANT CONCEPTS

THE CONCEPT OF A FUNCTION $f : x \mapsto f(x)$

Note that $f(x) = y$ usually.

A **function** is a *relation* that is *well-defined,* i.e., it must satisfy the rule that for each x there is only one y or $f(x)$.

Graphically, this is equivalent to satisfying the **vertical line test**, i.e., no vertical line can intersect the graph more than once.

The equation $x^2 + y^2 = 1$, the unit circle, has a circular graph and thus is not a function.

A relation that is
- *one-to-one*, (for each x there is only one y and for each y there is only one x, i.e., it satisfies the vertical and horizontal line test) *or*
- *many-to-one* (only satisfies the vertical line test)

is a function.

Relations that are **one-to-many** (satisfy the horizontal line test) or **many-to-many** (do not satisfy either line test) are **not functions**, as each type never satisfies the vertical line test.

The **domain** of a function is the set of all values that x (the independent variable) can take. Note if the domain is the set of real numbers then the statement "$x \in \mathbb{R}$" will be omitted.

To find the *domain* of a function it is best to remember 3 important facts:
- you cannot divide by zero
- you cannot get the square (or even) root of a negative number
- you cannot get the log of a non-positive number

The **range** of a function is the set of all values y or $f(x)$ (the dependent variable) can take. We often refer to $f(x)$ or y as the **image value** (y is the image of the corresponding x value).

In finding the *domain* and *range* of any function it is often useful to use a graphics calculator (gdc).

Composite functions $f \circ g$

If $f : x \mapsto f(x)$ and $g : x \mapsto g(x)$ then
$f \circ g : \ x \mapsto f(g(x))$, i.e., $(f \circ g)(x) = f(g(x))$.

Identity function: $e(x) = x$, i.e., $y = x$,

an oblique straight line with slope 1 passing through the origin.

Inverse functions f^{-1}

If the function f is given by $f : x \mapsto f(x)$ then its inverse f^{-1} is given by $f^{-1} : f(x) \mapsto x$.

A *function* f will only **have an inverse function** if it is *one-to-one*.

The inverse of a *many-to-one* function will be *one-to-many* and thus will not be a function.

Remember that $(f \circ f^{-1})(x) = x = (f^{-1} \circ f)(x) = e(x)$, the *identity function*.

The *domain* (*range*) of a function is the *range* (*domain*) of its inverse.

THE GRAPH OF THE FUNCTION $y = f(x)$

This is about your ability to use a gdc to draw graphs of all sorts of functions (even those not specifically stated in the syllabus), to find key features of these graphs and to solve equations graphically.

To find **vertical asymptotes**; if $y = \dfrac{f(x)}{g(x)}$ find where $g(x) = 0$;

if $y = \log_a (f(x))$ find where $f(x) = 0$.

To find *other asymptotes* (*horizontal* in this syllabus) find what happens to y as $x \to \pm\infty$.

An asymptote is a line (or curve) that the graph approaches (or begins to look like after some point).

When solving equations we obtain the *roots* of the *equation* or the *zeros* of the corresponding *function*, i.e., where the graph meets the x-axis.

TRANSFORMATIONS OF GRAPHS

Transformations of graphs: translations, stretches and reflections.

- $y = f(x) + b$ **translates** $y = f(x)$, b units vertically (up if $b > 0$, down if $b < 0$)
- $y = f(x - a)$ **translates** $y = f(x)$ a units horizontally (right if $a > 0$, left if $a < 0$)
- $y = pf(x)$ **stretches** $y = f(x)$ vertically by scale factor p in the y-direction.
- $y = f(\dfrac{x}{q})$ **stretches** $y = f(x)$ horizontally by scale factor q in the x-direction.

Examples:
- $y = x^2$ is used to obtain $y = 2x^2 - 3$ by a *stretch* of scale factor 2 in the y-direction followed by a *translation* of $\begin{bmatrix} 0 \\ -3 \end{bmatrix}$, i.e., 3 units vertically down.
- For $y = f(x)$,
  $y = -f(x)$ is a *reflection* in the x-axis and
  $y = f(-x)$ is a *reflection* in the y-axis.
  Try some examples on your gdc.

The graph of $y = f^{-1}(x)$

The graph of $y = f^{-1}(x)$ is the reflection in the line $y = x$ of the graph of $y = f(x)$.

Every point (x, y) on the graph of $y = f(x)$, becomes the point (y, x) on the graph of $y = f^{-1}(x)$.

The **invariant points** have the same x- and y-coordinates, i.e., points with coordinates (x, x). They lie on the line $y = x$.

The graph of $y = \dfrac{1}{f(x)}$ from $y = f(x)$

You need to remember :
- If $f(x) > 0$ then $\dfrac{1}{f(x)} > 0$.
- If $f(x) < 0$ then $\dfrac{1}{f(x)} < 0$.
- When $f(x)$ has a **max (min)** then $\dfrac{1}{f(x)}$ has a **min (max)**
- Where $f(x) = 0$ then $\dfrac{1}{f(x)}$ has vertical asymptotes.
- Where $f(x)$ has vertical asymptotes then $\dfrac{1}{f(x)}$ has zeros (x-intercepts).
- **Invariant points** occur where $f(x) = \pm 1$.

The graphs of absolute value functions, $y = |f(x)|$ and $y = f(|x|)$.

To graph $y = |f(x)|$, simply reflect in the x-axis that part of $f(x)$ that lies below the x-axis. The rest remains invariant.

To graph $y = f(|x|)$, simply reflect in the y-axis that part of $f(x)$ that lies to the right of the y-axis. The rest remains invariant.

THE RECIPROCAL FUNCTION $x \mapsto \dfrac{1}{x}, \ x \neq 0$:

The reciprocal function, its graph and its self inverse nature.

Sketch using your gdc and a square window.

The inverse of $y = \dfrac{1}{x}$ is also $y = \dfrac{1}{x}$.

THE QUADRATIC FUNCTION $x \mapsto ax^2 + bx + c$

The quadratic function and its graph (real coefficients a, b, c).

The graph is a *parabola*,
concave up if $a > 0$, *concave down* if $a < 0$.

Axis of symmetry, $x = \dfrac{-b}{2a}$. Refer to information booklet.

The form $x \mapsto a(x-h)^2 + k$, gives the vertex (h, k).

The form $x \mapsto a(x-p)(x-q)$, gives the x-intercepts at p and q.

QUADRATIC EQUATIONS

The solution of $ax^2 + bx + c = 0$, $a \neq 0$, the quadratic formula, and the use of the discriminant $\Delta = b^2 - 4ac$

Refer to information booklet.

The **discriminant** indicates whether the quadratic has
- *no real solutions* when $\Delta < 0$
- *one real (repeated) solution* when $\Delta = 0$
- *two real distinct solutions* when $\Delta > 0$.

It also indicates whether graphs
- *do not meet* when $\Delta < 0$
- *touch tangentially* when $\Delta = 0$
- *cut* when $\Delta > 0$.

THE EXPONENTIAL FUNCTION $x \mapsto a^x$, $a > 0$

Growth if $a > 1$, *decay* if $0 < a < 1$.

The inverse function (logarithmic) $x \mapsto \log_a x$, $x > 0$:

Note that $\log_a a^x = x$ and $a^{\log_a x} = x$, $x > 0$.

Graphs of $y = a^x$ and $y = \log_a x$

The graph of $y = a^x$ has a horizontal asymptote.

The graph of $y = \log_a x$ has a vertical asymptote.

Solution of $a^x = b$ **using logarithms**

You need to be able to recognise exponential equations and be able to solve by getting the same base if possible or otherwise using logs.

THE EXPONENTIAL FUNCTION $x \mapsto e^x$

$x \mapsto e^x$ has HA $y = 0$.

The logarithmic function $x \mapsto \ln x$

$x \mapsto \ln x$ has VA $x = 0$.

Note that $a^x = e^{x \ln a}$.

Examples of compound interest, growth and decay.

INEQUALITIES IN ONE VARIABLE

Inequalities in one variable, using their graphical representation.

Use of the absolute value sign in inequalities.

Solution of $g(x) \geqslant f(x)$, **where** f **and** g **are linear or quadratic**

For the analytic solution in simple cases, you need to find the critical values and draw a sign diagram. Note some rules for manipulating inequalities.
- $a > b \Rightarrow a + c > b + c$
- $a < b \Rightarrow a + c < b + c$
- $a > b$ and $c > 0 \Rightarrow ac > bc$
- $a > b$ and $c < 0 \Rightarrow ac < bc$
- $a > b \geqslant 0 \Rightarrow a^2 > b^2$
- $a < b \leqslant 0 \Rightarrow a^2 > b^2$

POLYNOMIAL FUNCTIONS

Polynomial functions; the factor and remainder theorems, with application to the solution of polynomial equations and inequalities.

If a polynomial $P(x)$ is divided by $x - k$ until a constant remainder R is obtained then, $R = P(k)$. **(Remainder theorem)**

$x - a$ is a factor of $P(x)$ if and only if ($\Leftrightarrow$) $P(a) = 0$, i.e., each *zero* a of a polynomial gives a *linear factor* $x - a$ of that polynomial.

A repeated (*double*) root of a *real polynomial* $\Rightarrow$ graph just touches the x-axis.

A repeated (*triple*) root of a *real polynomial* $\Rightarrow$ graph has a stationary point of inflexion on the x-axis.

TOPIC 2 – FUNCTIONS AND EQUATIONS ▰▰▰▰▰
SKILL BUILDER QUESTIONS

16 Find the domain and range of the function
$f : x \mapsto \sqrt{3x - 1} - 3$

17 Two functions f, g are defined as follows:
$f : x \to 2x + 1$ and $g : x \to 2 - x$.
Find: **a** $(g \circ f)(-4)$ **b** $f^{-1}(2)$.

18 On the same axes, sketch the graphs of
$y = e^{x-2}$ and $y = 2 - e^{-x}$, where $-1 \leqslant x \leqslant 5$.
Hence find correct to 3 decimal places any points of intersection of the graphs.

19 Sketch the graph of $f(x) = e^{2x-1} \sin 2x$ for $0 \leqslant x \leqslant 2\pi$.
Hence find the maximum and minimum values of the function over the given domain.

20 Find the equation of the quadratic function $y = 3x^2 + 2x$ if it has been stretched vertically by a factor of 2 and then translated by the vector $\begin{bmatrix} 3 \\ -1 \end{bmatrix}$.

21 Find $f^{-1}(x)$ when $f(x) = x^2 + 2x$ for $x \in \,]-\infty, -1]$.
State any invariant points.

22 Sketch the graph of $f(x) = \cos x$ and the graph of
$y = -1 + 2f(2x + \frac{\pi}{2})$ on the same set of axes for
$-\pi \leqslant x \leqslant \pi$.

23 Sketch the graph of $f(x) = x^2 - 2x$ for $x \in \mathbb{R}$, showing clearly the x-intercepts and any turning points. Hence sketch the graph of
a $y = f(|x|)$ for $x \in \mathbb{R}$ **b** $y = |f(x)|$ for $x \in \mathbb{R}$

24 Sketch the graph of $f(x) = \dfrac{2x + 1}{x - 2}$ showing clearly any asymptotes and intercepts.

Hence, sketch the graph of $y = \dfrac{1}{f(x)}$, again showing clearly and asymptotes, axes intercepts and invariant points.

25 For the quadratic function $f : x \mapsto 2x^2 + 4x - 30$,
a state the equation of the axis of symmetry
b find the coordinates of the turning point
c write the equation in the form $y = a(x - h)^2 + k$
d write the equation in the form $y = a(x - p)(x - q)$.

26 For what value(s) of k will the line $y = kx - 2$ be a tangent to the curve $y = 3x^2 + x + 1$?

27 Find the inverse function of $f : x \mapsto e^{2x+1}$.
Hence, evaluate $f^{-1}(7)$.

28 Find the inverse of $g : x \mapsto \log_2(2x - 1)$.
Hence, evaluate $g^{-1}(-6)$.

29 Solve analytically the inequality $\left| \dfrac{2x-1}{x+1} \right| \leqslant 3$.

30 Sketch the graph of the function
$f : x \mapsto 3(x-1)^2(x+2)(x-4)$,
showing clearly any axes intercepts.

IMPORTANT CONCEPTS

The coordinates of any point P on the **unit circle**, where the angle θ, made by OP and the positive direction of the x-axis, are $(\cos\theta, \sin\theta)$.

θ is **positive** when taken in an **anticlockwise** direction from the positive x-axis.

To simplify $\sin\left(\frac{n\pi}{2} \pm \theta\right)$, $\cos\left(\frac{n\pi}{2} \pm \theta\right)$ and $\tan\left(\frac{n\pi}{2} \pm \theta\right)$ or their reciprocals:

- If n is **odd**, change to the **complementary ratio**.

  For example: $\sin\left(\frac{\pi}{2} + \theta\right) = \cos\theta$,

  $$\cos\left(\frac{3\pi}{2} - \theta\right) = -\sin\theta, \quad \tan\left(\frac{\pi}{2} + \theta\right) = -\cot\theta.$$

  The sign is determined by the quadrant of the first angle.

  For this purpose, without loss of generality, it can always be assumed that θ is acute.

  The results apply whatever the size of θ.

- If n is **even**, the ratio is **unchanged**.

  For example: $\sec(\pi - \theta) = -\sec\theta$,

  $$\tan(3\pi + \theta) = \tan\theta, \quad \sin(2\pi - \theta) = -\sin\theta$$

To convert a degree measure to a radian measure, multiply by $\frac{\pi}{180}$.

To effect the conversion from radians to degrees, multiply by $\frac{180}{\pi}$.

To find the area of a segment of a circle, use the area of a triangle formula and the area of a sector formula.

The area of a segment $= \frac{1}{2}\theta r^2 - \frac{1}{2}r^2\sin\theta$

The double angle identities follow from replacing B by A in the formulas for $\sin(A+B)$, $\cos(A+B)$ and $\tan(A+B)$.

The sine, cosine and tangent of any angle can be expressed in terms of half the angle.

For example: $\cos(2x) = 2\cos^2 x - 1$

$$\Rightarrow 2\cos^2 x = 1 + \cos(2x)$$
$$\Rightarrow \cos^2 x = \frac{1}{2} + \frac{1}{2}\cos(2x)$$

Similarly, $\sin^2 x = \frac{1}{2} - \frac{1}{2}\sin(2x)$

These formulas are often useful in integral calculus.

The period of $\sin nx$ and $\cos nx$ is $\frac{2\pi}{n}$.

The period of $\tan nx$ is $\frac{\pi}{n}$.

For the function $f(x) = a\sin(b(x+c))+d$ related to $g(x) = \sin x$:
- a affects the amplitude.
  There is a vertical stretch of $g(x)$ by a factor of a.
- The period of $f(x)$ is $\frac{2\pi}{b}$.
- $f(x)$ is a translation of $g(x)$ of $\begin{bmatrix} -c \\ d \end{bmatrix}$.

When using a graphics calculator to help sketch the graphs of trigonometric functions, the following may be useful:
- If, for example the domain of the function is $[0, \ 2\pi]$, set the x values for the window to $x = -\frac{\pi}{6}$ and $x = \frac{13\pi}{6}$.
  This avoids missing any essential features at the edges of the screen.
- Set the x scale to $\frac{\pi}{6}$.
- Set a suitable y scale and turn the grid function on.

When graphing the reciprocal functions, remember that wherever sine, cosine or tangent are zero, the reciprocal function will have vertical asymptotes.

Whenever $\tan x$ is undefined, $\cot x$ will be zero.

The domains and ranges of the inverse trigonometric functions are as follows:

Function	Domain	Range
$x \mapsto \arcsin x$	$[-1, 1]$	$\left[-\frac{\pi}{2}, \frac{\pi}{2}\right]$
$x \mapsto \arccos x$	$[-1, 1]$	$[0, \pi]$
$x \mapsto \arctan x$	$]-\infty, \infty[$	$\left]-\frac{\pi}{2}, \frac{\pi}{2}\right[$

Solving trigonometric equations:

An equation of the form $a\sin x = b\cos x$ can always be solved by dividing both sides by $a\cos x$ to give $\tan x = \frac{b}{a}$.

The compound angle, double angle and Pythagorean identities can often be used to factorise an expression and lead to a method of solution.

In general, the sine rule is used in a triangle when dealing with two sides and two angles, one of which is unknown. The cosine rule is used when three sides and an angle, one of which is unknown, are involved.

Remember that the range of $\arcsin x$ is $\left[-\frac{\pi}{2}, \frac{\pi}{2}\right]$ and consequently only acute angles will be found when using the sine rule and a calculator in a triangle. Always check to determine whether the angle could be obtuse. Sometimes both acute and obtuse angles will be correct, on other occasions only one will work.

TOPIC 3 – CIRCULAR FUNCTIONS AND TRIGONOMETRY
SKILL BUILDER QUESTIONS

31 A chord of a circle has length 6 cm. If the radius of the circle is 5 cm, find the area of the minor segment cut off by the circle.

32 Simplify $\sin\left(\frac{3\pi}{2} - A\right)\tan(\pi + A)$.

33 Simplify $1 - \dfrac{\sin^2 A}{1 + \cos A}$.

34 Find the exact value of $\cos 79^o \cos 71^o - \sin 79^o \sin 71^o$.

35 Find the exact value of $\sin x$ if $\cos 2x = \frac{5}{8}$.

36 If θ is obtuse and $\sin\theta = \frac{2}{3}$, find the exact value of $\sin 2\theta$.

37 Find the largest angle of the triangle with sides 11 cm, 9 cm and 7 cm.

38 In triangle ABC, AB = 15 cm, AC = 12 cm and angle ABC is 30°, find the size of angle ACB.

39 Solve for x: $\sin x = \sin 2x$ for $-\pi \leqslant x \leqslant \pi$, giving your answers as exact values.

40 Solve for x: $2\sin^2 x - \cos x = 1$ for $0 \leqslant x \leqslant 2\pi$, giving your answers as exact values.

41 Find the exact coordinates of the first maximum turning point for $x > 0$ of the function $f(x) = -2\cos\left(\frac{1}{3}\left(x - \frac{\pi}{6}\right)\right) + 1$.

42 Find the exact period of the function $f(x) = \tan 2x + \tan 3x$.

43 Sketch the graph of $y = \arccos x$, clearly showing axes intercepts and endpoints.

44 Simplify: $\arcsin\left(-\frac{1}{2}\right) + \arctan 1 + \arccos\left(-\frac{1}{2}\right)$, giving your answer as an exact value.

45 Solve for x: $\sin x + \cos x = 1$ where $0 \leqslant x \leqslant \pi$, giving your answers as exact values.

IMPORTANT CONCEPTS

DEFINITION OF A MATRIX

Definition of a matrix: the terms element, row, column and order.

Be aware of the use of matrices to store data.

Order refers to the number of rows and columns.

ALGEBRA OF MATRICES

Algebra of matrices: equality, addition, subtraction and multiplication by a scalar.

Make sure you know when you can add and subtract and know the meaning of a scalar.

Multiplication of matrices

Be certain you know how to multiply (rows by columns) and know when you can multiply.

Important property for multiplication $AB \neq BA$ in general. (not commutative)

Ensure you can do these processes manually and by using your gdc.

Identity and zero matrices $I = \begin{bmatrix} 1 & 0 \\ 0 & 1 \end{bmatrix}$ and $O = \begin{bmatrix} 0 & 0 \\ 0 & 0 \end{bmatrix}$

I is always square and satisfies $AI = IA = A$ for all matrices A for which the product exists.

O is any shape and satisfies $A + O = O + A = A$ for all matrices A for which the sum exists.

DETERMINANT OF A MATRIX

If the det $A = 0$, then matrix A is **singular**.

If det $A \neq 0$, then matrix A is non-singular.

The notation for det A is $|A|$.

Calculation of 2 × 2 and 3 × 3 determinants

Refer to information booklet. Ensure you can do these processes manually and by gdc.

Note that   det (AB) = det A det B for matrices A and B. (They must have same shape and be square.)

Inverse of A matrix: conditions for its existence.

For 2×2 matrices refer to information booklet. Be sure you can find the inverse of a 3×3 matrix using gdc. Only square, non-singular matrices have an inverse.

A^{-1} is the inverse of A and satisfies the rule $AA^{-1} = A^{-1}A = I$

SOLUTION OF SYSTEMS OF LINEAR EQUATIONS

Solution of systems of linear equations (a maximum of three equations in three unknowns)

Either   matrix algebra can be used provided det $A \neq 0$

     e.g.,   Find X if $AX = B \Rightarrow X = A^{-1}B$.

     In this case a unique solution exists.

or   Use elementary row operations on the augmented matrix (row reduction).

     When det $A \neq 0$ a unique solution exists.

     When det $A = 0$ we get either *no* solutions (inconsistent) or *infinite* solutions (consistent).

Note: When manipulating matrix equations be careful of the non-commutative property of multiplication. So when you multiply both sides of an equation by a matrix you must either **pre-** or **post-multiply**.

46 State the conditions for m, n, p, q if we can evaluate $2A - 3B$ where A is a matrix of order $m \times n$ and B is a matrix of order $p \times q$.

47 School A bought 2 soccer balls, one softball and 3 basketballs for a total of \$90, school B bought 3 soccer balls, 2 softballs and 1 basketball for a total of \$81 and school C bought 5 soccer balls and 2 basketballs for a total of \$104.

Write this information down as a matrix equation that will enable you to calculate the cost of each soccer ball, softball and basketball. Find the cost of each type of ball.

48 State the 2 conditions under which the equation $A = B$ is true for matrices A and B.

49   **a**   Under what conditions does $AB = C$ for matrices A, B and C. Clearly state the orders of each of the matrices.

     b   How would you find the element in the product matrix C above if it is in the 3rd row and 4th column. State your answer precisely.

50 Under what conditions will $A + O = O + A$? What matrix will they be equal to?

51 Under what conditions will $AI = IA = A$? State clearly the order of each matrix and the elements in I.

52 Find real k for which the matrix $\begin{bmatrix} k & 5 \\ 1 & k \end{bmatrix}$ is singular. For these real values of k explain the implications for the matrix.

53 Solve for X, the matrix equation $3AXB - 2C = O$.

54 Find the real value(s) of m for which the matrix $\begin{bmatrix} 2 & -1 & 1 \\ m & 2 & 1 \\ 3 & -1 & 2 \end{bmatrix}$ has an inverse.

55 Find the value(s) of a for which the equations

$$3x - ay + 2z = 4$$
$$x + 2y - 3z = 1$$
$$-x - y + z = 12 \quad \text{has a unique solution.}$$

56 Calculate det(AB) without finding the product

AB if $A = \begin{bmatrix} 2 & -1 \\ 1 & 3 \end{bmatrix}$ and $B = \begin{bmatrix} -2 & 5 \\ 1 & 3 \end{bmatrix}$.

Check your answer by using your calculator.

57 How many solutions could I get if I have 2 equations in 3 unknowns?

58 What must I be careful about if I solve 3 equations in 2 unknowns (in general more equations than unknowns)?

59 Use row reduction on the system of equations

$$x + 3y + kz = 2$$
$$kx - 2y + 3z = k$$
$$4x - 3y + 10z = 5 \quad \text{to:}$$

     a   show that for one value of k, the system of equations has infinitely many solutions

     b   find the value(s) of k for which the system has no solutions

     c   find the value(s) of k for which the system has a unique solution.

60   **a**   Find the values of a and b for which the matrix $\begin{bmatrix} 2 & 1 & 1 \\ 1 & 1 & 1 \\ 2 & 2 & 1 \end{bmatrix}$

        has an inverse of the form $\begin{bmatrix} a & b & 0 \\ b & 0 & a \\ 0 & 2 & b \end{bmatrix}$.

     b   Use your answer to part **a** above to solve the system of equations

$$2x + y + z = 1$$
$$x + y + z = 6$$
$$2x + 2y + z = 5$$

IMPORTANT CONCEPTS

Refer extensively to the information booklet for this section.

VECTORS AS DISPLACEMENTS (IN 2D AND 3D)

Components of a vector; column representation

$$\mathbf{v} = \begin{bmatrix} v_1 \\ v_2 \\ v_3 \end{bmatrix} = v_1\mathbf{i} + v_2\mathbf{j} + v_3\mathbf{k}.$$

The components are with respect to the unit vectors **i**, **j** and **k** (standard basis).

Be clear about the algebraic and geometric approaches to the following topics:

- the sum and difference of two vectors; the zero vector, the vector $-\mathbf{v}$
  The difference of **v** and **w** is $\mathbf{v} - \mathbf{w} = \mathbf{v} + (-\mathbf{w})$.
- multiplication by a scalar k, i.e., $k\mathbf{v}$. $k\mathbf{v}$ is parallel to **v**.
- magnitude of vector **v**, $|\mathbf{v}| = \sqrt{v_1^2 + v_2^2 + v_3^2}$
  The *distance* between two points in space is the *length* of the vector obtained by joining the two points.
  This is also the *magnitude* of the vector.
  $|k\mathbf{v}| = |k|\,|\mathbf{v}|$
- unit vectors; base vectors **i**, **j**, **k**
  Unit vectors have a magnitude of 1.

$$\mathbf{i} = \begin{bmatrix} 1 \\ 0 \\ 0 \end{bmatrix}, \quad \mathbf{j} = \begin{bmatrix} 0 \\ 1 \\ 0 \end{bmatrix}, \quad \mathbf{k} = \begin{bmatrix} 0 \\ 0 \\ 1 \end{bmatrix}$$

It is important to distinguish between scalars (magnitude only) and vectors (magnitude and direction) by using appropriate notation.

- Hence, when we write a scalar unknown simply use something like k. When we write an unknown vector we write either $\overrightarrow{a}$ or $\underline{a}$
- In examinations bold type will be used for vectors, i.e., **a**.

Position vectors

$\overrightarrow{OA} = \mathbf{a}$.
The position vector of the point A(x, y, z) is $\begin{bmatrix} x \\ y \\ z \end{bmatrix}$
which has the same coordinates as A.

Thus in problems if we wish to find **a** all we have to do is find $\overrightarrow{OA} = \mathbf{a}$.

Note: $\overrightarrow{AB} = \overrightarrow{OB} - \overrightarrow{OA} = \mathbf{b} - \mathbf{a}$.

THE SCALAR PRODUCT OF TWO VECTORS, v • w

$\mathbf{v} \bullet \mathbf{w} = |\mathbf{v}||\mathbf{w}|\cos\theta$ (geometric)
$\mathbf{v} \bullet \mathbf{w} = v_1w_1 + v_2w_2 + v_3w_3$ (algebraic)

The scalar product is also known as the **dot product** or the **inner product**.

Perpendicular vectors:

$\mathbf{v} \perp \mathbf{w} \iff \mathbf{v} \bullet \mathbf{w} = 0$,   (for non-zero vectors, **v**, **w**).

Parallel vectors:

$\mathbf{v} \parallel \mathbf{w} \iff \mathbf{v} = k\mathbf{w}$ (or $\mathbf{w} = k\mathbf{v}$) or $\mathbf{v} \bullet \mathbf{w} = \pm|\mathbf{v}||\mathbf{w}|$.

The angle between two vectors:

The angle θ between **v** and **w** emanating from the same point is found using $\cos\theta = \dfrac{\mathbf{v} \bullet \mathbf{w}}{|\mathbf{v}||\mathbf{w}|}$.

If $\mathbf{v} \bullet \mathbf{w} > 0$, the angle is acute, if $\mathbf{v} \bullet \mathbf{w} < 0$, the angle is obtuse.

THE VECTOR EQUATION OF A LINE, r = a + λb.

This is the form for the vector equation of a line in the plane (2-D) and in space (3-D).

Here, **r** is the position vector for any point on the line, **a** is the position vector for a known point on the line, **b** is a vector parallel to the line and λ is a parameter ($\lambda \in \mathbb{R}$).

Each value of λ corresponds to a unique point on the line.

Parametric form for the equation of a line:

$$x = x_o + \lambda l, \quad y = y_o + \lambda m, \quad z = z_o + \lambda n.$$

Connecting with the vector equation above

$$\mathbf{r} = \begin{bmatrix} x \\ y \\ z \end{bmatrix}, \quad \mathbf{a} = \begin{bmatrix} x_o \\ y_o \\ z_o \end{bmatrix}, \quad \mathbf{b} = \begin{bmatrix} l \\ m \\ n \end{bmatrix}.$$

Cartesian form for the equation of a line:

$$\frac{x - x_o}{l} = \frac{y - y_o}{m} = \frac{z - z_o}{n} \ (= \lambda).$$

The connection here is the same as above.

The angle between two lines

Normally we are only interested in the **acute** angle between 2 lines.

Hence, the acute angle θ is given by $\cos\theta = \dfrac{|\mathbf{a} \bullet \mathbf{b}|}{|\mathbf{a}||\mathbf{b}|}$

where **a** and **b** are any vectors parallel to each of the lines, called the **direction vectors** of the lines.

Examples of applications: interpretation of t as time and **b** as velocity, with $|\mathbf{b}|$ representing speed.

HOW PLANES MEET

Coincident, parallel, intersecting and skew lines, distinguishing between these cases.

- Lines are **parallel** if their direction vectors are parallel, i.e., $\mathbf{a} = k\mathbf{b}$.
- Lines are **coincident** if they are parallel and have a common point.
- Lines are **intersecting** if you can solve simultaneously and get a common point that fits both equations.
  (These are all coplanar.)
- Lines are **skew** if they are not parallel and do not have a point of intersection, i.e., no solutions when you solve simultaneously. They are said to be non-coplanar, i.e., are not in the same plane.

Points of intersection

To find these solve simultaneously. Be careful to ensure you use different pronumerals for the parameters of each line.

THE VECTOR PRODUCT OF TWO VECTORS, v × w.

The vector product is also known as the cross product.

To find the cross product of two 3-D vectors, use the rule

$$\mathbf{v} \times \mathbf{w} = \begin{bmatrix} \mathbf{i} & \mathbf{j} & \mathbf{k} \\ v_1 & v_2 & v_3 \\ w_1 & w_2 & w_3 \end{bmatrix} \text{ refer to information booklet.}$$

It is important to note that $\mathbf{v} \times \mathbf{w}$ is perpendicular to both **v** and **w**. Thus it is easy to check that you have found $\mathbf{v} \times \mathbf{w}$ correctly.

Geometric interpretation of $|\mathbf{v} \times \mathbf{w}|$

$|\mathbf{v} \times \mathbf{w}| = |\mathbf{v}||\mathbf{w}|\sin\theta$ and this leads to

$|\mathbf{v} \times \mathbf{w}| = $ area of parallelogram formed by vectors **v** and **w**.

$\frac{1}{2}|\mathbf{v} \times \mathbf{w}| = $ area of triangle formed by vectors **v** and **w**.

VECTOR EQUATION OF A PLANE IN 3D $\mathbf{r} = \mathbf{a} + \lambda\mathbf{b} + \mu\mathbf{c}$.

Here, $\mathbf{r}$ is the position vector of any point on the plane, $\mathbf{a}$ is the position vector of a known point on the plane, $\mathbf{b}$ is any vector parallel to the plane, $\mathbf{c}$ is another vector parallel to the plane (with $\mathbf{b}$ not parallel to $\mathbf{c}$) and λ and μ are parameters ($\lambda, \mu \in \mathbb{R}$).

Given values for λ and μ correspond to a point on the plane.

Use of a normal vector to obtain the form $\mathbf{r} \bullet \mathbf{n} = \mathbf{r} \bullet \mathbf{a}$.

Here $\mathbf{r}$ and $\mathbf{a}$ are as described before. $\mathbf{n}$ is any vector normal to the plane.

You can use any $\mathbf{n}$ where $\mathbf{n} \parallel \mathbf{b} \times \mathbf{c}$, where $\mathbf{b}$ and $\mathbf{c}$ are described before.

Cartesian equation of a plane $ax + by + cz = d$.

This can be obtained using $\mathbf{r} \bullet \mathbf{n} = \mathbf{a} \bullet \mathbf{n}$ where $d = \mathbf{a} \bullet \mathbf{n}$

and $\mathbf{n} = \begin{bmatrix} a \\ b \\ c \end{bmatrix}$.

INTERSECTION OF LINES AND PLANES

The intersection of: a line with a plane; two planes; three planes

To find these intersections solve their equations simultaneously.

For finding the intersection of 3 planes you can use

- the **inverse matrix method** if there is a unique solution (i.e., there is only one point that lies on all 3 planes) **or**

- the row reduction method whether the planes have a unique solution (a point) or infinite solutions (planes meet in a line or are coincident) or have no solutions (at least 2 of the planes are parallel or the line of intersection of any two of the planes is parallel to the third plane).

Geometrical Interpretation:

The solution to a system of 3 equations in 3 unknowns (x, y, and z) can be interpreted as the common points of three planes in space.

- If two or more planes are **parallel** (the coefficients of x, y, and z are multiples) then there are *no points common* to all three planes. So, the system has *no solutions*.

- If two planes are **coincident** (the coefficients of x, y, and z and the constant terms are multiples) and the third plane is not parallel then the planes meet in a line. There are an infinite number of points on a line so there are an *infinite number of solutions* to the system of equations.

- If all three planes are **coincident** then any one of the three planes represents the common points.
  Assuming no parallelism or coincidence for these planes, there are three possible forms of solution indicated in the table below.

Algebraic solution	Geometrical interpretation
• No solution	No common points. The line of intersection of any pair of planes is parallel to the third plane.
• An infinite number of solutions	The three planes meet in a line.
• A unique solution	The three planes meet in a common point.

Angle between: a line and a plane; two planes.

To find these angles you are expected to find the acute angle.

- For a line and a plane simply find the acute angle θ between the direction vector of the line and the normal to the plane. You then need to take this answer θ from 90° to get the correct answer α (see diagram).

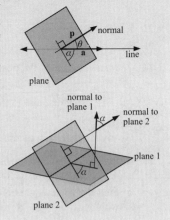

- For the angle between two planes simply find the acute angle α between the normal vectors of the two planes.

TOPIC 5 – VECTORS (SKILL BUILDER QUESTIONS)

61 Clearly explain what is special about the *position vector* of a point A$(1, -2, 3)$.

62 For the *position vector* of A in question **61** above:
  a write it in terms of the base vectors, $\mathbf{i}$, $\mathbf{j}$, and $\mathbf{k}$
  b find the magnitude of this vector
  c write down a unit vector in the opposite direction of the position vector of A.

63 On grid paper, draw accurately how to find geometrically the vector $2\mathbf{a} - \mathbf{b} + 3\mathbf{c}$ where

$\mathbf{a} = \begin{bmatrix} 4 \\ -3 \end{bmatrix}$, $\mathbf{b} = \begin{bmatrix} -5 \\ 7 \end{bmatrix}$ and $\mathbf{c} = \begin{bmatrix} 1 \\ 2 \end{bmatrix}$.

Check your answer by doing a simple calculation.

64 a Draw a clear diagram of a parallelogram ABCD formed by two vectors $\overrightarrow{AB} = \mathbf{a}$ and $\overrightarrow{AD} = \mathbf{b}$ along its sides.
  b Write the vectors $\overrightarrow{BC}$, $\overrightarrow{CD}$ and the diagonals $\overrightarrow{AC}$ and $\overrightarrow{BD}$ in terms of $\mathbf{a}$ and $\mathbf{b}$.
  c Hence, calculate the product $\overrightarrow{AC} \bullet \overrightarrow{BD}$ in terms of $\mathbf{a}$ and $\mathbf{b}$ given that the parallelogram is a rhombus, i.e., $|\mathbf{a}| = |\mathbf{b}|$.
  d Explain clearly why $\overrightarrow{AC}$ is perpendicular to $\overrightarrow{BD}$ using your answer to part **c** above.

65 a Given $\mathbf{a} \bullet \mathbf{b} < 0$, what conclusion can you draw about he angle between $\mathbf{a}$ and $\mathbf{b}$?
  b Find $\mathbf{a} \bullet \mathbf{b}$ for the vectors $\mathbf{a} = \begin{bmatrix} -2 \\ 1 \\ 3 \end{bmatrix}$ and $\mathbf{b} = \begin{bmatrix} 3 \\ -1 \\ 1 \end{bmatrix}$

  and hence find the angle between these vectors in degrees correct to one decimal place.

66 Find the value(s) of k for which the vectors $\begin{bmatrix} k \\ 1 \\ 3 \end{bmatrix}$ and $\begin{bmatrix} 4 \\ k \\ 3k \end{bmatrix}$ are:
  a parallel to each other
  b perpendicular to each other.

67 For the line with equations $\dfrac{x-1}{2} = \dfrac{3-y}{3} = z$, find
  a a vector parallel to the line
  b a point on the line
  c if the point $(7, -3, 2)$ lies on the line, giving reasons.

68 a Find an equation of a line perpendicular to the line in question **67** above passing through the point $(5, -3, 2)$. Give your answer in parametric form.
  b Find if the line in question **67** intersects the line found in part **a** above. If they do intersect find the point of intersection. If not, state the relationship between the lines.

69 Find the acute angle between the line given in question **67**

and the line with equation $\mathbf{r} = \begin{bmatrix} 2 \\ -1 \\ 3 \end{bmatrix} + \lambda \begin{bmatrix} -1 \\ 2 \\ 1 \end{bmatrix}$, $\lambda \in \mathbb{R}$.

70 Briefly explain how you would show that two lines in 3-D are coincident.

71 Find an equation of the plane passing through the point

$(3, -1, 2)$ and parallel to the vectors $\begin{bmatrix} -2 \\ 1 \\ 3 \end{bmatrix}$ and $\begin{bmatrix} 3 \\ -1 \\ 1 \end{bmatrix}$.

Give your answer in parametric and Cartesian form.

72 a Find an equation of the plane passing through the points $A(-1, 2, 1)$, $B(2, 1, 3)$ and $C(4, -3, 5)$.
   b Find the acute angle between the plane ABC and the line with equation $\mathbf{r} = 2\mathbf{i} + \mathbf{j} - 3\mathbf{k} + \lambda(\mathbf{i} - \mathbf{j} + \mathbf{k})$, $\lambda \in \mathbb{R}$.

73 For the plane with equation $3x - 2y + 7z = 6$, find
   a a vector normal to the plane
   b a point on the plane
   c the shortest distance of the plane from the point $(2, -1, 1)$.

74 Given two planes with equations: $\begin{aligned} 2x + 4y + z &= 1 \\ 3x + 5y &= 1 \end{aligned}$, find

   a the acute angle between the two planes
   b any solutions to the system of equations interpreting your answer geometrically
   c all the points that lie on the two planes and also on the plane with equation $5x + 13y + 7z = 4$.

75 Find the distance from the point $(2, -1, 3)$ to the line $\dfrac{x-1}{2} = \dfrac{3+y}{3} = z$.

TOPIC 6   STATISTICS AND PROBABILITY

IMPORTANT CONCEPTS

POPULATIONS AND SAMPLES

Concepts of population, sample, random sample and frequency distribution of discrete and continuous data.

The **population** consists of the set of all possible members under consideration.

A **sample** consists of any subset of that population.

A **random sample** is one in which each member of the population has an equal chance of being selected in that sample. It is usually intended that a sample reflects the true population.

Refer to information booklet for relevant formulae.

PRESENTATION OF DATA

Presentation of data: frequency tables and diagrams, box and whisker plots.

You must be aware of discrete and continuous data.

Discrete data does not take in-between values, e.g., number of children in a family, shoe size in a shop.

Continuous data does take on in-between values, e.g., weight of babies at birth, height of students.

Grouped data: mid-interval values, interval width, upper and lower boundaries

Grouped data refers to data that can be grouped because frequency is greater than one, or because it is simpler to classify data in *groups* or *classes*.

Mid-interval values are the scores mid-way between classes.

Interval width refers to the upper score minus the lower score for that class.

A **frequency histogram** is a graph that measures frequency against class scores. A frequency histogram *uses equal* class intervals.

MEAN, MEDIAN, MODE, QUARTILES, PERCENTILES

You must be aware that the **population mean**, μ, is generally unknown, and that the **sample mean**, $\overline{x}$, serves as an **unbiased estimate** of this quantity.

The **mean** of a set of scores is the *average* of those scores.

Depending on how the data is classified the mean is calculated using:

$$\overline{x} = \frac{\sum x}{n} = \frac{\sum fx}{\sum f}, \quad \text{where } f \text{ is the frequency.}$$

The **median** is the "middle" score of an ordered sample. It has as many scores below it as above it. It is the 50th *percentile*.

The **modal score** is the most frequently occurring score. Data can be *bi-modal* or even *multi-modal*. With continuous data, we may refer to the *modal class*.

The **quartiles** are: • Q_1 (25% of scores are $< Q_1$),
                   • Q_2 or median   (50% of scores are $< Q_2$),
                   • Q_3 (75% of scores are $< Q_3$).

The kth **percentile** is that score a such that $k\%$ of the scores are less than a.

A **box and whisker plot** indicates 5 key statistics for a set of data

These are: •   the *minimum* score
             •   the 25th percentile (*lower quartile* or Q_1)
             •   the *median* (50th percentile or Q_2)
             •   the 75th percentile (upper quartile or Q_3)
             •   the maximum score.

It enables you to see at a glance the spread of the scores in each quartile and compare them. Be certain you can draw a box and whisker plot on your gdc.

Range, interquartile range, variance, standard deviation.

These terms are measures of **dispersion** because they are different ways of measuring how a set of scores is **spread**.

The **range** measures the spread from highest to lowest score.

The **interquartile range** measures the difference between the 75th percentile and the 25th percentile, i.e., $\mathbf{IQR = Q_3 - Q_1}$.

It is the width of the box in the box and whisker plots and is used to eliminate the distorting effects of outliers.

The **variance** $s_n^{\,2}$ measures the **spread** of the scores about the sample **mean**. It is obtained by calculating the mean square deviation of the scores from the mean of the scores. Units obtained are square units.

The **sample standard deviation**, s_n, is simply the square root of the variance.

The formulae for calculating the variance and sample standard deviation and for calculating an **unbiased estimate**, s_{n-1}, of the *population standard deviation*, σ, are given in your information booklet.

The **population variance**, σ, is generally unknown, and

$$s_{n-1}^{\,2} = \frac{n}{n-1} s_n^{\,2} \quad \text{serves as an unbiased estimate of } \sigma.$$

CUMULATIVE FREQUENCY

Cumulative frequency, cumulative frequency graphs, use to find median, quartiles, percentiles

The **cumulative frequency** refers to all scores that lie below a given score or class boundary value (if grouped).

A **cumulative frequency graph** (ogive) measures cumulative frequency against class scores. It enables you to read off **percentiles** and **quartiles** from the graph. Be sure you know how to do this!

PROBABILITY

Concepts of trial, outcome, equally likely outcomes, sample space (U) and event

A **trial** occurs when you perform some experiment once.

The result achieved from a trial is called an **outcome**. Outcomes are equally likely if they have the same chance of occurring.

The **sample space (U)** is the set of all possible outcomes that could occur if one trial is performed.

The **probability** of an event A is given as P(A) where $P(A) = \dfrac{n(A)}{n(U)}$.

This rule only applies if each of the outcomes is equally likely.

The calculation of $n(A)$ and $n(U)$ may involve counting principles (refer to section 1.3). Hence, $0 \leqslant P(A) \leqslant 1$ always.

The **complementary events** A and A' (not A) are such that $P(A) + P(A') = 1$.

$A \cup A' = U$ and $A \cap A' = \varnothing$

COMBINED EVENTS

The formula: $P(A \cup B) = P(A) + P(B) - P(A \cap B)$

This can easily be verified using a Venn diagram. $A \cup B$ means A or B or both (not just A or B).

For mutually exclusive events $A \cap B = \varnothing$.

$P(A \cap B) = 0$ for mutually exclusive events.

This implies $P(A \cup B) = P(A) + P(B)$ for mutually exclusive events.

Mutually exclusive events are also called **disjoint events**.

CONDITIONAL PROBABILITY

The definition: $P(A \mid B) = \dfrac{P(A \cap B)}{P(B)}$

This can be justified by considering B as the sample space.

Independent events

The definition: $P(A \mid B) = P(A) = P(A \mid B')$.

The term "independent" is equivalent to "statistically independent".

The rule implies $P(A \cap B) = P(A)\,P(B)$.

Bayes' theorem for two events.

$$P(B \mid A) = \dfrac{P(B)\,P(A \mid B)}{P(B)\,P(A \mid B) \;+\; P(B')\,P(A \mid B')}.$$

Bayes' theorem is used in cases where we know $P(B \mid A)$ usually represented on a tree diagram and we want to find $P(B \mid A)$, sometimes called inverse probability.

VENN DIAGRAMS, TREE DIAGRAMS AND TABLES

The use of Venn diagrams, tree diagrams and tables of outcomes to solve problems.

It is important you know when and how to use these tools for calculating probabilities and solving problems.

RANDOM VARIABLES

Concept of discrete and continuous random variables and their probability distributions.

A **random variable** X which can take on exactly n numerical values, each of which corresponds to one and only one of the events in the sample space is called a *discrete random variable*.

A **discrete random variable** is one in which we can produce a *countable* number of outcomes.

For a discrete random variable,

$$0 \leqslant P(x) \leqslant 1 \quad \text{and} \quad \sum P(x) = 1.$$

A **continuous random variable**, X, takes on all possible *measured* values not just whole numbers. For example, weight, height, but *not* the number of children in a family or shoe size.

We do not consider $X = 3.7$ kg , rather $X \in [3.65, 3.75[$.

Definition and use of **probability density functions (pdf)**

Continuous random variables are described by a pdf $f(x)$ with the requirement that $0 \leqslant f(x) \leqslant 1$ and $\int_{-\infty}^{\infty} f(x)\,dx = 1$, or the area under the graph of $f(x)$ over which $f(x)$ is defined is 1.

Probability density functions are used to calculate probabilities of continuous random variables,

$$\text{e.g.} \quad P(a \leqslant x \leqslant b) = \int_a^b f(x)\,dx.$$

Expected value (mean), mode, median, variance and standard deviation

The **expected value** of X is denoted by E(X). It is the mean value of X.

- for a discrete RV $\quad E(X) = \mu = \sum x\,P(x)$
- for a continuous RV $\quad E(X) = \mu = \int_{-\infty}^{\infty} f(x)\,dx$

The **mode** is the most frequently occurring score.

- for a discrete RV $\quad$ **mode** = score with **highest frequency**
- for a continuous RV $\quad$ **mode** = x for which $f(x)$ is a **maximum**

The **median** is the middle score (50th percentile)

- for a discrete RV $\quad$ **median** = middle score
- for a continuous RV $\quad$ **median** = a where $\int_{-\infty}^{a} f(x)\,dx = \frac{1}{2}$

The **variance** is a measure of the spread (variability) of the scores. It is measured in square units.

The **standard deviation** is also a measure of the spread (dispersion) of the scores. It is measured in the same units as the random variable.

- for a discrete RV $\quad$ **variance**, $\sigma^2 = \text{Var}(X)$
$$= \sum (x - \mu)^2\,P(x)$$
$$= \sum x^2\,P(x) - \mu^2$$
  standard deviation $\sigma = \sqrt{\text{variance}}$

- for a continuous RV $\quad$ **variance**, $\sigma^2 = \text{Var}(X)$
$$= \int_{-\infty}^{\infty} (x - \mu)^2 f(x)\,dx$$
$$= \int_{-\infty}^{\infty} x^2 f(x)\,dx - \mu^2$$
  standard deviation $\sigma = \sqrt{\text{variance}}$

BINOMIAL DISTRIBUTION

The binomial distribution, its mean and variance

We say the random variable X has a **binomial distribution** if there are n independent trials of the same experiment with the probability of success being a constant p for each trial, i.e., $X \sim B(n,\, p)$

So, $P(X = x) = \binom{n}{x} p^x (1 - p)^{n-x}$ where $x = 0, 1, 2, 3, \ldots n$, and X is the number of successes in n trials of the experiment.

$E(X) = \mu = np$ and $\text{Var}(X) = \sigma^2 = np(1 - p)$.

POISSON DISTRIBUTION

We say the random variable X has a **Poisson distribution** if the events occur singly and at random in a given interval of time or space and m, the mean number of occurrences in the given interval, is finite, i.e. $X \sim \text{Po}(m)$

This implies that $P(X = x) = \dfrac{m^x e^{-m}}{x!}$, for $x = 0, 1, 2, 3, \ldots$

$E(X) = \mu = m$ and $\text{Var}(X) = \sigma^2 = m$.

The Binomial and the Poisson random variables are both examples of discrete random variables and you must use the appropriate rules for discrete random variables.

NORMAL DISTRIBUTION

We say the random variable X has a normal distribution with mean μ, and variance σ^2, i.e., $X \sim N(\mu, \sigma^2)$.

If X is a normal random variable then its probability density function (pdf) takes the shape of a symmetrical bell-shaped curve.

The curve is symmetrical about the mean (μ).

Properties of a normal distribution

The pdf has the property that:

- approx. 68% of all scores lie within one σ of the mean
- approx. 95% of all scores lie within two σs of the mean
- approx. 99.7% of all scores lie within three 3σs of the mean.

Standardisation of normal variables

We can **standardise** the random variable $X \sim N(\mu, \sigma^2)$ to the normal random variable $Z \sim N(0, 1)$ with mean 0 and variance (and standard deviation) 1, by using the rule

$$z = \frac{x - \mu}{\sigma}, \quad \text{i.e.,} \quad X \sim N(\mu, \sigma^2) \Rightarrow Z = \frac{X - \mu}{\sigma} \sim N(0, 1).$$

A value x of the random variable X has a corresponding value z of the random variable Z which indicates how many standard deviations the x is above the mean (if z is positive) or below the mean (when z is negative).

With modern calculators we do not need to use z-scores as often as in pre-calculator days and generally we only need to use z-scores in problem solving when

- we are looking for an unknown mean (μ) or (σ) or
- we are comparing scores from two different normal distributions.

It is important to note that normal random variables are examples of continuous random variables and you must use the appropriate rules for continuous random variables.

You are expected to be able to use calculators or tables to find normal probabilities and also the reverse process of finding scores if probabilities are known.

TOPIC 6 – STATISTICS AND PROBABILITY
SKILL BUILDER QUESTIONS

76 A random sample of the distances of drives hit by a famous golfer, Cheetah Trees, was recorded in the following table:

Distance (m)	Frequency (f)
240–	1
245–	3
250–	6
255–	2
260–	7
265–	6
270–	3
275– but < 280	2

Use the results in the table to answer the following questions:

a How many drives were chosen in the sample?

b Construct a *frequency histogram* of the data using your gdc.

c Find estimates of the *mean, median, mode* and the *standard deviation* of this sample and use these answers to comment on the *symmetry* of the data.

d Draw a *box plot* of this data using your gdc and find the *range* and *interquartile* range of the data. What do these values give an indication of?

e Find an *unbiased estimate* of the *mean* and *standard deviation* of the population from which this sample came.

77 a Use the data in question **76** to prepare a *cumulative frequency* table and graph.

b From your graph determine the *median* and *inter-quartile* range. Comment on these answers and those from question **76**.

c Use the graph to find the 10th *percentile* of drives that Cheetah hit in his sample data.

78 In a sample of data, we know that $\sum f = 30$, $\bar{x} = 80.9$ and the standard deviation of this sample is 296.

Find $\sum f x$ and $\sum f x^2$ for this sample of data, giving your answers to the nearest integer.

79 a In a horse race with 10 horses in the field, why is the probability of a given horse winning *not* necessarily equal to $\frac{1}{10}$?

b Hence, explain when the rule $P(A) = \dfrac{n(A)}{n(U)}$ does not necessarily apply.

80 A bucket contains 7 red, 3 blue, 2 black and 1 yellow ball of the same size. A random selection of 5 balls is taken from the bucket:

a Find the probability that the random selection from the bucket will contain 2 red, 1 blue, and 2 black balls.

b Find the probability that the random selection will contain at least 1 red ball.

81 a Tickets in a raffle are numbered 1 to 100. A ticket is drawn at random. Suppose A is the event that a ticket with number strictly less than 45 is drawn and B is the event that a ticket with numbers between 40 and 55 are drawn.

  i Are A and B mutually exclusive events? Give a reason.

  ii Find $P(A \cup B)$.

b Let $P(A)$ and $P(B)$ both be non-zero. Explain why events A *and* B cannot be both *independent* and *mutually exclusive* at the same time.

82 It is said that events A and B are *independent* if
$P(A \mid B) = P(A)$.

Use this result and the rule for conditional probability to show that this implies $P(A \cap B) = P(A) P(B)$.

83 Events A and B are independent.
Given that $P(A \cup B) = 0.63$ and $P(B) = 0.36$, find $P(A)$.

84 A year 12 IB Maths class has 38% female students. Of the female students in this class, 73% are left handed whereas 44% of the male students are left handed.

a Find the probability that a randomly chosen student from this class is left handed.

b Find the probability that a randomly chosen left handed student is a female.

85 Two unbiased six-sided cubic dice are rolled and the difference between the scores is noted. Using a table of outcomes, find the probability that the difference between the scores is '3'.

86 Given that $P(A) = 0.46$, $P(B) = \frac{5}{7}$ and $P(A \cup B)' = \frac{1}{12}$, find $P(A \cap B)$.

87 A random variable X has the following distribution table:

$X = x$	-2	0	3	5
$P(X = x)$	$\frac{1}{3}$	$\frac{1}{6}$	k	$\frac{1}{12}$

a Is the random variable discrete or continuous?

b Find k.

c Find $E(X)$, $\text{Var}(X)$ and the standard deviation of X.

d Find the *median* and *modal* values of X.

88 A random variable X has a probability density function given by $f(x) = \begin{cases} \sin(0.5x), & 0 \leqslant x \leqslant a \\ 0, & \text{elsewhere} \end{cases}$.

   a Is the random variable discrete or continuous?
   b Find the *exact* value of a.
   c Find $\mathrm{E}(X)$, $\mathrm{Var}(X)$ and the standard deviation of X.
   d Find the *median* and *modal* values of X.

89 Classify the following random variables as Binomial or Poisson:
   a The number (X) of errors in a document consisting of 12 pages made by a typist if on average he makes 1 error per page.
   b The number (Y) of correct answers in a multiple choice test consisting of 30 questions with 5 answers to choose from in each question and only one answer being correct, with each choice being randomly guessed.

90 a For **a** in question **89** above, find
   i the *mean* and *standard deviation* of the random variable X in a document
   ii $\mathrm{P}(X = 10)$ in a document
   iii the probability the typist will be chastised if he makes at least 10 errors in this document.

   b For **b** in question **89** above, find
   i the *mean* and *standard deviation* of the random variable Y
   ii $\mathrm{P}(Y = 20)$
   iii the probability of getting a *distinction* if you require a score of at least the mean plus twice the standard deviation for a *distinction*.

91 The random variable X is distributed normally with *mean* 37 and *variance* 9.
   a Is the random variable discrete or continuous?
   b Why is it almost impossible to have a score of 27?
   c How many standard deviations away from the mean is the score of 33?
   d Explain why $\mathrm{P}(X \geqslant 39)$ is smaller than 0.5.
   e Find $\mathrm{P}(X \geqslant 39)$.
   f Find $P(31 \leqslant X \leqslant 39)$.
   g Find $P(|X - 37| \leqslant 2)$.
   h Find k if $P(X \geqslant k) = 0.56$.

TOPIC 7 — CALCULUS

IMPORTANT CONCEPTS

The list of derivatives together with the chain, product and quotient rules will greatly assist in any question involving differentiation.

Logarithmic rules are often useful.

For example: To find $\dfrac{dy}{dx}$ if $y = \ln \dfrac{(2x+3)^2}{\sqrt{x^2+5}}$

we first use logs: $\ln y = 2\ln(2x+3) - \frac{1}{2}\ln(x^2+5)$

then $\dfrac{1}{y}\dfrac{dy}{dx} = \dfrac{4}{2x+3} - \dfrac{x}{x^2+5}$, etc

When determining the nature of stationary points, remember that, if both the first and second derivatives of a function are zero, no conclusion can be made. Checking the sign diagram for the first or second derivative will be necessary.

For trigonometric integrals, these trigonometric identities are useful:

- $\tan^2 x = \sec^2 x - 1$
- $\cos^2 x = \frac{1}{2} + \frac{1}{2}\cos 2x$
- $\sin^2 x = \frac{1}{2} - \frac{1}{2}\cos 2x$

There is a difference between a definite integral and an area. The former can be negative, the latter cannot.

If using the gdc to determine the total area enclosed by $y = f(x)$ and the x axis between $x = a$ and $x = b$, use $\int_a^b |f(x)|\, dx$.

This is not necessary if the graph is above the x axis between a and b but it is possibly safer to always use it.

The formula $a = v\dfrac{dv}{ds}$ will be useful in **kinematic problems** where the acceleration is given as a function of the displacement rather than time.

When velocity is given as a function of displacement, the differential equation $\dfrac{ds}{dt} = f(s)$ can usually be solved by separation of variables.

For **optimisation problem**s, it is important to remember that a local maximum or minimum does not always give the maximum or minimum values of the function in a particular domain.

Check to see whether there are any other turning points for that domain or whether the end values of the domain give higher or lower values.

When using the calculator for graphing functions, make sure you choose appropriate windows so that essential properties of the function are not missed. Sometimes a calculator shows a graph finishing in "mid air" when the function is asymptotic. Zooming in or out may

For a rational function $F(x) = \dfrac{f(x)}{g(x)}$:

- $f(x) = 0$ gives x-intercepts
- $F(0)$ gives the y-intercept
- $g(x) = 0$ gives the equations of **vertical asymptotes**
- If the degree of $f(x) <$ the degree of $g(x)$, the **horizontal asymptote** is $y = 0$.
- If the degree of $f(x) =$ the degree of $g(x)$, the **horizontal asymptote** is $y = a$ where a is the quotient found when $f(x)$ is divided by $g(x)$.
- If the degree of $f(x) = 1 +$ the degree of $g(x)$, the **oblique asymptote** will be $y = ax + b$ where $ax + b$ is the quotient found when $f(x)$ is divided by $g(x)$.

The graph of a function will never cross its vertical asymptotes, but may cross its horizontal or oblique asymptote.

Equations which are expressed implicitly are not always functions. For any x value there may be more than one y value. Information in the question may indicate whether a particular value should be chosen.

When finding $\dfrac{dy}{dx}$ if, for example $x^2 + xy - y^2 = 7$, a common error is to forget to differentiate the right hand side.

When using substitution on a definite integral, there is no need to change back to the original variable as long as you have changed the limits of integration.

For example, $\int_a^b f(x)\, dx$.

If using the substitution $u = x - 2$, the limits of the integral become $a - 2$ and $b - 2$.

If using $x = g(u)$, then the limits become $g^{-1}(a)$ and $g^{-1}(b)$.

TOPIC 7 – CALCULUS (SKILL BUILDER QUESTIONS)

92 Find $f'(x)$ if $f(x) = \sqrt{3x^2 + 5x - 2}$.

93 Find $\dfrac{dy}{dx}$ if $y = \ln(2x^2 + 8)$.

94 Find $f'(x)$ if $f(x) = x^2 e^{2x-3}$.

95 Find $f'(x)$ if $f(x) = 3^{x^2 - x - 2}$.

96 Find $\dfrac{dy}{dx}$ if $y = \dfrac{x+2}{x^2+3}$, fully simplifying your answer.

97 Find $f'(x)$ if $f(x) = (\sin x)e^{\cos x}$.

98 Find $\dfrac{dy}{dx}$ if $y = \arcsin(2x+3)$.

99 Find $\dfrac{d^2y}{dx^2}$ if $y = x^2 \sin 2x$.

100 Find the equation of the tangent to the function

$f(x) = \dfrac{x-4}{x-2}$ at the point where $x = 3$.

101 Find the equation of the normal to the curve $y = x^2 - 2x - 1$ at the point where $x = -1$.

102 For what values of x is the graph of the function

$f(x) = \dfrac{x}{x^2 - 2}$ concave down?

103 Find the exact coordinates of the stationary points of the function $f(x) = 2x^3 - 3x^2 - 12x + 7$.

104 Find the exact coordinates of the stationary points of the function $f(x) = \dfrac{x-3}{x^2-5}$.

105 Find all asymptotes of the graph of $y = f(x)$ if

$f(x) = \dfrac{2x^2 - 3x + 6}{x^2 - x - 6}$.

106 Find $\dfrac{dy}{dx}$ if $x^2 - xy^2 + y = 21$.

107 Find $\displaystyle\int \dfrac{2x^2 - x - 3}{x^2}\, dx$.

108 Find the exact value of $\displaystyle\int_3^5 \dfrac{x}{x^2 - 8}\, dx$.

109 Find $\displaystyle\int \sin^2 3x\, dx$.

110 Find $\displaystyle\int \tan^2 2x\, dx$.

111 Find the exact value of k, $k > 0$, if $\displaystyle\int_0^k \dfrac{x}{\sqrt{x^2+4}}\, dx = 1$.

112 Use integration by parts to find $\displaystyle\int x \ln x\, dx$.

113 Use integration by parts to find $\displaystyle\int \arctan x\, dx$.

114 Find the exact value of $\displaystyle\int_0^4 \dfrac{1}{\sqrt{x+4}}\, dx$.

115 Find the total distance travelled by a particle in the first 5 seconds of motion if the particle is moving in a straight line and its velocity is given by $v = t^3 - 3t^2 e^{0.05t}$.

116 Find the exact area of the region enclosed by the graph of $y = 8x - x^2$ and the x-axis.

117 Find the exact value of the area of the region enclosed by the graphs of $y = x^2 - 3x$ and the line $y = x$.

118 Find the volume of the solid formed when the region enclosed by the graph of $y = x^2 - 2x$ and the x-axis is rotated about the x-axis. Give your answer as an exact value.

119 Find the volume of the solid formed when the region enclosed by the graph of $y = \ln x$, the x-axis, the y-axis and the line $y = \ln 3$ is rotated about the y-axis. Give your answer as an exact value.

120 Solve for y: $y\dfrac{dy}{dx} = 2x - 3$ given that, when $x = 0$, $y = 4$.

121 Solve for y: $\dfrac{dy}{dx} = 3x^2 y + y$ given that, when $x = 0$, $y = 2$.

EXAMINATION PRACTICE SET 1

122 a The sum of the first eight terms of an arithmetic sequence is -4 whilst the sum of the next eight terms is 188. Find an expression for u_n, the nth term of the sequence.

b x and y are integers such that 9, x, and y are consecutive terms of a geometric sequence and x, y and 2 are consecutive terms of an arithmetic sequence. Find the values of x and y.

123 Eight different books are to be placed in a row on a bookshelf. Three of the books are mathematics books. How many arrangements are possible if

a there are no restrictions

b the mathematics books are always placed together

c there has to be a mathematics book at each end of the shelf?

124 Given the two sets of equations,

$y_1 = x_1 + x_2 - x_3$ $x_1 = 2z_1 + 3z_2 - z_3$

$y_2 = 2x_1 - x_2 + 5x_3$ $x_2 = 4z_1 - 2z_2 + z_3$

$y_3 = 3x_1 - 2x_2 + x_3$ $x_3 = z_1 - 6z_2 + 7z_3$

use matrix methods to obtain three equations that express y_1, y_2, and y_3 directly in terms of z_1, z_2 and z_3.

125 The coordinates of X and Y are $(3\mu, 2, 1)$ and $(\mu, 1 - 3\mu, 2\mu - 1)$ respectively, where μ is a constant.

If O is the origin, find all values of μ for which $\overrightarrow{OX}$ is perpendicular to $\overrightarrow{OY}$.

126 Let $f(x) = x^2 + 4x$ for $-\infty < x \leqslant -2$ and $g(x) = \sqrt{3 - 2x}$.

Find: **a** $f^{-1}(x)$ **b** $(g \circ f)(-3)$.

127 If the polynomial $x^n + ax^2 - 6$ leaves a remainder of -3 when divided by $(x - 1)$ and a remainder of -15 when divided by $(x + 3)$, find the values of a and n.

128 A sector cuts off an angle of $53°$ at the centre of a circle of radius 7 cm. Find:

a the perimeter of the sector   **b** the area of the sector.

129 In triangle ABC, $A\widehat{B}C = 2\theta$, $A\widehat{C}B = \theta$, AB = 3 cm and AC = 5 cm. Find the exact value of the area of the triangle.

130 Find the exact values of x if $-\pi \leqslant x \leqslant \pi$ and $\sin^2 x + \cos x = \frac{5}{4}$

131 For what values of x in the interval $[0, 2\pi]$ is $\arccos(\sin 3x + \cos 2x)$ defined?

132 A receptionist walks to work every day.

If it is not raining, the probability that he is late is $\frac{1}{6}$.

If it is raining, the probability that he is late is $\frac{3}{5}$.

The probability that it rains on a particular day is $\frac{1}{5}$.

On one particular day the receptionist is late.

Find the probability that it was raining on that day.

133 A discrete random variable X has the probability distribution.

x	0	1	2	3	4
$P(X = x)$	$\frac{1}{6}$	$2k$	$\frac{1}{5}k$	$\frac{1}{3}$	$\frac{2}{5}k$

a Find the exact value of k.   **b** Calculate $P(0 < X < 4)$.

134 X is a binomial random variable, where the number of trials is 7 and the probability of success of each trial is p. Find the possible values of p if $P(X = 4) = 0.25$

135 Find the exact values of the coordinates of the point of intersection of the normal at the point where $x = \frac{\pi}{6}$, to the graph of $y = \sin x$, and the x-axis.

136 The graph of the function $f : x \mapsto ax^3 + bx^2 + cx + d$ has a maximum turning point at $(0, 1)$ and a minimum turning point at $(-2, -2)$. Find a, b, c and d.

137 AB is a diameter of a circle of radius 5 cm and P is a point on the circle. P moves at a constant rate in a clockwise direction on the circle and completes one rotation every 10π seconds. Find, as an exact value, the rate of change in the area of triangle ABP when $\widehat{PAB} = \frac{\pi}{3}$ and P is moving towards B.

138 Find the exact value of $\displaystyle\int_0^{\frac{\pi}{6}} (\sin 3x \cos 2x + \cos 3x \sin 2x)\ dx$

139 The region enclosed by $y = \arccos x$, $y = \frac{\pi}{3}$, $y = \frac{\pi}{6}$ and the y-axis is rotated about the y-axis. Find the exact value of the volume of the solid generated.

140 Use the substitution $x = \sin u$ to find the exact value of $\displaystyle\int_0^{\frac{1}{2}} \sqrt{1 - x^2}\ dx$

141 Find the exact value of p if $p > 0$ and $\displaystyle\int_0^p x^3 + x\ dx = \frac{15}{4}$.

142 The graph of $f(x)$ is given.

a Draw the graph of $|f(x)|$, on the same set of axes as shown.

b Find the y-intercept of $\dfrac{1}{f(x)}$.

c Draw the graph of $y = \dfrac{1}{f(x)}$ on the same set of axes as shown.

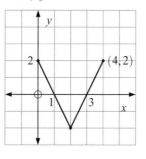

143 Given two lines with equations:
line l_1: $x = 3\lambda + 4$, $y = \lambda + 4$, $z = 2\lambda - 1$.
line l_2: $x + 1 = \dfrac{y - k}{2} = \dfrac{z - 1}{-2}$.

a Find the value of k for which these lines are coplanar, and hence determine the point of intersection of the two lines.

b Find a vector $\mathbf{p}$ which is perpendicular to both l_1 and l_2.

c Show that an equation of the plane which is normal to vector $\mathbf{p}$ and contains l_1 is $-6x + 8y + 5z = 3$.

144 A police radar gun measuring the speeds of cars on the road is known to produce errors at random that are distributed normally with mean 0 and standard deviation σ.

We say the error E is distributed normally as
$E \sim N\ (\mu = 0,\ \text{variance} = \sigma^2)$.

The police will not prosecute without being 99% confident that a car is travelling at greater than 60 km/h in a 60 km/h zone.

Suppose they are 99% sure that a car is travelling at greater than 60 km/h (i.e., it is speeding) when they record a speed of more than 65 km/h on the radar gun.

a Explain why the distribution of readings for a car travelling at 60 km/h is given by the random variable $X = 60 + E$.

b Find the standard deviation σ, of the distribution of errors given by the radar gun.

145 The function f is defined by: $f(x) = \dfrac{k \ln x}{x}$, $k > 0$, $x > 0$.

a Find the exact coordinates of the stationary point on the graph of $y = f(x)$.

b Find the exact coordinates of the point of inflection on the graph of $y = f(x)$.

c Find k if $\displaystyle\int_1^{e^2} \dfrac{k \ln x}{x}\ dx = 10$.

d Use integration by parts to show that
$$\int \frac{(\ln x)^2}{x^2}\ dx = -\frac{1}{x}(\ln x)^2 - \frac{2}{x}\ln x - \frac{2}{x} + c$$

e Hence, find the exact value of the volume of the solid formed by rotating the region enclosed by the x axis, $y = f(x)$, where $k = 1$, and the line $x = e^2$ about the x-axis.

146 On the unit circle shown, $\widehat{AOP} = \alpha$ and $\widehat{BOP} = \beta$. OA is produced to meet the line through B parallel to the y-axis at C. CB produced meets the x-axis at D.

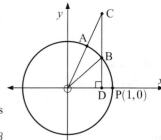

a Write down the lengths of OD and BD.

b Show that $OC = \dfrac{\cos \beta}{\cos \alpha}$.

c Show that $BC = \cos \beta \tan \alpha - \sin \beta$

d Use the sine rule in triangle OBC to show that $\sin(\alpha - \beta) = \sin \alpha \cos \beta - \cos \alpha \sin \beta$.

e Hence find the exact value of $\sin 15°$.

147 Given **A** such that $\mathbf{A} = \begin{bmatrix} 1 - k & -2 & -1 \\ 1 & -1 & -2 \\ 1 & k & -1 \end{bmatrix}$, $k \in \mathbb{R}$

a For what values of k is the matrix non-singular.

b Find $\mathbf{A}^{-1}$ if $k = 0$.

c Hence find the point of intersection of the planes:
$x - 2y - z = 2$
$x - y - 2z = -1$
$x - y = 2$

d Show that the point of intersection of the plane lies on the line, l, given by: $\dfrac{x + 3}{2} = y + 4 = \dfrac{7 - z}{-1}$.

e Find the angle between l and the plane $x - 2y - z = 2$.

EXAMINATION PRACTICE SET 2

148 A geometric series with common ratio r, where $0.5 < r < 1$ has second term 6 and a sum of 49. Find:
a r **b** u_n, the nth term of the series.

149 Find the exact value of x if $2^{2x} + 2^{x+1} - 15 = 0$.

150 Find the term independent of x in the expansion of $\left(2x^2 + \dfrac{1}{x}\right)^9$.

151 Let two functions f and g be given such that $g(x) = 3x - 2$ and $(f \circ g)(x) = x + 2$, find $f(9x - 8)$.

152 Find the points of intersection of the graphs of $x^2 y = 4 + x$ and $y = e^x - 3x + 1$, where $-5 \leqslant x \leqslant 5$.

153 When a cubic polynomial $p(x)$ is divided by $x(2x - 3)$, the remainder is $ax + b$, (where a and b are real).

a If the quotient is the same as the remainder, write down an expression for $p(x)$.

b Prove that $(2x - 1)$ and $(x - 1)$ are both factors of $p(x)$.

c Find the equation of $p(x)$ given that it has a y-intercept $(0, 7)$ and passes through the point $(2, 39)$.

154 Each of two circles with the same radius passes through the centre of the other. Find the area common to both circles if the radii are 6 cm, giving your answer as an exact value.

155 Find the exact value of x in the diagram below.

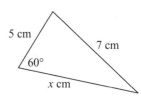

156 Find the exact values of $\tan x$ if $2\sin\left(x + \frac{\pi}{6}\right) = \sin x$

157 Simplify $\sin(\arcsin a + \arcsin b)$, giving your answer in terms of a and b.

158 a Find the inverse of the matrix $\mathbf{A} = \begin{bmatrix} -1 & k \\ k & 1 \end{bmatrix}$ where $k \in \mathbb{R}$

    b Hence, or otherwise, solve the simultaneous equations
$$-x + ky = 2k$$
$$kx + y = 1 - k^2$$

159 Find a unit vector parallel to $\lambda\mathbf{i} + \mathbf{j} - \lambda\mathbf{k}$ and perpendicular to $3\mathbf{i} - 4\mathbf{j} + \mathbf{k}$.

160 In a school, $\frac{2}{7}$ of the students travel to school by bicycle.

Seven students are chosen at random.

Find the probability that exactly 4 of them travel to school by bicycle.

161 A box contains 1000 fish with 3.7% not suitable for sale. If 20 fish are chosen at random from the box, what is the probability that

    a all of them are suitable for sale

    b exactly one of them is not suitable for sale?

162 Find the exact value of the x coordinate of the stationary point of the function $f : x \mapsto e^{x \ln x}$, $x > 0$

163 Find the exact value of the coordinates of the stationary points on the curve $y = \sin x(1 + \cos x)$ for $0 \leqslant x \leqslant 2\pi$.

164 The radius of the base of a right circular cylinder is r cm and its height is $2r$ cm. Find the rate at which the surface area of the cylinder is increasing when the radius is 5 cm and the volume is increasing at 5π cm^{3}s^{-1}.

165 Find the exact value of $\displaystyle\int_{\frac{\pi}{6}}^{\frac{\pi}{3}} (\cos^2 x + \tan^2 x)\, dx$

166 a Find the exact value of the area enclosed by the curve

$$y = \frac{1}{\sqrt{4 - x^2}},$$ the y-axis, the x-axis and the line $x = 1$.

    b The region in **a** is rotated about the x-axis. Find the volume of the solid generated.

167 Find $\displaystyle\int \frac{x^2}{\sqrt{x+2}}\, dx$

168 Find k where $k > 0$ if $\displaystyle\int_1^k 3\sqrt{10 - x}\, dx = 38$.

169 When a biased die is rolled the numbers from 1 to 6 appear according to the following probability distribution.

Result	1	2	3	4	5	6
$P(X = x)$	$\frac{2}{7}$	$\frac{1}{7}$	$\frac{3}{14}$	$\frac{1}{14}$	$\frac{1}{7}$	y

    a Find the value of y.

    b If X is the random variable which takes on values 1 to 6 of the above table find the exact values of $E(X)$ and $Var(X)$.

    c Write a brief interpretation of the values found in part **b**.

170 a i Prove that $\sin(A + B) + \sin(A - B) = 2\sin A \cos B$

      ii Hence, or otherwise, find the exact value of the period of the function $f(x) = \sin 5x \cos 2x$.

      iii Find $\int \sin 5x \cos 2x\, dx$

      iv Hence find the exact value of $\int_0^{\frac{\pi}{3}} \sin 5x \cos 2x\, dx$

    b i Prove that $\cos(A + B) - \cos(A - B) = -2\sin A \sin B$

      ii Prove by mathematical induction that, for all $n \in \mathbb{Z}^+$,

$$\sin x + \sin 3x + \sin 5x + \ldots + \sin(2n - 1)x = \frac{\sin^2 nx}{\sin x}$$

171 a In the triangle shown, find a in terms of b.

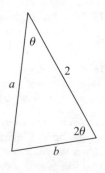

    b Prove that for all $n \in \mathbb{Z}^+$,

$$\int_0^{\frac{\pi}{4}} \tan^n x\, dx + \int_0^{\frac{\pi}{4}} \tan^{n-2} x\, dx = \frac{1}{n - 1}$$

172 Let $\mathbf{r} = \begin{bmatrix} 2t + 5 \\ -2t - 1 \\ t \end{bmatrix}$, $t \in \mathbb{R}$ be an equation of line L.

The plane P has a normal vector $3\mathbf{i} - 4\mathbf{j} - \mathbf{k}$ and passes through the point A(-1, 0, 4).

    a Show that the point B(9, -5, 2) lies on the line L.

    b Give an equation of the plane P.

    c Show that the line L meets the plane P at the point C(1, 3, -2).

    d The line N through the point B(9, -5, 2) is perpendicular to the plane P. Find an equation of the line N.

    e Show that the point of intersection of the line N and the plane P is the point D(3, 3, 4).

    f Find the coordinates of the point B$'$ on the line N such that the plane P bisects the line segment BB$'$.

    g Decide if the vector $\mathbf{i} - 2\mathbf{j} - 2\mathbf{k}$ is parallel to the line CB$'$. Give reasons for your answer.

173 A survey of 100 people is conducted to find out how long people spend travelling to work. The following results were recorded:

Travelling time (min)	Frequency
1 - 10	11
11 - 20	19
21 - 30	32
31 - 40	22
41 - 50	9
51 - 60	7

    a Use you gdc to input this data and then to calculate the important statistics: *mean, median, mode, upper* and *lower quartiles, range, interquartile range* (IQR).

    b Add to the table above by including headings for cumulative frequency and mid-point.

    c Use your gdc to draw the following diagrams: *histogram, cumulative frequency graph*, and a *box plot*.

    d Use the *cumulative frequency graph* (ogive) you have drawn to calculate the 10th percentile and the 90th percentile of these scores. What do these answers mean?

    e Let Y be a binomial random variable with mean 3 and standard deviation $\frac{3}{2}$. Find $P(Y \leqslant 4)$.

174 a Find $\sum_{r=1}^{3} (2r + 2^r)$

   b Find an expression for $\sum_{r=1}^{n} (2r + 2^r)$.

175 If $\log_a 2 = b$ and $\log_a 3 = c$, express $\log_a \sqrt{72}$ in terms of b and c.

176 The coefficient of x^4 in the expansion of $(ax + 3)^5$ is equal to the coefficient of x^5 in the expansion of $(ax + 3)^7$. Find a.

177 Consider the functions $f(x) = \dfrac{1}{x + 5}$, $x \neq -5$ and $g(x) = 3x$.

   a Calculate $(g \circ f)(4)$ as a rational number.

   b Find $g^{-1}(x)$.

   c Find the domain of g^{-1}.

178 a On the graph drawn alongside, sketch the graph of the inverse of $y = f(x) = -x^2 + 3$.

   b Briefly explain why the inverse of $y = f(x)$ is not a function.

   c Find the equation of the inverse of $x \mapsto -x^2 + 3$, $x \leqslant 0$ and illustrate this function on your sketch.

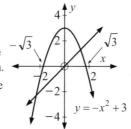

179 Factorise $f(x) = 2x^3 - x^2 - 8x - 5$ into real factors and hence, determine the values of x for which $f(x) \geqslant 0$.

180 The radius of a circle is 4 cm. Find the exact value of the area of the minor segment of the circle cut off by a chord of length $4\sqrt{3}$ cm.

181 In triangle PQR, $\sin \widehat{PRQ} = \dfrac{3\sqrt{3}}{14}$, $QP = 3$ cm and $PR = 7$ cm. Find the possible values of $\widehat{PQR}$, giving your answer in degrees.

182 Find the exact value of $\sin\theta$ if $3\cos 2\theta + 2 = 7\sin\theta$.

183 Find the exact value of $\cos\left(\arcsin\frac{3}{5} + \arccos\frac{2}{3}\right)$.

184 a Find the values of **A** and **B** if

$$\mathbf{A} = \begin{bmatrix} 2 & 1 & a \\ a & 2 & 1 \\ 0 & 6 & 1 \end{bmatrix} \text{ is the inverse of } \mathbf{B} = \begin{bmatrix} -2b & 7 & -3 \\ a & b & 1 \\ 6 & -6b & -5 \end{bmatrix}$$

   b Hence, solve simultaneously the equations

$$\begin{aligned} 4u + 7v - 3w &= -8 \\ -u - 2v + w &= 3 \\ 6u + 12v - 5w &= -15 \end{aligned}$$

185 If $\mathbf{a} + \mathbf{b} + \mathbf{c} = \mathbf{0}$, show that $\mathbf{a} \times \mathbf{b} = \mathbf{b} \times \mathbf{c}$.

186 The diameters of discs produced by a machine are normally distributed with a mean of 73 mm and standard deviation of 1.1 mm. Find the probability of the machine producing a disc with a diameter larger than 75 mm.

187 Independent events A and B are such that $P(A) = 0.35$ and $P(A \cup B) = 0.75$. Find $P(B)$.

188 A couple is told that the probability that they will have blonde-hair children is $\frac{1}{7}$. The couple would like to have 5 children.

   a What is the expected number of blonde-haired children?

   b What is the probability that 3 of the children will have blonde-hair?

   c What is the probability that more than 3 children will have blonde-hair?

189 The probability that a salesperson leaves her mobile phone in a shop is $\frac{1}{6}$. After visiting two shops in succession, the salesperson discovers her mobile phone is missing. What is the probability that she left the mobile phone in the first shop?

190 If $y = \ln(x^2 - 3)$, simplify $\dfrac{d^2y}{dx^2} + \left(\dfrac{dy}{dx}\right)^2$.

191 For the graph of the function $f : x \mapsto \dfrac{e^{x^2}}{e^x - 1}$

   a i Find the equation of any vertical asymptotes, given in exact form.

   ii Find the coordinates of the turning points.

   b Sketch the graph of $y = \dfrac{e^{x^2}}{e^x - 1}$ for $x \in [-1, 2]$.

192 Find the exact value of $\displaystyle\int_0^{\frac{\pi}{4}} \left(\tan x - \dfrac{\tan x - 1}{\tan x + 1}\right) dx$

193 The region enclosed by the graph of $y = 1 + \tan x$, the x and y axes and $x = \frac{\pi}{4}$ is rotated about the x-axis. Find the exact value of the volume generated.

194 The velocity of a particle, in metres per second at time t seconds, is given by $v = t^3 - 3t^2 + 2t$. Calculate the distance travelled by the particle in the first 3 seconds of motion.

195 Solve the differential equation $xy\dfrac{dy}{dx} + 1 = x^2$ for $x > 0$ given that $y = 2$ when $x = 1$. Give your answer in the form $y = f(x)$.

196 ABCD is a rectangle such that A and B are points on the graph of $y = \sqrt{1 - x^2}$ and C and D lie on the x-axis. Let C have coordinates $(a, 0)$.

   a Write an expression for the area of ABCD

   b Find the exact value of x when the area is a maximum.

   c Find the maximum area of the rectangle.

197 a Given the points $A(3, 0, 2)$, $B(1, 0, 3)$ and $C(2, -3, 5)$, show that $\overrightarrow{AB} \times \overrightarrow{AC} = \begin{bmatrix} 3 \\ 5 \\ 6 \end{bmatrix}$.

   b Students are using equations of planes to model two hillsides that meet along a river. The river is modelled by the line where the two planes meet.

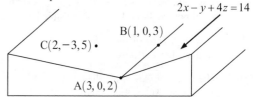

One of the hillsides contains the points with coordinates A(3, 0, 2), B (1, 0, 3) and C(2, -3, 5). The other hillside has an equation $2x - y + 4z = 14$.

   i Show that A and B are two points on the river.

   ii Show that an equation for the river is

$$\mathbf{r} = \begin{bmatrix} 3 - 2\lambda \\ 0 \\ 2 + \lambda \end{bmatrix} \text{ for } \lambda \in \mathbb{R}.$$

   iii Show that B is the closest point on the river to C.

   iv Find the shortest distance from the river to C.

198 a Let $P(u, \cos u)$ be any point on the graph of $y = \cos x$ in the first quadrant

   i Find the equation of the tangent to the curve $y = \cos x$ at P.

   ii The tangent at P meets the x-axis at A and the y-axis at B. Find the coordinates of A and B.

   iii Find an expression for the area of triangle AOB.

   iv Find the coordinates of P for which the area of triangle AOB is a minimum.

b The hour hand and minute hand of a large railway station clock are 2 metres and 3 metres long respectively. Find the rate at which the distance between the ends of the hands is changing at 4.00 pm

199 a Given the sequence defined by $u_{n+2} = u_n + u_{n+1}$ where $u_1 = u_2 = 1$ and $n \in \mathbb{Z}^+$, use mathematical induction to prove that

$$\begin{bmatrix} 1 & 1 \\ 1 & 0 \end{bmatrix}^n = \begin{bmatrix} u_{n+1} & u_n \\ u_n & u_{n-1} \end{bmatrix} \text{ for } n \geqslant 2.$$

b i Use integration by parts to show that
$$\int (\ln x)^2 dx = x(\ln x)^2 - 2x\ln x + 2x + c$$

ii The region bounded by $y = \ln x$, the x-axis and the line $x = 3$ is rotated about the x axis. Find the exact value of the volume of the solid generated.

iii The region described in **b** is rotated about the y-axis. Find the exact value of the volume of the solid generated.

EXAMINATION PRACTICE SET 4

200 For the arithmetic series $3 + 8 + 13 + \ .....$
a find an expression for S_n, the sum of the first n terms of the series
b Find the smallest value of n for which the sum of the series is greater than 1000.

201 Simplify: $\log_2 27 \times \log_3 16$

202 When $(1 + ax)^n$, $n \in \mathbb{Z}^+$ is written in expanded form as far as the third term, the result is $1 + 35x + 525x^2$.
Find a and n.

203 Let the function $f : x \mapsto a + \dfrac{b}{x + c}$.
The graph of f has asymptotes at $x = -2$ and $y = 3$ and passes through $(2, 4)$.
a Find the values of a, b and c.
b State the domain and range of f.
c Find f^{-1} and state the domain and range of f^{-1}.

204 The graph of $x \mapsto kx^2 - 3x + (k+2)$ cuts the x-axis in two distinct points. Find the set of possible real values of k.

205 $1 - 2i$ is a zero of the polynomial $2z^3 - 9z^2 + 20z - 25$. Find the other two zeros.

206 In the diagram, AB is the diameter of the circle, AC = 6 cm, and BC = 8 cm. Find the area of the minor segment cut off by AC.

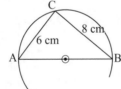

207 In triangle ABC, AB = 7 cm, BC = 5 cm and $\cos A\widehat{C}B = \frac{3}{5}$, find the exact length of AC.

208 Find the exact value of $\cot A$ if $\cot 2A = \frac{3}{5}$ and A is obtuse.

209 Find the exact value of $\sin 2(\arcsin \frac{3}{5})$.

210 Find the value(s) of λ for which $|\mathbf{A} - \lambda\mathbf{I}| = -2$ where
$$\mathbf{A} = \begin{bmatrix} 0 & 4 \\ 1 & 3 \end{bmatrix} \text{ and } \mathbf{I} = \begin{bmatrix} 1 & 0 \\ 0 & 1 \end{bmatrix}.$$

211 Find all values of k for which this system of equations has a non-zero solution (that is, $(x, y, z) \neq (0, 0, 0)$).
$$2x - 2y + kz = 0$$
$$x + 4z = 0$$
$$kx + y + z = 0$$

212 A discrete random variable takes the values $X = 0, 2, 7$ with probabilities $\frac{1}{4}$, $\frac{3}{7}$, and k respectively.
a Find k.
b Find the mean, median, and mode of X.
c Find the variance and standard deviation of X.

213 The random variable X is normally distributed and $P(X \geqslant 20) \approx 0.386$ and $P(X \geqslant 25) \approx 0.183$. Find the mean and standard deviation of X.

214 For what values of a does the function $f(x) = \dfrac{ax + 2}{x^2 + 1}$ have stationary points?

215 Find the x-coordinate of the stationary point of $y = xe^{2x} - 3e^{2x}$.

216 Find $\int \sec x \tan x \ dx$.

217 Find the exact value of $\displaystyle\int_0^{\frac{1}{2}} \frac{1}{\sqrt{1 - x^2}} dx$.

218 a Find the exact value of the area of the region enclosed by the curve $y = xe^{-0.1x^2}$, the x axis and $x = 4$.
b Find the volume generated when the region in **a** is rotated about the x-axis.

219 A particle starts from O with initial velocity of 5 ms^{-1}. After t seconds, the acceleration of the particle is given by $a = 3t^2 - 2t + 1$. Find an expression for s, the displacement of the particle at time t.

220 Solve the differential equation $\dfrac{dy}{dx} = x \sec y$ given that $y = \frac{\pi}{6}$ when $x = 0$.

221 In the figure, $\overrightarrow{OB}$ is three times longer than $\overrightarrow{OA}$, $\overrightarrow{BC}$ is parallel to $\overrightarrow{OA}$ and twice its length. $\overrightarrow{CD}$ is parallel to $\overrightarrow{BA}$. Angle AOB is $60°$.

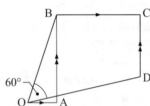

If A and B have position vectors **a** and **b** respectively, relative to O, and $\overrightarrow{CD} = k(\overrightarrow{BA})$, determine,
a vector expressions for **i** $\overrightarrow{BA}$ **ii** $\overrightarrow{OD}$.
b k if $\overrightarrow{OD}$ is perpendicular to $\overrightarrow{AB}$.

222 The table below shows the number of components produced by machines I and II, and the probability of machines I and II producing faulty components.

Machine	Number of components made	Probability of making faulty ones
I	1700	5.2%
II	3300	4.3%

a If a component is chosen at random from the total number of components produced, what is the probability that it is faulty?
b If a component is selected at random and it is found to be faulty, what is the chance that it is produced by machine II?

223 A machine is set to produce bags of sugar, whose weights are distributed normally, with a mean of 120 g and a standard deviation of 1.063 g. If the weight of a bag of sugar is less than 118 g, the bag is rejected.
a With these settings, find the percentage of the bags are rejected, correct to *3 decimal places*.
b The settings of the machine are altered and it is found that 6% of the bags are rejected. If the mean has not changed, find the new standard deviation, correct to *3 decimal places*.
c The machine is adjusted to operate with this new value of the standard deviation. Find the value, correct to *two decimal places*, at which the mean should be set so that only 3% of the bags are rejected.

d With the new settings from part **c**, it is found that 70% of the bags of sugar have a weight which lies between x g and y g , where x and y are symmetric about the mean. Find the values of x and y, giving your answers correct to *two decimal places*.

224 For the graph of the function $y = f(x)$ where
$$f(x) = \frac{x - 2}{x^2 + cx - 6}$$
   a Write down the intercepts on the axes.
   b Determine the equation of the horizontal asymptote.
   c For what values of c is there at least one vertical asymptote?
   d Find an expression for $f'(x)$
   e For what values of c does the function have at least one stationary point?
   f For $c = 0$, find the coordinates of the point of inflection of the curve, giving your answer to 3 significant figures.
   g For $c = -4$, find the exact value of $\displaystyle\int_{-1}^{1} \frac{x - 2}{x^2 + cx - 6}\, dx$.

225 **a** **i** By expanding $(\cos\theta + i\sin\theta)^5$ and using De Moivre's Theorem, find an expression for $\sin 5\theta$ in terms of $\sin\theta$.
      ii Hence, determine that the exact value of $\sin 36°$ is $\frac{1}{4}\sqrt{10 - 2\sqrt{5}}$.
   b **i** In triangle ABC, $BC = a$, $AC = b$ and $AB = c$. D is the midpoint of BC. Let the length of the median AD be m. Show that $m^2 = \frac{1}{4}\left(2b^2 + 2c^2 - a^2\right)$
      ii Hence show that, the area of an isosceles triangle with equal sides x units and base a units is given by $\frac{1}{4}a\sqrt{4x^2 - a^2}$.

EXAMINATION PRACTICE SET 5

226 Find the sum of the first 100 terms of the series $\ln\sqrt{2} + \ln 2 + \ln\sqrt{8} + \ldots\ldots$ giving your answer in the form $n\ln 2$ where $n \in \mathbb{Z}$.

227 If $\log_a 3 = 7$, find
   a the exact value of $\log_a 27$
   b the exact value of $\log_{\sqrt{a}} 3$
   c the value of a, to 3 significant figures.

228 Given two complex numbers, $z = 5 - 3i$ and $w = b + 2i$, $b \in \mathbb{Q}$, find b if $\dfrac{z}{w} \in \mathbb{R}$.

229 Let $f : x \mapsto \sqrt{\dfrac{1}{x^2} - 4}$. Find:
   a the set of real values of x for which $f(x)$ is real and finite
   b the range of f.

230 For what real values of m will the line $y = mx + 16$ be a tangent to the parabola $y = x^2 + 25$?

231 Solve for x, the equation $\log_3\left(4x^2 - 5x - 6\right) = 1 + 2\log_3 x$

232 The diagram below shows a major sector of the circle with centre O. The perimeter of the sector is 100 cm. Find the area of the sector.

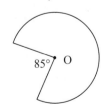

233 Find the exact value of a in the diagram:

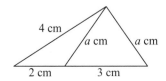

234 Find the exact values of θ if $\theta \in [0, 2\pi]$ and $\cos\theta + \sin\theta = \sqrt{2}$.

235 Find the exact value of x if $\arctan\left(\dfrac{x}{3}\right) + \arctan 6 = \arctan 3$.

236 Consider the matrices $\mathbf{M} = \begin{bmatrix} 2 & 3 \\ 1 & 0 \end{bmatrix}$ and $\mathbf{N} = \begin{bmatrix} 1 & 6 \\ 2 & -3 \end{bmatrix}$,
   a show that **i** $\mathbf{MN} = \mathbf{NM}$ **ii** $(\mathbf{MN})^{-1} = \mathbf{N}^{-1}\mathbf{M}^{-1}$.
   b Explain clearly why $\mathbf{M}^2 - \mathbf{N}^2 = (\mathbf{M} - \mathbf{N})(\mathbf{M} + \mathbf{N})$ for these particular values of $\mathbf{M}$ and $\mathbf{N}$.
    Hence find the matrix $\mathbf{M}^2 - \mathbf{N}^2$.

237 Given the vectors $\mathbf{a} = -2\mathbf{i} + p\mathbf{j} - \mathbf{k}$ and $\mathbf{b} = \mathbf{i} + 3(p + 4)\mathbf{j} + (2p - 5)\mathbf{k}$, find all values of p for which $\mathbf{a}$ is perpendicular to $\mathbf{b}$.

238 Two dice are rolled. The score is the smaller of the two numbers that appear. If the same number appears on both dice, then the score is that number. What is the probability that the score is 4?

239 Find the term independent of x in the expansion of $\left(\dfrac{5x^2}{2} - \dfrac{2}{5x}\right)^{12}$.

240 Let X be a continuous random variable with the probability density function
$$f(x) = \begin{cases} \dfrac{x}{8} + c & 0 \leqslant x \leqslant 2 \\ 0 & \text{elsewhere} \end{cases}$$
Find:
   a the value of c
   b the expected value of X
   c the standard deviation of X.

241 For what values of x is the graph of the function $f(x) = x^2 e^x$ concave down? Give your answer using exact values.

242 Find the exact value of the x-coordinates of the stationary points of the function $f : x \mapsto \log_3\left(\dfrac{x^2 + 1}{3x + 1}\right)$.

243 Find $\int \sin^3 x\, dx$.

244 Find the area enclosed by the curve $y = ax^2$, $a > 0$ and the line $y = x$.

245 Use integration by parts to find $\int x^2 e^x dx$.

246 After t seconds, the velocity, v metres per second, of a particle moving in a straight line is given by $v = \dfrac{2t}{4 + t^2}$.
   a Find an expression for the displacement, s metres, of the particle if the initial position is $s = -3$.
   b Find an expression of the acceleration, a ms^{-2}, of the particle after t seconds. Simplify your answer.

247 Solve the differential equation $\dfrac{dy}{dx} = 2xy^2 + y^2$ given that $y = 0.5$ when $x = 0$.

248 In a Maths Quiz there are 30 multiple choice questions with five alternative answers for each question, only one of which is correct.
   a Assuming that you guess every question and you answer all the questions, what is the probability of obtaining:
      i exactly 20 correct answers?
      ii at least 15 correct answers?
      iii no more than 25 correct answers?
   b Assuming you have studied hard and have an 85% chance of obtaining a correct answer for each question, what is now the probability of obtaining:
      i exactly 20 correct responses?
      ii at least 15 correct answers?

249 a i Show that the lines: $\mathbf{r} = \begin{bmatrix} 3+4t \\ 4+t \\ 1 \end{bmatrix}$ and $\mathbf{r} = \begin{bmatrix} -1+12\lambda \\ 7+6\lambda \\ 5+3\lambda \end{bmatrix}$

intersect, and find the coordinates of the point of intersection.

ii Find an equation of the plane containing these 2 lines.

b An aeroplane approaches the end of a runway from the east with an angle of descent $24°$. A tower is 20 m high and it is situated 110 m north and 270 m east of the end of the runway.

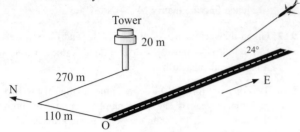

i Write down the position vector of the top of the tower relative to an origin at the end of the runway, and a vector in the direction of the line of descent of the aeroplane.

ii Hence, or otherwise, calculate how close, to the nearest metre, the aeroplane comes to a warning light that is at the top of the tower.

Note: The distance between a point with position vector $\mathbf{a}$ and a line through the origin and in the direction $\mathbf{b}$ is given by $\dfrac{|\mathbf{a} \times \mathbf{b}|}{|\mathbf{b}|}$.

250 a i Expand and simplify $\begin{bmatrix} r\cos\theta & -r\sin\theta \\ r\sin\theta & r\cos\theta \end{bmatrix}^2$.

ii Use the result from **i** to expand and simplify: $\begin{bmatrix} r\cos\theta & -r\sin\theta \\ r\sin\theta & r\cos\theta \end{bmatrix}^3$.

iii Using **i** and **ii**, make a conjecture for an expression for $\begin{bmatrix} r\cos\theta & -r\sin\theta \\ r\sin\theta & r\cos\theta \end{bmatrix}^n$ where n is a positive integer.

iv Use mathematical induction to prove your conjecture in **iii**.

b i Find the six roots of the equation $z^6 = 1+i$ giving your answer in the form $r\cos\theta + i\sin\theta$

ii Plot the roots found in **i** on an Argand diagram.

251 The function f is defined by $f(x) = \dfrac{2x^2 - 17x + 8}{x^2 - 5x + 4}$.

a For the graph of $y = f(x)$, find

i the exact values of the intercepts on the axes.

ii the equations of the vertical asymptotes.

iii the equation of the horizontal asymptote.

iv the coordinates of the point at which the graph crosses its horizontal asymptote.

b i Find $f'(x)$, fully simplifying your answer.

ii Hence, find the exact coordinates of the stationary points of the function and determine their nature.

c i Sketch the graph of $y = f(x)$ for $-5 \leqslant x \leqslant 10$ showing all the features found above.

ii Clearly indicate on your graph the approximate location of any points of inflection.

EXAMINATION PRACTICE SET 6

252 An infinite geometric series with common ratio r, $0 < r < 1$ is such that the sum of the first 3 terms is half the sum of the series. Find the exact value of r.

253 Solve for x: $\ln(x^2 + 9) - 2 = \ln|x + 5|$

254 If $z = 2 - i$ is a solution of the equation $z^3 - 6z^2 + 13z - 10 = 0$, find the other two solutions.

255 For these functions state the domain and range:

a $x \mapsto \sqrt{5-x}$ **b** $x \mapsto$ "distance from nearest integer"

256 Given $f(x) = e^{-\frac{1}{2}x^2}$ and $g(x) = e^{\frac{1}{2}x^2} - 1$ for $0 \leqslant x \leqslant 1.5$. Let the x-coordinate of the point of intersection of the curves $y = f(x)$ and $y = g(x)$ be a. Find the value of a correct to three decimal places.

257 Let $f(x) = \ln|4x - x^3|$, $-1 < x < 2.5$, $x \neq h$, $x \neq k$ (h, k are values of x for which $f(x)$ is not defined).

a Sketch the graph of $f(x)$, indicating on your sketch the number of zeros of $f(x)$. Show also the position of any asymptotes.

b Find all the zeros $f(x)$.

c Find the *exact* values of h and k.

258 Given $f(x) = x^2 + x(2 - k) + k^2$, find the possible real values of k for which $f(x) > 0$ for all real values of x.

259 A farm produces 200 tonnes of grain in its first year of operation. If the yield improves by 3% p.a. due to improved efficiency, how long will it take for the annual crop to double? How much crop was produced in total over the first 8 years of production?

260 The area of a sector of a circle is 15 cm^2 and the perimeter of the sector is 16 cm. Find the radius of the circle and the angle cut off at the centre of the circle by the sector.

261 The area of triangle ABC is 23 cm^2. If $BA = 10$ cm and $AC = 8$ cm, find two possible values for the length of BC.

262 Find the x-coordinates of the points of intersection of the graphs of $y = 3\sin^2 x$ and $y = 1.9x$.

263 Find a vector in the same direction as $2\mathbf{i} - 3\mathbf{j} + \mathbf{k}$ which is 5 units in length.

264 Given the following two matrices,

$$\mathbf{M} = \begin{bmatrix} 1 & -1 & -2 \\ 1 & 1 & -2 \\ 1 & 2 & a \end{bmatrix} \text{ and } \mathbf{M}^{-1} = \frac{1}{2}\begin{bmatrix} b & -5 & 4 \\ -1 & 1 & 0 \\ 1 & -3 & 2 \end{bmatrix}$$

Find the values of a and b.

265 A box contains two dice with faces that are numbered 1 to 6. One of the dice is fair, and the other is weighted so that the probability of a one appearing is 0.5.

a If a die is selected at random and tossed, what is the probability that a one appears?

b If a one appears, what is the probability that the chosen die was the weighted one?

266 Find the positive integer value of n such that the coefficients of x^2 in the binomial expansions of $(1+x)^{2n}$ and $(1+15x^2)^n$ are equal.

267 Smith and Co. produce jars of jam in such a way that the net weight of a jar of jam is normally distributed with mean 475 g, and standard deviation 7.5 g. What percentage of jars has a net weight of less than 460 g?

268 Find the equation of the tangent to the curve $3x^2 - 2y^2 = 10$ at the point where $x = 2$ and $y < 0$.

269 A function is defined by $f(x) = x^3 + 3x^2 + bx + 4$, where b is a constant.

a Find the coordinates of the point of inflection of this function.

b For what values of b would the point of inflection found in **a** be a stationary point of the function?

c For what values of b would the function have no stationary points?

270 a Find $\displaystyle\int \frac{1+x}{4+x^2}\, dx$

b Use integration by parts to find $\int x^2 \ln x\, dx$

271 Find the area enclosed by the graphs of $y = \dfrac{4}{1+x^3}$ and $y = 4(x-1)^4$ in the first quadrant.

272 Solve the differential equation $\dfrac{dy}{dx} = 3x^2 y + 3x^2$ given that $y = 3$ when $x = 0$.

273 The displacement, s metres, of a particle moving in a straight line at time t seconds is given by $s = t\sin\left(\frac{t}{2}\right) + 2\cos\left(\frac{t}{2}\right)$.

a Find an expression for v, the velocity of the particle at time t, in metres per second.

b The particle starts at rest. When does the particle first change direction?

c Find the exact value of the acceleration of the particle after $\frac{\pi}{3}$ seconds.

274 A student takes a Maths test weekly over an entire year with each test marked out of 10.

He randomly selects the results of 25 of these tests and finds that
$$\sum_{r=1}^{25} x_r = 109 \quad\text{and}\quad \sum_{r=1}^{25} x_r^2 = 579,$$
where x_r refers to the score obtained in the rth test.

Calculate an unbiased estimate of

a the mean score obtained in his tests over the year

b the variance of the scores obtained during the year.

275 a Use mathematical induction to prove that, for all $n \in Z^+$, $2^{4n+3} + 3^{3n+1}$ is divisible by 11.

b a, b and c are three consecutive terms of an arithmetic sequence whilst a, $b+1$ and $c+29$ are three consecutive terms of a geometric sequence. If $a+b+c = 33$, find all possible values of a, b and c.

c For the infinite geometric series
$\ln x + (\ln x)^2 + (\ln x)^3 + \dots$ where $x > 0$

i Find the values of x for which the series converges.

ii Find the exact value of x for which the sum of the series is 2.

276 a $\cos x + \sin x\cos x + \sin^2 x\cos x + \dots$ is an infinite series defined for $0 < x < \frac{\pi}{2}$

i Find the sum of the series.

ii Determine the exact values of x for which the sum of the series is $\sqrt{3}$.

b Prove that $\dfrac{\cos x}{1 - \sin x} = \sec x + \tan x$.

c Find $\int \dfrac{\cos x}{1 - \sin x}\, dx$ for $0 < x < \frac{\pi}{2}$.

d Hence prove that $\int \sec x\, dx = \ln(\sec x + \tan x) + c$ for $0 < x < \frac{\pi}{2}$.

e Find the exact value of the area enclosed by the graph $y = \sec x$, the x-axis and the lines $x = \frac{\pi}{4}$ and $x = \frac{\pi}{3}$

277 Consider the lines L: $\begin{bmatrix} x \\ y \\ z \end{bmatrix} = \begin{bmatrix} 2 \\ -3 \\ 1 \end{bmatrix} + \lambda \begin{bmatrix} 1 \\ 2 \\ -1 \end{bmatrix}$

and M: $\begin{bmatrix} x \\ y \\ z \end{bmatrix} = \begin{bmatrix} 1 \\ 0 \\ -1 \end{bmatrix} + \mu \begin{bmatrix} 2 \\ -1 \\ 1 \end{bmatrix}$, where λ, $\mu \in \mathbb{R}$

a Find the acute angle between a vector in the direction of L and a vector in the direction of M.

b Find a vector $\mathbf{n}$ that is perpendicular to both lines.

c Find an equation of the plane P that contains the line L and is perpendicular to $\mathbf{n}$.

d Show that a vector $\overrightarrow{AB}$, where $A \in L$ and $B \in M$, is of the form
$$\begin{bmatrix} -1-\lambda+2\mu \\ 3-2\lambda-\mu \\ -2+\lambda+\mu \end{bmatrix}$$

e Find the values of λ and μ such that $\overrightarrow{AB}$ is parallel to $\mathbf{n}$ and hence, or otherwise, find the distance between the lines L and M. Comment on the nature of these two lines.

EXAMINATION PRACTICE SET 7

278 Find real numbers a and b such that $(a+2i)(b-i) = 17+7i$

279 Find the exact value of x if $\log_{64}(x+5) + \log_2 \sqrt[6]{3x-1} = 1$

280 Visitors to an island have increased by 6% per annum each year since the year 2000.

a If 4000 people visited the island in 2000, how many would be expected to visit the island in 2010?

b If for each of the years 2000 to 2010 inclusive, each visitor to the island is charged \$5, what is the total amount paid over these years.

281 Find the largest set of values of x such that the following functions take real values.

a $f(x) = \sqrt{x^2 - 1}$ **b** $g(x) = \ln(1 - x^2)$

c $F(x) = \dfrac{|x-1|}{x}$ **d** $G(x) = \sqrt{\dfrac{2x-3}{x+2}}$

282 Sketch the graph of the function
$f : x \mapsto 3 + \dfrac{2}{x+1}$, $-5 \leqslant x \leqslant 5$, $x \neq -1$, showing clearly all asymptotes. Hence:

a on the same axes sketch the graph of $|f(x)|$.

b Now graph on the same axes the sketch of $\dfrac{1}{f(x)}$.

283 Consider the function $g : x \mapsto 2x^2 - 3x + \sin x$.
Find simplified expressions for the functions f and h where the graphs of f and h are reflections of g in the x- and y-axes respectively.

284 The weight W_t, of radioactive uranium remaining after t years is given by the formula $W_t = W_0 e^{-\frac{t}{5000}}$ grams, $t \geqslant 0$. Find:

a the time required for the weight to fall to 50% of its original value (half-life)

b the time required for the weight to fall to 0.1% of its original value

c the percentage weight loss after 1000 years.

285 If $\sin A = \frac{3}{4}$ and $\cos B = \frac{2}{3}$ where A and B are acute, find the exact value of $\sin(A - B)$.

286 In triangle ABC, $\widehat{ABC} = 60°$, AB = 5 cm, BC = 2 cm and AC = $k\sqrt{3}$ cm. Find the value of k.

287 If $\tan\alpha = \frac{3}{\sqrt{5}}$ and α lies in the interval $]\,\pi, \frac{3\pi}{2}\,[$, find the exact value of $\sin 2\alpha$.

288 Find the acute angle between the two planes with equations

$\mathbf{r} = \begin{bmatrix} 1 \\ 1 \\ -3 \end{bmatrix} + \lambda \begin{bmatrix} 2 \\ -1 \\ 1 \end{bmatrix} + \mu \begin{bmatrix} 1 \\ -1 \\ 2 \end{bmatrix}$, λ, $\mu \in \mathbb{R}$

$\mathbf{r} = \begin{bmatrix} 0 \\ 1 \\ -2 \end{bmatrix} + s \begin{bmatrix} 1 \\ 1 \\ 1 \end{bmatrix} + t \begin{bmatrix} 2 \\ 0 \\ -1 \end{bmatrix}$, $s, t \in \mathbb{R}$

289 Given that $\mathbf{A} = \begin{bmatrix} 3 & 2 & 1 \\ 0 & -2 & 0 \\ 2 & 1 & -2 \end{bmatrix}$ and $\mathbf{B} = \begin{bmatrix} 2 & -1 & 1 \\ 0 & 2 & 3 \\ -3 & 1 & 2 \end{bmatrix}$

solve the matrix equation $\mathbf{AX} = \mathbf{BA} + \mathbf{A}$.

290 Three suppliers A, B and C produce respectively 40%, 25%, and 35% of the total number of a certain component that is required by a washing machine manufacturer. The percentages of faulty components in each suppliers output are, again respectively, 5% , 3% and 4%.

What is the probability that a component selected at random is faulty?

291 A zoologist knows that the lengths of a certain type of tropical fish are normally distributed with mean length m cm and standard deviation 0.12 cm. If 20% of the fish are longer than 13 cm, find the value of m.

292 The random variable Y follows a Poisson distribution that satisfies the property that $(E(Y))^2 = 2\,\text{Var}(Y) + 3$.

Find $P(Y \geqslant 3)$.

293 Find the exact values of the coordinates of the stationary point of the curve $y = xe^{-x^2}$.

294 Find the coordinates of the points where the tangents to the curve $6x^2 + 4xy + 2y^2 = 3$ are horizontal.

295 Find $\displaystyle\int \frac{1 - 2x}{\sqrt{1 - x^2}}\, dx, \quad -1 < x < 1$

296 Find the area of the region enclosed by the graphs of $y = e^{0.1x}$ and $y = 2\ln x$.

297 Use integration by parts to find $\int x \arctan x\, dx$

298 The displacement of a particle moving in a straight line at time t seconds is given by $s = 4e^{0.2t} - e^{0.3t} + 10$ m. Find
  a the initial displacement of the particle
  b the initial velocity of the particle
  c the exact time at which the particle first comes to rest.

299 Solve the differential equation $e^y \dfrac{dy}{dx} = 2xe^y + 2x$ if $y = 0$ when $x = 0$.

300 An alarm clock is used to wake a swimmer for early morning training. The probability that the alarm rings is $\frac{9}{10}$.

If the alarm rings, there is a probability of $\frac{5}{6}$ that the swimmer arrives for training, but, if the alarm does not ring, the probability that the swimmer arrives for training is $\frac{2}{15}$. Find:

  a the probability that the swimmer arrives for early morning training on a given day
  b the probability that, on a randomly chosen morning on which the swimmer does not arrive for training, the alarm did not ring.

301 The function f is defined by $f(x) = x - 3 + \dfrac{6}{x + 4}$.

  a For the graph of $y = f(x)$
    i Write down the equation of the vertical asymptote
    ii Write down the equation of the oblique asymptote.
    iii Find the axes intercepts.

  b Sketch the graph of $y = f(x)$ showing all the features found in **a**.

  c For what real values of k does the equation $f(x) = k$ have no real solutions?

  d Find the exact coordinates of the points on the graph where the slope of the normal to the graph is -3.

  e Find the exact value of the area of the region enclosed by the graph of $y = f(x)$ and the x-axis.

302 a Find the exact value of $\sin 77^\circ \cos 17^\circ - \cos 77^\circ \sin 17^\circ$.

  b **i** Use mathematical induction to prove that
  $$\cos\theta + \cos 3\theta + \ldots + \cos(2n - 1)\theta = \frac{\sin 2n\theta}{2\sin\theta}$$
  for $n \in \mathbb{Z}^+$, $\sin\theta \neq 0$

  ii Expand $(\cos\theta + i\sin\theta)^3$

  iii Using **ii** and DeMoivre's theorem, find an expression for $\cos 3\theta$ in terms of $\cos\theta$.

  iv Using **i** and **ii**, find an expression for $\sin 4\theta$ in terms of $\sin\theta$ and $\cos\theta$

  c Find the exact value of $\displaystyle\int_{\frac{\pi}{6}}^{\frac{\pi}{2}} \frac{\sin 6\theta}{2\sin\theta}\, d\theta$.

303 Consider the two lines L_1 and L_2.
$$L_1\colon \frac{x - 1}{2} = \frac{y - 3}{3} = \frac{z - 1}{2} \quad \text{and}$$
$$L_2\colon \frac{3 - x}{4} = \frac{2y - 3}{3} = \frac{z + 1}{2}.$$

  a Write the vector equation of each line in the form $\overrightarrow{r} = \overrightarrow{r_0} + \lambda\overrightarrow{u}$.

  b Show that the two lines do not intersect, and state whether or not they are parallel.

  c Find, in the form $ax + by + cz = d$, an equation of a plane that is perpendicular to L_2 and intersects L_1.

  d Find a vector that is perpendicular to both lines.

  e Hence, or otherwise, find the distance between L_1 and L_2.

EXAMINATION PRACTICE SET 8

304 On the first day of an exercise program, Paula jogs for 500 metres. Each day she plans to jog 50 metres further than her distance on the previous day.
  a How far will she jog on the 30th day?
  b What would be the total distance she has jogged after 30 days?

305 Find the exact value of x if $\dfrac{6}{7^x} - 2(7^x) = 1$

306 Find p and q where $p,\ q \in \mathbb{R},\ p > 0$ such that $(p + qi)^2 = -3 + 6i\sqrt{6}$

307 Find the coefficients of $\dfrac{1}{x}$ and $\dfrac{1}{x^2}$ in the expansion of $(x + \frac{1}{x})^9$.

308 Given the function $f(x) = \dfrac{1}{\sqrt{9 - x^2}}$, find
  a the domain of f **b** the range of f.

309 a Sketch the graph of $f(x) = \left|\, e^{3x} - \dfrac{2}{x + 1}\,\right|$
  b Hence solve the equation $f(x) = 1$.

310 The roots of the equation $x^2 - kx + 4 = 0$ are α and β. Find in terms of k,
  a $\alpha^2 + \beta^2$ **b** a quadratic equation whose roots are $\dfrac{1}{\alpha}, \dfrac{1}{\beta}$.

311 If $\log(x^2 y^3) = a$ and $\log(\frac{x}{y}) = b$, express $\log x$ and $\log y$ in terms of a and b.

312 Find the exact value of $\tan x$ if $\sin x = \cos\left(x + \frac{\pi}{3}\right)$

313 The sides AB, BC and AC of triangle ABC have lengths 5 cm, 3 cm and 7 cm respectively.
  a Find $\cos \widehat{ABC}$.
  b Hence find the exact value of the area of the triangle.

314 If $\sin\gamma = \frac{\sqrt{3}}{7}$, find the exact value of $\cos 2\gamma$.

315 The points A(2, -1, 3), B(6, 1, 1), C and D(7, 5, 6) form a parallelogram. Find the area of this parallelogram.

316 Given the points A(4, 2, −1), B(2, 1, 5) and C(9, 4, 1),
  a show that $\overrightarrow{AB}$ is perpendicular to $\overrightarrow{AC}$
  b find the size of the angle ABC.

317 In a group of 45 students, 25 hold an American passport, 15 hold a Australian passport, and 8 have neither an American nor Australian passport. Draw a Venn diagram to illustrate this situation. If a student is selected at random, find
  a the probability that the student has both an American and Australian passport.
  b The probability that the student holds neither an American nor Australian passport.
  c The probability that the student holds only one passport.

318 Suppose a professional typist makes on average 2 errors per 500 words of typing. Find the probability that when typing a 1500 word essay the typist will:
  a make no more than 5 errors
  b make no more than 5 errors given that at least one error has been made.

319 A random variable, X, has probability density function, $f(x)$, where
$$f(x) = \begin{cases} \frac{1}{3}x & 0 \leqslant x < 1 \\ \frac{1}{3} & 1 \leqslant x < 2 \\ \frac{1}{12}(6-x) & 2 \leqslant x < a \\ 0 & \text{elsewhere} \end{cases}$$
Find:
  a the value of a **b** the median value of X.

320 **a** Find the equations of all the asymptotes of the graph of the function $y = f(x)$ where $f(x) = \dfrac{x^3 + 5x^2 - 2x}{x^2 + 3x - 10}$
  b Find the coordinates of the point where the graph of $y = f(x)$ crosses its oblique asymptote.

321 Find the equation of the tangent to the curve $x^3y^2 - xy + y = 4$ where $y > 0$ at the point where $x = 1$.

322 Find $\int x\sqrt{x-3}\,dx$, $x > 3$.

323 Let $f(x) = \sin 2x + \sin 4x$
  a Sketch the graph of $y = f(x)$ for $0 \leqslant x \leqslant \pi$ clearly showing intercepts on axes.
  b Show that the line $y = \frac{4}{\pi}x$ cuts the curve at the origin and at $(\frac{\pi}{4}, 1)$.
  c Find the exact value of the area of the region enclosed by the line $y = \frac{4}{\pi}x$ and the curve $y = f(x)$ for $0 \leqslant x \leqslant \pi$.

324 Use integration by parts to find $\int \arcsin x\,dx$

325 A particle moving in a straight line has initial displacement $s = 3$ metres. Its velocity in metres per second at time t seconds is given by $v = 2s$. Find s as a function of time t.

326 Solve the differential equation $(x^2 + 1)\dfrac{dy}{dx} = 2xy$ given that $y = 10$ when $x = 2$.

327 The equations of two lines are:
$l_1 : \quad x = 3\lambda - 4, \ y = \lambda + 2, \ z = 2\lambda - 1$
$l_2 : \quad x = \dfrac{y-5}{2} = \dfrac{-z-1}{2}.$
  a Determine the point of intersection of l_1 and the plane $2x + y - z = 2$.
  b Find the point of intersection of l_1 and l_2.
  c Find an equation of the plane that contains l_1 and l_2.

328 The function f is defined by $f(x) = e^{\sin^2 x}$, $0 \leqslant x \leqslant \pi$.
  a **i** Find an expression for $f'(x)$.
    ii Hence find the exact coordinates of the minimum and maximum turning points of the graph of $y = f(x)$.
    iii Find $f''(x)$.

  b **i** Find the equation of the tangent to the curve $y = f(x)$ at the point where $x = \frac{3\pi}{4}$.
    ii Find the exact value of the x-intercept of the tangent found in **i**.
  c Find the area enclosed by the graph $y = f(x)$ and $y = 1$.

329 **a** In triangle ABC, BC $= a$, AC $= b$ and AB $= c$. D is a point on the segment BC such that AD $= b$ and BD:DC $= 1:3$. $A\widehat{B}C = 60^o$.
    i Use the cosine rule to find two different expressions for b^2.
    ii Hence, find an expression for a in terms of c.
  b Two circles with radii 5 cm and 8 cm respectively are such that their centres are 10 cm apart. Find the area common to the two circles.

EXAMINATION PRACTICE SET 9

330 **a** Find all non-real complex numbers z such that $z^2 = 2\bar{z}$.
  b Given $z = x + 2i$, where $x \in \mathbb{R}$, for what values of x is $|z| < 2|z - 1 - i|$?

331 Find x if $\log_6(x+3) = 1 - \log_6(x-2)$.

332 Each year, the population of seals on an island increases by 3%. In 2005 the population is 1250. Assuming the same rate of growth continues, during what year would the population be expected to exceed 2000 for the first time?

333 Given the function $f : \quad x \mapsto e^{x^2 - 1} + \sqrt{x^2 - 1}$, find the domain and range of $f(x)$.
Sketch, where possible, this graph for $-2 \leqslant x \leqslant 0$.

334 **a** Find the real domain of the function $f : x \mapsto \ln x + \ln (x+3) - \ln (x^2 - 9)$.
  b Show that $f(x)$ can be written in the form $\ln\left(\dfrac{x}{x-3}\right)$.
  c Find an expression for $f^{-1}(x)$.

335 Find the real number a, for which $1 + ai$, $(i = \sqrt{-1})$, is a zero of the quadratic polynomial $x^2 + ax + 5$.

336 Determine the quartic polynomial $f(x)$ which cuts the x-axis at -2 and 3 and touches it at 1. Give your answer in expanded form. The y-intercept is -12.

337 A and B are acute angles, $\sin A = \frac{4}{5}$ and $\sin B = \frac{8}{17}$. Find the exact value of $\tan(A + B)$.

338 Find the exact values of x such that $0 \leqslant x \leqslant 2\pi$ and $\sqrt{2}\sin x = \tan x$

339 If $\sin A = -\frac{2}{3}$ and $0 < A < \frac{3\pi}{2}$, find the exact value of $\tan 2A$.

340 Find the values of x and y given that $\begin{bmatrix} 16 & -8 \\ 2x & 16 \end{bmatrix} = \begin{bmatrix} x & y \\ x & 0 \end{bmatrix}\begin{bmatrix} 2 & x \\ 3 & -3 \end{bmatrix}$.

341 **a** Given $\mathbf{A} = \begin{bmatrix} 1 \\ 1 \\ -3 \end{bmatrix}$ and $\mathbf{B} = \begin{bmatrix} 0 \\ 1 \\ 2 \end{bmatrix}$, find $\mathbf{A} \times \mathbf{B}$.
  b Find a vector of length 5 units which is perpendicular to both $\mathbf{A}$ and $\mathbf{B}$.

342 How many times must a pair of dice be thrown so that there is a better than 70% chance of obtaining a double, that is, the same number on both dice?

343 In how many ways can nine different raffle tickets be divided between two students so that each student receives at least one raffle ticket?

344 Z is the standardised normal random variable with mean 0 and variance 1. Find a such that $P(|Z| \leqslant a) = 0.72$.

345 The function $f(x) = \dfrac{ax + b}{x^2 - 5x + 7}$ has a turning point at $(3, 5)$. Find the values of a and b.

346 Find the equation of the tangent to the curve $x^2 + x \ln y - y = 3$ at the point $(2, 1)$.

347 Find $\int \sin^3 x \cos^3 x \, dx$.

348 Find the exact value of the area enclosed by the curve $y = x\sqrt{4 - x^2}$ and the x-axis in the first quadrant.

349 Use integration by parts to find $\int e^x \sin x \, dx$.

350 A particle is moving along a straight line. It's displacement at time t seconds from O is s metres. After t seconds, the acceleration of the particle is given by $a = -4s$. The particle starts from rest at $s = 5$. Find the velocity of the particle at the time when it first has a displacement of 3 metres.

351 Solve the differential equation $(x^2 + 1) y \dfrac{dy}{dx} = 2$ given that $y = -\sqrt{2\pi}$ when $x = 0$.

352 Given points $A(4, 2, -1)$, $B(2, 1, 5)$, and $C(9, 4, 1)$.
  a Show that $\overrightarrow{AB}$ is perpendicular to $\overrightarrow{AC}$.
  b Find an equation of the plane containing A, B and C and hence determine the distance from this plane to the point $(8, 1, 0)$.
  c Find an equation of the line through A and B.
  d Determine the distance from D(8, 11, −5) to the line through A and B.

353 Vectors **a** and **b** are the position vectors of points A(−4, 12, 8) and B(4, 8, 0) respectively.
  a Find M, the point with position vector $\frac{1}{4}\mathbf{a} + \frac{3}{4}\mathbf{b}$.
  b State the ratio in which M divides $\overline{AB}$.
  c Find the point on $\overleftrightarrow{AB}$ that is three units from A in the direction of B.
  d Find D, the point that divides $\overrightarrow{AB}$ externally in the ratio 3:7.
  e Find the size of the angle ABO.

354 a Prove, using mathematical induction, that
$$\sum_{r=1}^{n} (r^2 + r) = \frac{n(n + 1)(n + 2)}{3} \quad \text{for } n \in Z^+.$$

  b Emma sets up a fund for her granddaughter, Amy. On the first day of each month, Emma deposits \$60 in an account. The account pays compound interest of 5% per annum, calculated monthly. The interest is added to the account on the last day of each month.
   i Find the value of the fund after 3 months.
   ii Write down an expression which would give the value of the fund after k years.
   iii Hence find the value of the fund after 20 years.

355 a Find the exact value of the the area of the region bound by the graph of $y = \cos^2 x$, the y-axis and $x = \frac{\pi}{2}$.

  b Use integration by parts to prove that, for $n \in \mathbb{Z}$, $n \geqslant 3$
$$\int \cos^n x \, dx = \frac{1}{n} \sin x \cos^{n-1} x + \frac{n - 1}{n} \int \cos^{n-2} x \, dx$$

  c Use **a** and **b** to find the exact value of the volume of the solid generated by rotating the region in **a** about the x axis.

EXAMINATION PRACTICE SET 10

356 a Find real numbers b and c such that $3 - 2i$ is a solution of the equation $x^2 + bx + c = 0$.

  b Solve for x: $\log_2 x + \log_2(x - 1) = 2 - \log_2\left(\frac{1}{3}\right)$

357 The first term of a geometric series exceeds the second term by 9. The sum of the series is 81. Find:
  a the common ratio of the series
  b the first term of the series.

358 If $f(x) = \dfrac{x}{x - 2}$, for $x \neq 2$ and $g(x) = (f \circ f)(x)$, find
  a $g(x)$ **b** $(g \circ g)(2)$.

359 Consider $f : x \mapsto \dfrac{x^2 - 2x + 4}{x^2 + 2x + 4}$. Find the range of
  a the function f **b** the composite function $f \circ f$.

360 a Find the *exact* domain of real numbers for which the function $f(x) = \dfrac{2}{\sqrt{5 - x^2}}$ takes real values.
  b Find the range of the image values of f for the domain found in part **a**.

361 Solve exactly for $x \in \,] - \infty, \infty [$, $\dfrac{5}{x + 2} \geqslant \dfrac{2}{x + 3}$.

362 Find the exact value of $\tan 75°$.

363 Find the exact value of θ, $\theta \in [0, \pi]$ if $2\cos\theta + 2\sec\theta = 5$

364 The graph of $y = a \sin bx + c$ where $a, b, c \in \mathbb{R}$ and $0 \leqslant x \leqslant \dfrac{2\pi}{b}$ is drawn below.

On the same set of axes, sketch the graph of $y = -2a \sin\left(\frac{b}{2}x\right)$

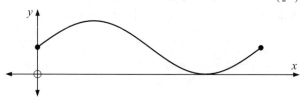

365 Find the value of x such that $\begin{vmatrix} 4 & x \\ x & x \end{vmatrix} = \begin{vmatrix} 2 & 0 & -1 \\ 4 & 5 & 0 \\ 0 & 1 & 2 \end{vmatrix}$.

366 Let $\mathbf{r} = 2\mathbf{i} - \mathbf{j} + 2\mathbf{k}$, $\mathbf{s} = 3\mathbf{i} - \mathbf{j} + 2\mathbf{k}$, $\mathbf{t} = 2\mathbf{i} + 2\mathbf{j} - \mathbf{k}$, be the position vectors of the points R, S, and T, respectively. Find the area of the triangle $\triangle$RST.

367 In the figure, ABCD is a parallelogram. X is the mid-point of BC, and Y is on AX such that AY:YX = 2:1.

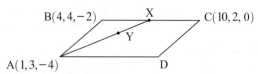

The coordinates of A, B and C are (1, 3, −4), (4, 4, −2), and (10, 2, 0) respectively.
  a Find the coordinates of D, X, and Y.
  b Prove that B, Y, and D are collinear.

368 A continuous probability density function is described by:
$$f(x) = \begin{cases} 0 & \text{for } x < k \\ 2 - 5x & \text{for } k \leqslant x \leqslant 0 \\ 0 & \text{for } x > 0 \end{cases}$$
  a Find the value of k.   **b** Find the mean of the distribution.

369 Given that events A and B are *independent events* with $P(A \cap B) = 0.3$ and $P(A \cap B') = 0.4$, find $P(A \cup B)$.

370 A publisher finds that in the draft of a new 750 page book, the probability of at least one typing error per page is 0.01. If X is the Poisson random variable representing the number of errors per page, find:
  a the expected number of errors per page
  b the expected number of pages with exactly one error.

371 Find k if $y = Ae^{kt}$ and $\dfrac{d^2y}{dt^2} + 3\dfrac{dy}{dt} + 2y = 0$.

372 Find all points on the graph of $y^2 = 3 - xy$ where the tangents have gradient $-\dfrac{3}{4}$.

373 Find $\int x^2\sqrt{1-x}\ dx$.

374 Find the area enclosed by the curve $y^2 + 2y - 3x = 0$ and the line $2x - y - 1 = 0$.

375 Use the substitution $u = 1 - x$ to find $\displaystyle\int \dfrac{x^2}{(1-x)^3}\ dx$.

376 The velocity of a particle, v metres per second, at time t seconds is given by $v = e^t \cos 2t$.
  a Write down an expression for the distance travelled by the particle in the first five seconds.
  b Find the distance travelled by the particle in the first five seconds.

377 Solve the differential equation $y\dfrac{dy}{dx} = xy^2 + x$ if $y = 2$ when $x = 0$.

378 **a** **i** Using mathematical induction, prove that
$$\sum_{r=1}^{n} r^3 = \frac{n^2(n+1)^2}{4} \quad \text{for } n \in \mathbb{Z}^+$$
  ii Hence find $1^3 + 2^3 + 3^3 + \ldots + 100^3$
  b Prove that $\displaystyle\sum_{r=1}^{n} r^3 = \left(\sum_{r=1}^{n} r\right)^2$

379 Vectors **a** and **b** are the position vectors of points A and B, two of the vertices of an equilateral triangle $\triangle OAB$. M is the mid-point of $\overline{AB}$.
  a Express $\overrightarrow{OM}$ in terms of **a** and **b**.
  b Use vectors to prove that $\overrightarrow{OM} \perp \overline{AB}$.
  c Explain why $|\mathbf{b} - \mathbf{a}| = |\mathbf{a}|$, and use this result to prove that $\mathbf{b} \bullet (\mathbf{b} - 2\mathbf{a}) = 0$.
  d Illustrate this on a sketch of $\triangle OAB$.

380 The functions f and g are defined by:
$$f(x) = 2x\sin x, \quad g(x) = x \quad \text{for } 0 \leqslant x \leqslant 2\pi$$
  a **i** Find the exact coordinates of the points of intersection of the graphs $y = f(x)$ and $y = g(x)$.
  ii Write down an equation which would give the x-coordinates of the stationary points of $y = f(x)$.
  iii Find the coordinates of the stationary points of the graph of $y = f(x)$.
  iv Sketch the graphs of $y = f(x)$ and $y = g(x)$ on the same set of axes.
  b **i** Use integration by parts to find $\int 2x\sin x\ dx$.
  ii Find the exact value of the area enclosed by the graphs of $y = f(x)$ and $y = g(x)$.

381 **a** Show that the plane $\mathbf{r} \bullet \begin{bmatrix} 2 \\ 1 \\ 1 \end{bmatrix} = 5$ contains the line
  $l_1: \quad \mathbf{r} = (-2t + 2)\mathbf{i} + t\mathbf{j} + (3t + 1)\mathbf{k},\ (t \in \mathbb{R})$.
  b Find k when the plane $\mathbf{r} \bullet \begin{bmatrix} 1 \\ k \\ 1 \end{bmatrix} = 3$ contains l_1.
  c Without using row operations, find the values of p and q for which the following system of equations has an infinite number of solutions. Clearly explain your reasoning.
$$2x + y + z = 5$$
$$x - y + z = 3$$
$$-2x + py + 2z = q$$

---

382 **a** Find integers a and b such that $(a + 3i)(b - i) = 13 + i$
  b The complex number $z = 5 + ai$ where $a \in \mathbb{Z}$ is such that $|z + 1 + i| = 2|z - 2 - i|$. Find the value of a.

383 An arithmetic sequence of 30 terms is such that the sum of the even numbered terms exceeds the sum of the odd numbered terms by 8. Find:
  a the common difference, d.
  b an expression for S_n, the sum of the first n terms.

384 Solve for x: $\log_6 x + \log_x(2x - 1).\log_6 x = 1$

385 Given $f \circ g : \mathbb{R} \to \mathbb{R}$, find the domain and range of $f \circ g$, where $f : x \mapsto \sqrt{x}$ and $g : x \mapsto 1 - \sin x$.

386 Consider the equation $e^{-\frac{1}{2}x} = \sin 3x$, $-\pi \leqslant x \leqslant \pi$.
  a Find the exact number of solutions to this equation.
  b Find the solution closest to $\frac{\pi}{2}$ giving your answer to 5 decimal places.

387 Find all real values of x for which $2|x - 3| \leqslant |x + 7|$.

388 The given diagram shows the graph of $y = f(x)$.

It has relative minimum and maximum points at $(0, 0)$ and $(1, \frac{1}{2})$ respectively.

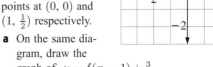

  a On the same diagram, draw the graph of $y = f(x - 1) + \frac{3}{2}$.
  b What are the coordinates of the minimum and maximum points of $y = f(x - 1) + \frac{3}{2}$?

389 Simplify $\sin\left(\frac{\pi}{2} - \theta\right) . \cos\left(\frac{\pi}{2} + \theta\right) . \csc(\pi - 2\theta)$

390 Find all values of x in the interval $[0, 2\pi]$ such that $\cos 2x = -\cos x$ giving your answers as exact values.

391 The graph of $y = a\sin bx + c$, where a, b and c are integers, is shown below.

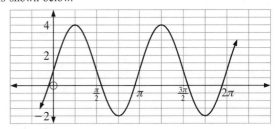

Find the value of **a** a **b** b **c** c.

392 Given matrices $\mathbf{A} = \begin{bmatrix} 1 & 3 \\ -2 & 1 \\ 0 & 4 \end{bmatrix}$ and $\mathbf{B} = \begin{bmatrix} 2 & -1 & a \\ -3 & 4 & 1 \end{bmatrix}$, find the products $\mathbf{AB}$ and $\mathbf{BA}$.

393 Find the angle between the plane $2x + 2y - z = 3$ and the line $\mathbf{r} = \begin{bmatrix} -1 \\ 4 \\ 3 \end{bmatrix} + \mu\begin{bmatrix} 1 \\ -2 \\ -1 \end{bmatrix}$, $\mu \in \mathbb{R}$.

394 Given $|\mathbf{a}| = 4$, $|\mathbf{b}| = 5$, and $\mathbf{a} \times \mathbf{b} = 12\mathbf{j} - 5\mathbf{k}$, find the possible values of $\mathbf{a} \bullet \mathbf{b}$.

395 How many different arrangements, each consisting of 5 different digits, can be formed from 1, 2, 3, 4, 5, 6 and 7, if
  a each arrangement begins and ends with an odd digit
  b in each arrangement odd and even digits alternate?

396 Given that A and B are *independent events*, and $P(A) = 0.27$, $P(A \cup B) = 0.8$, find $P(B)$.

397 Customers arrive at random at a grocery store at the rate of 12 per hour throughout the day. Find the probability that 5 customers will arrive at the store between 9:00 am and 9:30 am.

398 A sample of 80 batteries was tested to see how long they last. The results were:

Time (hours)	Number of batteries
$0 \leqslant t < 10$	3
$10 \leqslant t < 20$	6
$20 \leqslant t < 30$	9
$30 \leqslant t < 40$	8
$40 \leqslant t < 50$	12
$50 \leqslant t < 60$	14
$60 \leqslant t < 70$	11
$70 \leqslant t < 80$	8
$80 \leqslant t < 90$	7
$90 \leqslant t < 100$	2
Total	80

Find
a the sample standard deviation
b an unbiased estimate of the standard deviation of the population from which this sample is taken.

399 Find the exact value of the x-coordinate of the point of inflection on the graph of $y = x^2 \ln\left(\frac{1}{x^2}\right)$.

400 a Find the coordinates of the points on the curve
$3x^2 + 2xy - y^2 = 7$ where $x = -2$.
b Find the equation of the normal to the curve at one of these points.

401 Find $\displaystyle\int \frac{\arctan x}{1 + x^2}\, dx$.

402 Calculate the area of the region enclosed by the curve $x = 8y - 7 - y^2$ and the line $x - 2y + 2 = 0$.

403 Use integration by parts to find $\int \arcsin x\, dx$.

404 Find a if $a > 0$ and $\displaystyle\int_0^a x\sqrt{1 - x^2}\, dx = 0.2$.

405 Given two vectors $\mathbf{p}$ and $\mathbf{q}$ such that
$(\mathbf{p} + \mathbf{q}) \bullet (\mathbf{p} + \mathbf{q}) = 25$ and that $|\mathbf{p}|^2 + |\mathbf{q}|^2 = 25$
a find $|\mathbf{p} + \mathbf{q}|$
b prove that $\mathbf{p} \bullet \mathbf{q} = 0$
c hence draw a diagram that represents the relative positions of $\mathbf{p}$, $\mathbf{q}$ and $\mathbf{p} + \mathbf{q}$.

406 a Let $z = r(\cos\theta + i\sin\theta)$. By using $z = re^{i\theta}$ show that $z^n = r^n(\cos n\theta + i\sin n\theta)$
b i Express $1 + i$ and $1 - i$ in the form $r(\cos\theta + i\sin\theta)$
ii where r and θ are given as exact values and $r > 0$. Hence prove that
$(1 + i)^n + (1 - i)^n = 2^{\frac{n}{2}+1} \cos\left(\frac{n\pi}{4}\right)$
iii Prove that there is no integer, n, for which
$(1 + i)^n + (1 - i)^n = 64$

407 The function f is defined by $f(x) = \dfrac{x^2 + 1}{e^x}$
a Determine the behaviour of $f(x)$ as $x \to \infty$.
b Find $f'(x)$, fully simplifying your answer.
c Show that $\left(1, \dfrac{2}{e}\right)$ is a stationary point and state its nature.
d Find an expression for $f''(x)$, fully simplifying your answer.
e Hence find the exact coordinates of the non-stationary point of inflection on the graph of f.
f Sketch the graph of $y = f(x)$ for $0 \leqslant x \leqslant 5$, clearly showing the two points found in **d** and **e** and the exact coordinates of the endpoints of the graph.

408 Find the sum of all the positive integers less than 1000 that are divisible by neither 6 nor 8.

409 Given the equation $2^{x+1} = 5^{x-1}$:
a Find the exact value of x, giving your answer in terms of $\log_2 5$
b Find x to 3 significant figures.

410 Given two complex numbers w and z such that $|w| = |z|$, $\arg(w) = \frac{\pi}{6}$ and $\arg(z) = \frac{\pi}{3}$, find the exact values of:
a $\arg(wz)$ **b** $\arg(w + z)$

411 Find the domain and range of the function
$f : x \mapsto |x - 2| - 4|x+1|$.

412 Find the coordinates of all points of intersection of the graphs of $y = \ln|x - 5|$ and $y = x\cos x$ where $-5 \leqslant x \leqslant 5$.

413 Find where the graphs of the following functions meet:
$xy = 2$ and $x^3 + y^3 = 9$

414 The graph of a function with equation $y = 6x^2 + px + q$, cuts the x-axis at 2 and $-\frac{1}{2}$
Find the value of **a** p **b** q.

415 If $\tan\beta = \frac{2}{3}$ and $\pi < \beta < \frac{3\pi}{2}$, find the exact value of $\tan\left(\frac{\beta}{2}\right)$.

416 Find the exact values of x if $0 \leqslant x \leqslant \pi$ and
$2\sin^2 x - \sin x - 2\sin x \cos x + \cos x = 0$

417 a Sketch the graph of the function $f(x) = \cos 2x - \sin 2x$, $0 \leqslant x \leqslant \pi$.
b Find the maximum value of $\cos 2x - \sin 2x$.

418 Find the values of y so that the matrix $\begin{bmatrix} y & 2 & -1 \\ 1 & y & 3 \\ 4 & -1 & 1 \end{bmatrix}$ is singular, expressing your answer in surd (radical) form.

419 Given the vectors $\mathbf{a} = \begin{bmatrix} 1 \\ 2 \\ -2 \end{bmatrix}$ and $\mathbf{b} = \begin{bmatrix} -t \\ 1+t \\ 2t \end{bmatrix}$, find t if
a $\mathbf{a}$ and $\mathbf{b}$ are perpendicular **b** $\mathbf{a}$ and $\mathbf{b}$ are parallel.

420 Find, by considering the cuboid (rectangular prism) formed by the vectors $2\mathbf{i}$, $3\mathbf{j}$ and $5\mathbf{k}$, the acute angle between two diagonals of a cuboid.

421 Given the points A$(1, -2, 5)$, B$(-1, 2, 7)$ and C$(2, -4, 4)$ in space:
a prove that the three points are collinear
b find the ratio in which C divides $\overline{AB}$
c find the coordinates of P which divides $\overline{AB}$ in the ratio 2:1.

422 A machine fills bottles with orange juice. A sample of ten bottles is taken at random. The bottles contain the following amounts (in ml) of orange juice:
753, 748, 749, 752, 750, 751, 758, 744, 751, 750.
Find
a the sample standard deviation
b an unbiased estimate of the population standard deviation from which this sample is taken.

423 An employer randomly selects five new employees from twelve applicants, consisting of five men and seven women.
a Find the probability that no men are selected.
b Find the probability that 3 women and 2 men are selected.

424 In a certain university where 58% of the students are male, it is found that 13% of the female students, and 8% of the male students, do not own a car.

   a Find the probability that a student selected at random does not own a car.

   b If a student is selected at random and does not own a car, what is the probability that the student is male?

425 A random variable, X, is known to have a normal distribution with a mean of 90.

Given that the probability $P(X < 88) \approx 0.28925$, find the proportion of scores between 90 and 92, i.e. $P(90 < X < 92)$.

426 The function f is defined by $f(x) = 4xe^{-x}$ for $x \geqslant 0$.

   a Find the exact value of the coordinates of the turning point of the graph $y = f(x)$.

   b Find the exact value of the coordinates of the point of inflection on the graph $y = f(x)$.

427 O and B are fixed points such that $OB = 8$ cm. A is a point on the circle, centre O and radius 5 cm. A is initially on OB and rotates in a counter-clockwise direction about O, completing one rotation every 2 seconds. Find the rate of change in the area of triangle AOB when A is moving away from OB and $A\widehat{O}B = 30^o$.

428 Find $\int \tan^5 x \, dx$.

429 **a** Find $\displaystyle\int \frac{\sin x}{(1 + \cos x)^2} \, dx$.

   b Hence find the exact value of the area enclosed by the curve $y = \dfrac{\sin x}{(1 + \cos x)^2}$, the x-axis, $x = \frac{\pi}{3}$ and $x = \frac{2\pi}{3}$.

430 Find $\displaystyle\int \frac{1}{x^2} \ln x \, dx$.

431 Find a if $\displaystyle\int_{-a}^{a} 3x^2 - 8x + 2 \, dx = 12a$ and $a > 0$.

432 The function f is defined by $f(x) = \dfrac{\sin x}{\cos x + \sqrt{2}}$, for $0 < x < 2\pi$.

   a i Find $f'(x)$.

   ii Find the exact coordinates of the turning points of $y = f(x)$.

   b i Find $f''(x)$.

   ii Find the exact coordinates of the points of inflection of the graph of $y = f(x)$.

   c Sketch the graph of $y = f(x)$ for $0 < x < 2\pi$.

   d Find the exact value of the area enclosed by the graph of $y = f(x)$, the x-axis, $x = \frac{\pi}{4}$ and $x = \frac{3\pi}{4}$.

433 **a** Use mathematical induction to prove that, for all $n \in \mathbb{Z}^+$, $2^{n-1} \leqslant n!$.

   b The rate of growth of the area covered by a noxious weed is directly proportional to the area covered by the weed at time t years after the spread was first observed. After 5 years, an area of 32 square kilometres was affected and after 10 years, the area affected was 40 square kilometres.

      i Solve the differential equation $\dfrac{dA}{dt} = kA$.

      ii Find the value of k, correct to 4 significant figures.

      iii Find the area covered at the time of the initial observation.

      iv Assuming the growth continues in the same way, how long before 100 square kilometres would be covered?

434 The first term of an arithmetic sequence is 285 and the tenth term is 213.

   a Find, in terms of n, an expression for the nth term, u_n.

   b How many terms of the sequence are positive?

435 The first term of a geometric sequence is u_1 and the nth term is u_n.

   a Find an expression for the sum of the reciprocals of the first n terms.

   b Hence find $\frac{1}{3} + \frac{1}{6} + \frac{1}{12} + \ldots\ldots + \frac{1}{3072}$

436 Find n if $3\binom{n}{2} = \binom{n}{3}$

437 Simplify $\dfrac{\left(\cos \frac{\pi}{3} - i \sin \frac{\pi}{3}\right)^5 \left(\cos \frac{\pi}{4} + i \sin \frac{\pi}{4}\right)^3}{\left(\cos \frac{\pi}{12} - i \sin \frac{\pi}{12}\right)^7}$

giving your answer as an exact value in the form $a + bi$, where $a, b \in \mathbb{R}$

438 Two functions f, g are defined as follows:
$f : x \to 2x - 3$ and $g : x \to 3(2 - x)$.
Find: **a** $(f \circ g)(-4)$ **b** $f^{-1}(2)$

439 Given the function $f : x \mapsto \sqrt[3]{x}$, find an expression for $g(x)$ in terms of x in each of the following cases.

   a $(f \circ g)(x) = 2x - 1$ **b** $(g \circ f)(x) = 2x - 1$

440 The population P of a species after n months follows the rule: $P = 1000 + ae^{kn}$.

Given that initially the population was 2000 and after 1 year the population was 4000, find how long it would take for the population to reach $10\,000$ from the initial time.

441 A and B are acute angles such that $\sin A = \frac{3}{5}$ and $\tan(A + B) = -\frac{63}{16}$. Show that $\cos B = \frac{5}{13}$.

442 Find the exact values of x in the interval $[0, 2\pi]$ if $2 \sin x \cos x + 1 = 0$

443 Sketch the graph of $y = 2 \sin \left(x - \frac{\pi}{3}\right) + 1$ for $x \in [-\pi, \pi]$.

444 Let $\mathbf{A} = \begin{bmatrix} 2 & 1 & k \\ 3 & 0 & -2 \end{bmatrix}$, $\mathbf{B} = \begin{bmatrix} 0 & k \\ 5 & 1 \\ 6 & 2 \end{bmatrix}$, $\mathbf{C} = \begin{bmatrix} 23 & 13 \\ -12 & 5 \end{bmatrix}$.

   a Find $\mathbf{AB}$.

   b Find all values of k so that $\mathbf{AB} - \mathbf{C} = \mathbf{O}$.

445 Let the vectors $\mathbf{a}$, $\mathbf{b}$ and $\mathbf{c}$ be

$\mathbf{a} = 2\mathbf{i} - \mathbf{j} + 3\mathbf{k}$, $\mathbf{b} = \mathbf{i} - 3\mathbf{j} - \mathbf{k}$, $\mathbf{c} = 2\mathbf{i} - \mathbf{j} + \mathbf{k}$.

   a Show that $\mathbf{b} \times \mathbf{c} = -4\mathbf{i} - 3\mathbf{j} + 5\mathbf{k}$.

   b Verify, for the given vectors that,

$\mathbf{a} \times (\mathbf{b} \times \mathbf{c}) = \mathbf{b}(\mathbf{a} \bullet \mathbf{c}) - \mathbf{c}(\mathbf{a} \bullet \mathbf{b})$.

446 Given $A(3, -1, 5)$, $B(2, 0, -3)$, $C(1, 3, -3)$, find $\cos B\widehat{A}C$ and hence $B\widehat{A}C$.

447 Given that $\mathbf{a} \times (\mathbf{b} \times \mathbf{c}) = \mathbf{b}(\mathbf{a} \bullet \mathbf{c}) - \mathbf{c}(\mathbf{a} \bullet \mathbf{b})$, for any 3 vectors $\mathbf{a}$, $\mathbf{b}$ and $\mathbf{c}$

   a write an expression for $\mathbf{r} \times (\mathbf{s} \times \mathbf{t})$, where $\mathbf{r}$, $\mathbf{s}$ and $\mathbf{t}$ are *any* three vectors

   b simplify the vector $\mathbf{r} \times (\mathbf{s} \times \mathbf{t}) + \mathbf{s} \times (\mathbf{t} \times \mathbf{r}) + \mathbf{t} \times (\mathbf{r} \times \mathbf{s})$.

448 Vehicle licence plates are composed of three letters from a 26-letter alphabet, followed by a three-digit number whose first digit cannot be zero.

   a How many different licence plates are possible?

   b Find the probability of a randomly chosen number plate beginning with the letters AB and ending with the digit 0.

449 A bag contains 4 red and 9 blue balls. If two balls are drawn at random without replacement, what is the probability that one of them is red and the other is blue?

450 Given that $P(N) = \frac{3}{5}$, $P(M \mid N) = \frac{3}{7}$ and $P(M \mid N') = \frac{1}{6}$, find **a** $P(N')$ **b** $P(M' \cap N')$.

451 Find the exact values of the coordinates of the point of inflection on the graph of $y = \dfrac{\ln x}{x^2}$.

452 The diameter of the circular top of an inverted conical container is 20 cm. The height of the container is 20 cm. If the container is filled at a constant rate of 30 cm^{3}s^{-1}, find the rate at which the depth of water is increasing when the depth is 15 cm.

453 Find $\displaystyle\int \frac{\sin^3 x}{\cos^2 x}\,dx$.

454 Find the area enclosed by the curves
$y = x\arccos\frac{1}{2}(x-1) + 1$ and $y = x^2 - 1$

455 Find $\int x^2 \sin x\,dx$.

456 Find the exact value of u if $\displaystyle\int_0^2 \frac{1}{1+ux}\,dx = \frac{1}{u}$.

457 **a** **i** Write down the solutions of $w^6 = 64$, giving your answers in the form $x + iy$.

   ii Hence, determine the solutions of the equation $(z+1)^6 = 64(z-2)^6$.

   b Given the sequence defined by $u_{n+2} = u_n + u_{n+1}$ where $u_1 = u_2 = 1$ and $n \in \mathbb{Z}^+$, use mathematical induction to prove that
$$u_n = \frac{\left(\dfrac{1+\sqrt{5}}{2}\right)^n - \left(\dfrac{1-\sqrt{5}}{2}\right)^n}{\sqrt{5}}$$

458 **a** Use mathematical induction to prove that, for all $n \in \mathbb{Z}^+$,
$\dfrac{d^n}{dx^n}(xe^x) = (x+n)e^x$

   b A sloping wall makes an angle of $120°$ with horizontal ground. A 13 metre ladder leans up against the wall. The bottom of the ladder moves at a constant speed of 2 metres per minute away from the base of the wall. Find the speed at which the top of the ladder moves down the wall when the foot of the ladder is 7 metres from the base of the wall.

459 Consider the following normal distribution graph, modelling age at death (X) in a third world country, where the mean is 43 years and standard deviation is 7 years.

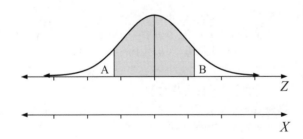

   a Complete a Z-scale and an X-scale on the number lines drawn above.

   b The unshaded region A corresponds to 9% of the population. What is the greatest age at death of any person in the smallest 9% of the population?

   c The un-shaded region B corresponds to 11% of the population. Find the lowest age at death of any person in the top 11% of the population.

   d Find the area of the shaded region.

460 **a** Write -8 in the form $r(\cos\theta + i\sin\theta)$

   b Find the exact value of a cube root of -8 in the form $a+bi$, where $a, b \in \mathbb{R}$

461 Find the coefficient of x^7 in the expansion of $(1+2x)(2-x)^8$.

462 On Peter's first birthday, his grandmother gave him \$100. For each subsequent birthday, she gave him 10% more than on the previous birthday.

   a Write down an expression for how much Peter received on his n^{th} birthday.

   b Write down an expression for the total amount Peter has received for the first n birthdays.

   c On which birthday does the total amount received by Peter first exceed \$4000?

463 Using the digits 2, 3, 4, 5, 6, 7, how many 3 digit numbers can be formed if

   a repetition of digits is permitted

   b digits cannot be repeated

   c digits cannot be repeated and the numbers formed are greater than 400 and even

   d the digits in each number are in ascending order from left to right?

464 The function f is defined by $f : x \to \sqrt{5 - 2x}$, $x \leqslant \frac{5}{2}$. Find $f^{-1}(5)$.

465 **a** Find the equation of the function F obtained by *stretching* the function f *vertically* by a factor of 2 and *horizontally* by a factor of $\frac{1}{2}$, followed by a translation of $\frac{1}{2}$ horizontally and -3 vertically, where $f(x) = x + 2$.

   b The point $(1, 3)$ remains invariant when stretched and translated as above. Hence, verify your answer to part **a** above by finding what happens to the points $(0, 2)$ and $(-1, 1)$.

466 Given $f(x) = 2x^3 - 9x^2 + 30x - 13$:
   a $f(\frac{1}{2})$ **b** factorise $f(x)$ completely into linear factors.

467 Find the exact value of $\tan A$ if $\tan\left(A + \frac{\pi}{4}\right) = 3$

468 Find the exact values of x in the interval $[-\pi, \pi]$ if $\cos 2x + \sqrt{3}\sin 2x = 1$

469 Sketch the graph of $\sin(x+y) = 0$ for $-2\pi \leqslant x \leqslant 2\pi$ and $0 \leqslant y \leqslant 4\pi$.

470 Given an $m \times n$ matrix $\mathbf{U}$ and an $n \times r$ matrix $\mathbf{V}$, find the orders of the matrices $\mathbf{W}$ and $\mathbf{D}$ such that $3\mathbf{U}(-4\mathbf{V} + \mathbf{W}) = -\mathbf{D}$.

471 Given two vectors $\overrightarrow{x}$ and $\overrightarrow{y}$, with $|\overrightarrow{x}| = 2$, find the value of $|\overrightarrow{x} + 2\overrightarrow{y}|$ in the following cases:
   a $\overrightarrow{y} = -2\overrightarrow{x}$
   b $\overrightarrow{x}$ and $\overrightarrow{y}$ are perpendicular and $|\overrightarrow{y}| = 3|\overrightarrow{x}|$.

472 The vectors $\mathbf{v} = \begin{bmatrix} 1 \\ 2 \\ -3 \end{bmatrix}$, $\mathbf{u} = \begin{bmatrix} 2 \\ 2 \\ 3 \end{bmatrix}$, and
$\mathbf{w} = \mathbf{i} + (2 - \lambda)\mathbf{j} + (\lambda + 1)\mathbf{k}$, are given. Find the parameter λ such that the three vectors $\mathbf{u}$, $\mathbf{v}$ and $\mathbf{w}$ are coplanar.

473 The line $\mathbf{r} = \begin{bmatrix} 2 \\ -1 \\ 1 \end{bmatrix} + t\begin{bmatrix} 1 \\ 2 \\ 2 \end{bmatrix}$ is reflected in the plane
$\mathbf{r} = \begin{bmatrix} 3 \\ -1 \\ 2 \end{bmatrix} + \lambda\begin{bmatrix} 1 \\ -1 \\ 1 \end{bmatrix} + \mu\begin{bmatrix} 0 \\ -1 \\ 2 \end{bmatrix}$.

Calculate the angle between the line and its reflection. Give your answer in radians.

474 The probability distribution of a discrete random variable X is given by $P(X = x) = a(\frac{1}{7})^x$, for $x = 0, 1, 2, 3, \dots$. Find the value of a.

475 If 20% of college students do not obtain a score of 35 or more in their IB aggregate, find the probability that out of 9 randomly selected IB students exactly 6 of them will obtain a score of 35 in their IB aggregate.

476 Eight committee members sit around a circular table for a meeting. Mr Jones and Mrs Smith must not sit together.
Calculate the number of different ways these eight people can sit at the table without Mr Jones and Mrs Smith together. (For this question assume the chairs are bolted to the floor. An arrangement is different if at least some of the members sit in a different chair.)

477 **a** Differentiate $x^{\frac{1}{x}}$ with respect to x.
b Hence find the exact values of the coordinates of the stationary point of the function $f : x \mapsto x^{\frac{1}{x}}$.

478 Find the exact values of the x-coordinates of the stationary points of the function $f : x \mapsto 2xe^x - 6e^x - 3x^2 + 12x + 5$.

479 Find $\displaystyle\int \frac{dx}{x^2 + 2x + 10}$

480 Find the exact value of the volume of the solid formed by rotating $y = \sin x$, $0 \leqslant x \leqslant \pi$ about the x-axis.

481 Find $\int x \tan^2 x \, dx$

482 Find the exact value of a if $\displaystyle\int_0^a \frac{x^2}{x^3 + 1} \, dx = 2$.

483 **a** **i** Write $1 - i\sqrt{3}$ and $1 - i$ each in the form $r(\cos \theta + i \sin \theta)$ where r, θ are given as exact values.
  ii Hence simplify $\dfrac{\left(1 - i\sqrt{3}\right)^{11}}{(1 - i)^{18}}$, giving your answer in the form $x + iy$ where x and y are real numbers, given in exact form.
b Solve for z: $z^5 = \sqrt{3} - i$ giving your answers in the form $r(\cos \theta + i \sin \theta)$ where r and θ are given as exact values.

484 **a** If $f(x) = 3x^2 + 5x - 2$, find $f'(x)$, from first principles.
b Given $f(x) = \dfrac{e^x - e^{-x}}{e^x + e^{-x}}$
  i Find $f'(x)$ and hence show that the graph of $y = f(x)$ has no stationary points.
  ii Find $f''(x)$.
  iii Find the exact value of $\displaystyle\int_0^{\ln 3} f(x) \, dx$, giving your answer in the form $\ln k$ where k is a rational number.

485 Scooter was born on the 6th of January 2001 in Adelaide. The day was an unusually hot day of 40°.
a Given that the daily maximum temperature in Adelaide in January is normally distributed with a mean of 33° and a standard deviation of 3.5^o, find the proportion of January days in Adelaide that will have a daily maximum temperature of more than 40°. (A sketch diagram may help.)
b Whilst travelling overseas in Prague, Scooter met Pokey who was born on the same day (January 6th 2001) as he was. After some conversation they discovered that there was a 52° temperature difference between the daily maximum temperature in Adelaide when Scooter was born and the daily minimum temperature in Prague when Pokey was born. Find the minimum temperature of the day that Pokey was born.
c Given that the daily minimum temperature in Prague in January is normally distributed with

$N(\mu = -3.2^o, \sigma = 4.9^o)$, calculate the proportion of January days in Prague that will have a daily minimum temperature of less than -12°.
d Use your knowledge of the normal distribution to explain which city experienced the most extreme temperature on the day that Scooter and Pokey were born.
e How cold would it have to be in January in Prague for the weather to be comparable with Adelaide's hottest January day on record, which was a scorching hot 46.4^o?

EXAMINATION PRACTICE SET 15

486 For the geometric series $1 - \tan^2 x + \tan^4 x - \dots$
a Determine the values of x where $0 \leqslant x \leqslant 2\pi$ for which the sum of the series converges.
b For the values of x found in **a**, determine the sum of the series.
c For what values of x in the interval $[0, 2\pi]$ does the sum of the series equal $\frac{1}{2}$?

487 **a** For what values of b does the infinite series
$$a + \frac{a}{b^2} + \frac{a}{b^4} + \dots \text{ converge?}$$
b For the values of b found in part **a**, find an expression for the sum of the series.
c Hence, by making suitable substitutions for a and b express $0.\overline{32}$ in the form $\dfrac{p}{q}$, $p, q \in \mathbb{Z}$.

488 How many different arrangements of the letters of the word DIPLOMA are possible if
a there is no restriction
b the arrangements begin and end with a vowel
c the vowels appear together?

489 The complex number z is such that $1 < |z| < 2$ and $0 < \arg(z) < \frac{\pi}{4}$.
The position of z is shown on the Argand diagram.
Mark, on the diagram the positions of **a** $-z$ **b** $\bar{z}$ **c** iz **d** z^2 **e** $\sqrt{z}$

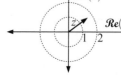

490 Given the functions $f: x \mapsto 2x - 1$ and $g : x \mapsto 2x^3$, find the function $(f \circ g)^{-1}$.

491 The graph of $f(x)$ is given.
a Draw the graph of $|f(x)|$, on the same set of axes as shown.
b Find the y-intercept of $\dfrac{1}{f(x)}$.
c Draw the graph of $y = \dfrac{1}{f(x)}$ on the same set of axes as shown.

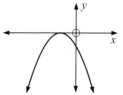

492 By observing the parabola drawn (with equation $y = ax^2 + bx + c$):
a State what you know about the value of a. Give a brief reason.
b State what you know about the value of c. Give a brief reason.
c What can be said about the solutions of the equation $ax^2 + bx = -c$?
d What can be stated about the value of $b^2 - 4ac$? Give a brief reason.

Mathematics HL – Exam Preparation & Practice Guide

e By writing the equation of the graph in the form $y = a(x - h)^2 + k$, find h and k in terms of a, b and c. Hence, briefly justify the formula for the axis of symmetry.

493 In triangle ABC, AB = 5 cm, BC = 7 cm, $A\widehat{C}B = \theta$, $B\widehat{A}C = 2\theta$. Find θ.

494 Find the exact values of x if $0 \leqslant x \leqslant 2\pi$ and $\sin 2x + \cos 2x = 1$.

495 Sketch the graph of $y = x \arcsin \left(\frac{x}{3} - 0.5 \right)$ for $-1 \leqslant x \leqslant 3$.

Indicate on your graph, the coordinates of the end points, axis intercepts and turning point.

496 State the range of values that k may take if the following system of equations
$$x - y - z = 1$$
$$2x + y + z = 2$$
$$4x - y - z = k$$
a has an infinite number of solutions **b** has no solution.

497 Find the area of the parallelogram determined by the vectors $\mathbf{a} = 3\mathbf{i} - 4\mathbf{j} + \mathbf{k}$ and $\mathbf{b} = 2\mathbf{i} + \mathbf{j} - 5\mathbf{k}$.

498 Consider the two planes P and Q, with equations
$$P: \quad \mathbf{r} \bullet \begin{bmatrix} 6 \\ -2 \\ 3 \end{bmatrix} + 8 = 0 \qquad Q: \quad \mathbf{r} \bullet \begin{bmatrix} 1 \\ -3 \\ 5 \end{bmatrix} = 0.$$

Find an equation of a third plane R which is perpendicular to both P and Q and contains the point (2, 2, 3).

499 The line $x + 1 = \frac{y - 1}{2} = \frac{z - 1}{-2}$ and the point (1, 3, −2) lie on the plane P.
a Find an equation of P.
b Calculate the distance of the plane from the origin.

500 In a game a player rolls a biased tetrahedral (four-faced) die. The probability of each possible score is shown below.

Score	1	2	3	4
Probability	$\frac{2}{7}$	$\frac{1}{3}$	x	$\frac{2}{21}$

Find the probability of a total score of six after two rolls.

501 An advanced mathematics class consists of 7 girls and 9 boys.
a How many different committees of 7 students can be chosen from this class?
b How many such committees can be chosen if class members Haakon (a male) and Josefine (a female) cannot both be on the committee?
c How many committees of 7 students can be chosen if there must be more boys than girls on the committee?

502 The mean test score for a mathematics class was 64 with a standard deviation of 8.352. Assuming that the test scores are normally distributed, find the proportion of students scoring an A if a student must score *more* than 80% in the given test to obtain an A.

503 a Differentiate $\frac{x}{\sqrt{x - 6}}$, simplifying your answer.
b Hence find the exact value of the x-coordinate of the minimum turning point of the function $y = \frac{x}{\sqrt{x - 6}}$, $x > 6$.

504 P is a point in the first quadrant on the graph of $y = 10 - xe^x$. A and B are points on the x and y axes respectively such that OAPB is a rectangle. Find the maximum area of the rectangle.

505 Find the exact value of $\int_0^{\frac{\pi}{2}} \frac{\sin x}{1 + \cos x} \, dx$.

506 The area bounded by the curve $y = \frac{x - 3}{x}$, the x-axis and

the line $x = 6$ is rotated about the x-axis. Find the exact value of the volume of the solid generated.

507 Use the substitution $x = 2 \sin \theta$ to find $\int \sqrt{4 - x^2} \, dx$

508 Find the exact value of a, $a > 0$ if $\int_0^a \frac{x}{x^2 + 1} \, dx = 1$.

509 a Let $f(x) = x^n$, $n \in \mathbb{Z}^+$
  i Express $f(x + h)$ in expanded form in decreasing powers of x, showing the first 3 and last 3 terms of the expansion.
  ii Hence find $f'(x)$ from first principles.

b The velocity, in metres per second at time t seconds, of a particle moving in a straight line is given by $v = 4t^3 - 9t^2 + 2$, $t \geqslant 0$
  i Find an expression for a, the acceleration of the particle after t seconds.
  ii Find the minimum velocity of the particle.
  iii Find an expression for s, the displacement from O of the particle at time t seconds, given that when $t = 0$, $s = -6$.
  iv Find when the particle first passes through O.
  v Find the total distance travelled in the first 5 seconds.

510 The scores in a Biology examination are distributed normally with a mean of 56% and a standard deviation of 30.512%.
a If you needed to get 72% to get a "6" or better in Biology, what percentage of students gained a "6" or better in Biology?
b If the pass mark was 40%, what percentage of students taking the Biology exam actually passed?
c What grade would Micah, with a score of 94%, receive if only the top 10% of students got a "7"? Show working for full marks.
d Micah, the same student in part **c** received a score of 87% for English, a subject with marks normally distributed with a mean of 63% and standard deviation of 18.31%. Clearly show a calculation to determine whether Micah performed better in Biology or English. What grade would he get in English if the same percentage of students got 7's and 6's in English as in Biology? Show all working for full marks.

511 a The depth of water, x metres in a shipping channel at the entrance of a harbour is given by $x = 6 + 2 \cos \left(\frac{4\pi}{25} t + \frac{\pi}{3} \right)$ where t is the number of hours after midday on Sept 1.
  i At what time will the first high tide occur?
  ii How much time elapses between consecutive high tides?
  iii A ship in the harbour is ready to leave at 3.00 pm on Sept 2. If it needs a depth of at least 5.5 metres, what is the earliest time it could safely pass through the entrance to the harbour?

b A field ABCD is in the shape of a quadrilateral with sides AB = 50 m, BC = 20 m, CD = 30 m AD = 40 m as shown. $B\widehat{A}D = \theta$ and $B\widehat{C}D = 2\theta$
  i Find the exact value of $\cos \theta$.
  ii Hence find the exact value of the area of the field.

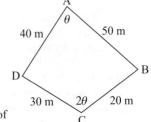

SKILL BUILDER SOLUTIONS

1 $18 + 16 + 14 + \ldots\ldots$ is arithmetic with $u_1 = 18$, $d = -2$

So, $S_{30} = \frac{30}{2}(2u_1 + 29d)$

$= 15 \times (36 + 29 \times -2)$

$= 15 \times (36 - 58)$

$= -330$

2 $u_1 = 27$ and $u_1 r^3 = 8$

$\Rightarrow \quad 27r^3 = 8$

$\Rightarrow \quad r = \sqrt[3]{\frac{8}{27}} = \frac{2}{3}$

and so $S_\infty = \frac{u_1}{1 - r} = \frac{27}{1 - \frac{2}{3}} = 81$

3   Let the terms be $x - d, x, x + d$

then the sum $= 3x = 18 \quad \Rightarrow \quad x = 6$

Sum of squares

$= (x - d)^2 + x^2 + (x + d)^2$

$= x^2 - 2dx + d^2 + x^2 + x^2 + 2dx + d^2$

$= 3x^2 + 2d^2$

$= 3 \times 36 + 2d^2$

$= 108 + 2d^2 \qquad \therefore \quad 108 + 2d^2 = 396$

$\Rightarrow \quad 2d^2 = 288$

$\Rightarrow \quad d^2 = 144$

$\Rightarrow \quad d = \pm 12$

Thus, the terms are: $-6, 6, 18$ or $18, 6, -6$.

4 $u_1 = 18$, $d = -3$ and $S_n = \frac{n}{2}(2u_1 + (n - 1)d)$

$= \frac{n}{2}(36 - 3(n - 1))$

$= \frac{n}{2}(39 - 3n)$

So, $\frac{n}{2}(39 - 3n) = -210$

$\Rightarrow \quad 3n(13 - n) = -420$

$\Rightarrow \quad n(13 - n) = -140$

$\Rightarrow \quad n^2 - 13n - 140 = 0$

$\Rightarrow \quad (n - 20)(n + 7) = 0$

$\Rightarrow \quad n = 20 \quad \{\text{as } n \neq -7\}$

i.e.,   20 terms in the series.

5 $\dfrac{x^a \sqrt{x^{3a}}}{x^{-2a}} = \dfrac{x^a x^{\frac{3a}{2}}}{x^{-2a}} = x^{a + \frac{3a}{2} + 2a} = x^{\frac{9a}{2}}$

6 $\left(\dfrac{3x^{-1}}{2a^2}\right)^{-2} \left(\dfrac{4x^2}{27a^{-3}}\right)^{-1} = \dfrac{3^{-2}x^2}{2^{-2}a^{-4}} \times \dfrac{2^{-2}x^{-2}}{3^{-3}a^3}$

$= \dfrac{2^2 x^2 a^4}{3^2} \times \dfrac{3^3}{2^2 a^3 x^2}$

$= 3a$

7 $8^{2x-3} = 16^{2-x}$

$\Rightarrow \quad 2^{3(2x-3)} = 2^{4(2-x)}$

$\Rightarrow \quad 6x - 9 = 8 - 4x$

$\Rightarrow \quad 10x = 17$

$\Rightarrow \quad x = 1.7$

8 $\log_9\left(\frac{1}{27}\right)$

$= \dfrac{\log\left(\frac{1}{27}\right)}{\log 9}$

$= \dfrac{\log 3^{-3}}{\log 3^2}$

$= \dfrac{-3 \log 3}{2 \log 3}$

$= -\dfrac{3}{2}$

9 $\dfrac{8}{\log_5 9}$

$= 8 \times \log_9 5 \quad \{\text{as } \log_b a \text{ and } \log_a b \text{ are reciprocals}\}$

$= 8 \times \dfrac{\log_3 5}{\log_3 9}$

$= 8 \times \dfrac{\log_3 5}{\log_3 3^2}$

$= 8 \times \dfrac{\log_3 5}{2}$

$= 4 \log_3 5$

10 $2 \ln x + \ln(x - 1) - \ln(x - 2)$

$= \ln x^2 + \ln(x - 1) - \ln(x - 2)$

$= \ln \dfrac{x^2(x - 1)}{(x - 2)}$

11 $\log_3 x + \log_3(x - 2) = 1$

$\log_3 x(x - 2) = \log_3 3$

$x(x - 2) = 3$

$x^2 - 2x - 3 = 0$

$(x + 1)(x - 3) = 0$

$x = -1 \text{ or } 3$

But $x > 0$ and $x - 2 > 0 \quad \Rightarrow \quad x > 2$

and so, $x = 3$.

12 $(2 - ai)^3$

$= 2^3 - 3(2)^2(ai) + 3(2)(ai)^2 - (ai)^3$

$= 8 - 12ai - 6a^2 + a^3 i$

$= (8 - 6a^2) + (a^3 - 12a)i$

13   In $(x + \frac{1}{x})^8$, $T_{r+1} = \binom{8}{r} x^{8-r} \left(\frac{1}{x}\right)^r$

$= \binom{8}{r} x^{8-r} x^{-r}$

$= \binom{8}{r} x^{8-2r}$

where $r = 0, 1, 2, \ldots\ldots, 8$

If $r = 4$, $T_5 = \binom{8}{4} x^0 = \binom{8}{4} = 70$

So, the constant term is 70 .

14 $3 - 3i\sqrt{3}$ has modulus $\sqrt{9 + 27} = \sqrt{36} = 6$

$\therefore \quad 3 - 3i\sqrt{3} = 6(\frac{1}{2} - \frac{\sqrt{3}}{2}i)$

$= 6 \operatorname{cis}\left(\frac{-\pi}{3}\right)$

$= 6\left[\cos\left(\frac{-\pi}{3}\right) + i\sin\left(\frac{-\pi}{3}\right)\right]$

15 $\left[\cos\left(\frac{2\pi}{3}\right) - i\sin\left(\frac{2\pi}{3}\right)\right]^{10}$

$= \left[\operatorname{cis}\left(-\frac{2\pi}{3}\right)\right]^{10} \quad \{\cos\theta - i\sin\theta = \operatorname{cis}(-\theta)\}$

$= \left[\operatorname{cis}\left(-\frac{20\pi}{3}\right)\right] \quad \{\text{DeMoivre}\}$

$= \left[\operatorname{cis}\left(-\frac{2\pi}{3}\right)\right] \quad \{\text{as } \operatorname{cis}(\theta + k2\pi) = \operatorname{cis}\theta\}$

$= -\frac{1}{2} - i\frac{\sqrt{3}}{2}$

SKILL BUILDER SOLUTIONS

16 f is defined if $3x - 1 \geqslant 0$ i.e., $x \geqslant \frac{1}{3}$.

Domain of f is $x \in \mathbb{R}$, $x \geqslant \frac{1}{3}$ or $[\frac{1}{3}, \infty[$.

17 a $(g \circ f)(-4) = g(f(-4))$

$= g(-8 + 1)$

$= g(-7)$

$= 2 - -7$

$= 9$

b   As f is $y = 2x + 1$,

then f^{-1} is $x = 2y + 1$ i.e., $y = \dfrac{x - 1}{2}$

Thus, $f^{-1}(x) = \dfrac{x - 1}{2}$ and $f^{-1}(2) = \dfrac{2 - 1}{2} = \frac{1}{2}$

18

They meet at $(-0.658, 0.070)$ and $(2.657, 1.930)$.

19

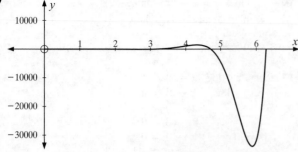

Maximum value of 1470 at $x = 4.320$

Minimum value of $-34\,010$ at $x = 5.891$

20 If $y = 3x^2 + 2x$ is stretched vertically by a factor of 2 then it becomes $y = 2(3x^2 + 2x)$, i.e., $y = 6x^2 + 4x$.

If this is then translated 3 units horizontally it becomes
$y = 6(x - 3)^2 + 4(x - 3)$ i.e., $y = 6x^2 - 32x + 42$

If this is then translated -1 units vertically it becomes
$y = 6x^2 - 32x + 42 - 1$ i.e., $y = 6x^2 - 32x + 41$

21 The function f is $y = x^2 + 2x$, $x \in\,]-\infty, -1]$. So, the inverse function f^{-1} is $x = y^2 + 2y$, $y \in\,]-\infty, -1]$

i.e., $y^2 + 2y - x = 0$ and so $y = \dfrac{-2 \pm \sqrt{4 - 4(1)(-x)}}{2}$

which is $y = -1 \pm \sqrt{1 + x}$

But, as $y \in\,]-\infty, -1]$, $y < 0$, $\therefore$ $y = -1 - \sqrt{1 + x}$

Invariant poits occur if

$$x = x^2 + 2x, \quad x \in\,]-\infty, -1]$$
$$\Rightarrow \quad x^2 + x = 0$$
$$\Rightarrow \quad x(x + 1) = 0$$
$$\Rightarrow \quad x = 0 \text{ or } -1. \quad \text{But } x \leqslant -1$$

So, $(-1, -1)$ is an invariant point.

22

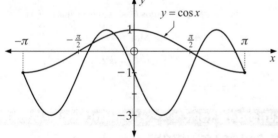

23 Graph of
$y = x^2 - 2x$, $x \in \mathbb{R}$

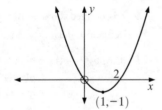

a Graph of
$y = f(|\,x\,|) = x^2 - 2\,|\,x\,|$

b Graph of
$y = |\,f(x)\,| = |\,x^2 - 2x\,|$

24 Graph of $y = \dfrac{2x + 1}{x - 2} = 2 + \dfrac{5}{x - 2}$

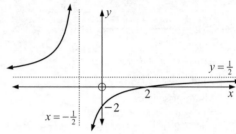

Graph of $y = \dfrac{1}{f(x)} = \dfrac{x - 2}{2x + 1} = \dfrac{1}{2} - \dfrac{3}{4x + 2}$

25 a Axis of symmetry of $f(x) = 2x^2 + 4x - 30$ is $x = \dfrac{-4}{2(2)}$
i.e., $x = -1$

b When $x = -1$, $f(-1) = 2 - 4 - 30 = -32$
$\Rightarrow$ turning point at $(-1, -32)$

c $\qquad y = 2x^2 + 4x - 30$
$\Rightarrow \quad y = 2(x^2 + 2x) - 30$
$\Rightarrow \quad y = 2[(x + 1)^2 - 1] - 30$
$\Rightarrow \quad y = 2(x + 1)^2 - 32$

d $\qquad y = 2(x + 1)^2 - 32$
$\Rightarrow \quad y = 2[(x + 1)^2 - 16]$
$\Rightarrow \quad y = 2[x + 1 + 4][x + 1 - 4]$
$\Rightarrow \quad y = 2[x + 5][x - 3]$

26 $y = kx - 2$ will be a tangent to the curve $y = 3x^2 + x + 1$ if the equation $3x^2 + x + 1 = kx - 2$ has a double root.

This equation becomes $3x^2 + (1 - k)x + 3 = 0$ where
$$\Delta = (1 - k)^2 - 4(3)(3)$$
$$= (1 - k)^2 - 36$$
$$= (1 - k + 6)(1 - k - 6)$$
$$= (7 - k)(-k - 5) \quad \text{and } \Delta = 0 \text{ when } k = 7 \text{ or } -5$$
So, the line is a tangent when $k = 7$ or -5.

27 The function f is $y = e^{2x+1}$, so the inverse function f^{-1} is $x = e^{2y+1}$

This becomes $\ln x = 2y + 1$ or $y = \dfrac{\ln x - 1}{2}$

Thus, $f^{-1}(x) = \dfrac{\ln x - 1}{2}$ and so $f^{-1}(7) = \dfrac{\ln 7 - 1}{2} \approx 0.473$.

28 The function g is $y = \log_2(2x - 1)$

So, the inverse function g^{-1} is $x = \log_2(2y - 1)$

This becomes $2y - 1 = 2^x$ and so $y = \dfrac{2^x + 1}{2}$

Thus, $g^{-1}(x) = \dfrac{2^x + 1}{2}$ and $g^{-1}(-6) = \dfrac{2^{-6} + 1}{2} \approx 0.508$.

29 If $x \neq -1$, $\left|\dfrac{2x - 1}{x + 1}\right| \leqslant 3$ $\Leftrightarrow$ $|\,2x - 1\,| \leqslant 3\,|\,x + 1\,|$

As $|\,2x - 1\,|$ and $|\,x + 1\,|$ behave differently around $\frac{1}{2}$ and -1 respectively, we need to consider 3 cases:

(1) $x \leqslant -1$ (2) $-1 \leqslant x \leqslant \frac{1}{2}$ (3) $x \geqslant \frac{1}{2}$

Case (3) :

if $x \geqslant \frac{1}{2}$ then $\qquad 2x - 1 \leqslant 3(x + 1)$
$$\Rightarrow \quad 2x - 1 \leqslant 3x + 3$$
$$x \geqslant -4$$

But $x \geqslant \frac{1}{2}$ and so $x \geqslant \frac{1}{2}$.

Case (2) :

if $-1 < x \leqslant \frac{1}{2}$ then $-(2x-1) \leqslant 3(x+1)$

$\Rightarrow \quad -2x+1 \leqslant 3x+3$

$\Rightarrow \quad 5x \geqslant -2$

$\Rightarrow \quad x \geqslant -\frac{2}{5}$

But $-1 < x \leqslant \frac{1}{2}$, $\therefore$ $-\frac{2}{5} \leqslant x \leqslant \frac{1}{2}$

Case (1) :

if $x < -1$ $-(2x-1) \leqslant 3(-x-1)$

$\Rightarrow \quad -2x+1 \leqslant -3x-3$

$\Rightarrow \quad x \leqslant -4$

But $x < -1$, $\therefore$ $x \leqslant -4$

Combining all three results we have $x \leqslant -4$ or $x \geqslant -\frac{2}{5}$.

30 The graph of $y = 3(x-1)^2(x+2)(x-4)$ is:

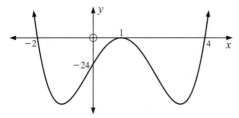

Note that the x-axis $(y=0)$ is a tangent to the curve.

SOLUTIONS TO TOPIC 3 **CIRCULAR FUNCTIONS AND TRIGONOMETRY**

SKILL BUILDER SOLUTIONS

31

$\sin\theta = \frac{3}{5}$

$\cos\theta = \frac{4}{5}$

$\sin 2\theta = 2(\frac{3}{5})(\frac{4}{5})$

$= \frac{24}{25}$

Area of segment

$= \frac{1}{2}r^2(2\theta - \sin 2\theta)$

$= \frac{1}{2} \times 25 \times (2\arcsin(0.6) - \frac{24}{25})$

$\approx 4.09 \text{ cm}^2$

32 $\sin(\frac{3\pi}{2} - A)\tan(\pi + A) = -\cos A \times \tan A$

$= -\cos A \times \frac{\sin A}{\cos A}$

$= -\sin A$

33 $1 - \frac{\sin^2 A}{1 + \cos A} = \frac{1 + \cos A - \sin^2 A}{1 + \cos A}$

$= \frac{1 + \cos A - (1 - \cos^2 A)}{1 + \cos A}$

$= \frac{1 + \cos A - 1 + \cos^2 A}{1 + \cos A}$

$= \frac{\cos A + \cos^2 A}{1 + \cos A}$

$= \frac{\cos A(1 + \cos A)}{1 + \cos A}$

$= \cos A$

34 $\cos 79^\circ \cos 71^\circ - \sin 79^\circ \sin 71^\circ = \cos(79^\circ + 71^\circ)$

$= \cos 150^\circ$

$= -\frac{\sqrt{3}}{2}$

35 $\cos 2x = \frac{5}{8} \quad \Rightarrow \quad 1 - 2\sin^2 x = \frac{5}{8}$

$\Rightarrow \quad 2\sin^2 x = \frac{3}{8}$

$\Rightarrow \quad \sin^2 x = \frac{3}{16}$

$\Rightarrow \quad \sin x = \pm\frac{\sqrt{3}}{4}$

---

36 $\sin\theta = \frac{2}{3} \quad \Rightarrow \quad \cos\theta = -\frac{\sqrt{5}}{3}$

$\Rightarrow \quad \sin 2\theta = 2\sin\theta\cos\theta$

$= 2(\frac{2}{3})(-\frac{\sqrt{5}}{3})$

$= -\frac{4\sqrt{5}}{9}$

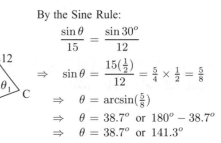

37

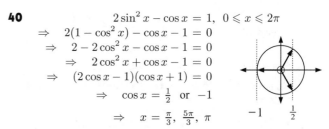

The largest angle is opposite the longest side.

By the Cosine rule,

$\cos\theta = \frac{7^2 + 9^2 - 11^2}{2 \times 7 \times 9} = \frac{9}{14 \times 9} = \frac{1}{14}$

$\Rightarrow \quad \theta = \arccos(\frac{1}{14}) \approx 85.9^\circ$.

38

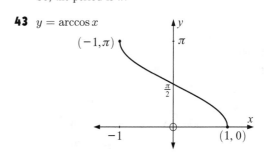

By the Sine Rule:

$\frac{\sin\theta}{15} = \frac{\sin 30^\circ}{12}$

$\Rightarrow \quad \sin\theta = \frac{15(\frac{1}{2})}{12} = \frac{5}{4} \times \frac{1}{2} = \frac{5}{8}$

$\Rightarrow \quad \theta = \arcsin(\frac{5}{8})$

$\Rightarrow \quad \theta = 38.7^\circ$ or $180^\circ - 38.7^\circ$

$\Rightarrow \quad \theta = 38.7^\circ$ or 141.3°

39 $\quad\quad\quad \sin x = \sin 2x$

$\Rightarrow \quad 2\sin x \cos x - \sin x = 0$

$\Rightarrow \quad \sin x(2\cos x - 1) = 0$

$\Rightarrow \quad \sin x = 0$ or $\cos x = \frac{1}{2}$

$\Rightarrow \quad x = -\pi, -\frac{\pi}{3}, 0, \frac{\pi}{3}, \pi$

40 $\quad 2\sin^2 x - \cos x = 1, \quad 0 \leqslant x \leqslant 2\pi$

$\Rightarrow \quad 2(1 - \cos^2 x) - \cos x - 1 = 0$

$\Rightarrow \quad 2 - 2\cos^2 x - \cos x - 1 = 0$

$\Rightarrow \quad 2\cos^2 x + \cos x - 1 = 0$

$\Rightarrow \quad (2\cos x - 1)(\cos x + 1) = 0$

$\Rightarrow \quad \cos x = \frac{1}{2}$ or -1

$\Rightarrow \quad x = \frac{\pi}{3}, \frac{5\pi}{3}, \pi$

41 $f(x) = -2\cos\left(\frac{1}{3}(x - \frac{\pi}{6})\right) + 1$

has max. value $-2(-1) + 1 = 3$ when

$\cos\left(\frac{1}{3}(x - \frac{\pi}{6})\right) = -1$

$\frac{1}{3}(x - \frac{\pi}{6}) = \pi + k2\pi$

$x - \frac{\pi}{6} = 3\pi + k6\pi$

$x = \frac{\pi}{6} + 3\pi + k6\pi$

$x = \frac{19\pi}{6} + k6\pi$

For $x > 0$, $x = \frac{19\pi}{6}$ gives the first such point, i.e., $\left(\frac{19\pi}{6}, 3\right)$.

42 $f(x) = \quad \tan 2x \quad + \quad \tan 3x$

$\quad\quad\quad\quad\quad \uparrow \quad\quad\quad\quad\quad \uparrow$

$\quad\quad\quad \text{period } \frac{\pi}{2} \quad\quad \text{period } \frac{\pi}{3}$

$\tan 2x$ repeats after $\frac{\pi}{2}, \pi, \frac{3\pi}{2}, 2\pi, ...$

$\tan 3x$ repeats after $\frac{\pi}{3}, \frac{2\pi}{3}, \pi, \frac{4\pi}{3}, ...$

So, the period is π.

43 $y = \arccos x$

---

44 $\arcsin(-\frac{1}{2}) + \arctan 1 + \arccos(-\frac{1}{2}) = -\frac{\pi}{6} + \frac{\pi}{4} + \frac{2\pi}{3}$

$$= \pi(-\frac{1}{6} + \frac{1}{4} + \frac{2}{3})$$
$$= \frac{3\pi}{4}$$

45

$$\sin x + \cos x = 1$$
$$\Rightarrow \quad (\sin x + \cos x)^2 = 1$$
$$\Rightarrow \quad \sin^2 x + 2\sin x \cos x + \cos^2 x = 1$$
$$\Rightarrow \quad 1 + \sin 2x = 1$$
$$\Rightarrow \quad \sin 2x = 0$$

Reminder: Sometimes squaring equations produces incorrect solutions, so each solution must be checked.

$$\Rightarrow \quad 2x = 0 + k\pi, \ k \in \mathbb{Z}$$
$$\Rightarrow \quad x = \frac{k\pi}{2}$$
$$\Rightarrow \quad x = 0, \ \frac{\pi}{2}, \ \pi$$

Check: $x = 0, \ \sin 0 + \cos 0 = 0 + 1 = 1 \ \checkmark$

$x = \frac{\pi}{2}, \ \sin \frac{\pi}{2} + \cos \frac{\pi}{2} = 1 + 0 \ \checkmark$

$x = \pi, \ \sin \pi + \cos \pi = 0 + -1 = -1 \ \times$

$\therefore$ the solutions are: $x = 0, \ \frac{\pi}{2}$.

SOLUTIONS TO TOPIC 4 — MATRICES

SKILL BUILDER SOLUTIONS

46 To evaluate $2\mathbf{A} - 3\mathbf{B}$, $\mathbf{A}$ and $\mathbf{B}$ must have the same order. Since $\mathbf{A}$ has order $m \times n$, $\mathbf{B}$ must have order $m \times n$, i.e., $p = m$ and $q = n$.

47 Let the cost of 1 soccer ball be $\$x$, the cost of 1 softball be $\$y$ and the cost of 1 basketball be $\$z$.

School A paid $2x + 1y + 3z = 90$,

school B paid $3x + 2y + 1z = 81$

and school C paid $5x + 0y + 2z = 104$.

In matrix form $\begin{bmatrix} 2 & 1 & 3 \\ 3 & 2 & 1 \\ 5 & 0 & 2 \end{bmatrix} \begin{bmatrix} x \\ y \\ z \end{bmatrix} = \begin{bmatrix} 90 \\ 81 \\ 104 \end{bmatrix}$

This system has solution $x = 14, \ y = 11, \ z = 17$

i.e., a soccer ball costs \$14, a softball costs \$11 and a basketball costs \$17.

48 $\mathbf{A} = \mathbf{B}$ if (1) $\mathbf{A}$ and $\mathbf{B}$ have the same order

(2) each element a_{ij} of $\mathbf{A}$ is equal to the corresponding element b_{ij} of $\mathbf{B}$.

49 a If $\mathbf{A}$ has order $m \times n$ and $\mathbf{B}$ has order $n \times p$

then $\mathbf{C}$ has order $m \times p$ and $c_{ij} = \sum_{k=1}^{n} a_{ik} b_{kj}$

b $c_{34} = \sum_{k=1}^{n} a_{3k} b_{k4}$

50 If $\mathbf{O}$ is the matrix with all entries 0, then $\mathbf{A} + \mathbf{O} = \mathbf{O} + \mathbf{A}$ if $\mathbf{A}$ and $\mathbf{O}$ have the same order. $\mathbf{A} + \mathbf{O} = \mathbf{O} + \mathbf{A} = \mathbf{A}$

51 If $\mathbf{I}$ is $n \times n$ then $\mathbf{A}$ must be of order $n \times n$.

The elements, e_{ij} of $\mathbf{I}$ are: $e_{ii} = 1$, for all i

$e_{ij} = 0$, for all $i \neq j$.

52 $\begin{bmatrix} k & 5 \\ 1 & k \end{bmatrix}$ is singular if $\begin{vmatrix} k & 5 \\ 1 & k \end{vmatrix} = k^2 - 5 = 0$ i.e., if $k = \pm\sqrt{5}$.

If $\begin{bmatrix} k & 5 \\ 1 & k \end{bmatrix}$ is singular it has no inverse.

53 Assuming $\mathbf{A}$ and $\mathbf{B}$ are square matrices with inverses $\mathbf{A}^{-1}$ and $\mathbf{B}^{-1}$ respectively

$$3\mathbf{AXB} = 2\mathbf{C} \quad \Leftrightarrow \quad 3\mathbf{AXBB}^{-1} = 2\mathbf{CB}^{-1}$$
$$\Leftrightarrow \quad 3\mathbf{AX} = 2\mathbf{CB}^{-1}$$
$$\Leftrightarrow \quad \mathbf{AX} = \tfrac{2}{3}\mathbf{CB}^{-1}$$
$$\Leftrightarrow \quad \mathbf{A}^{-1}\mathbf{AX} = \tfrac{2}{3}\mathbf{A}^{-1}\mathbf{CB}^{-1}$$
$$\Leftrightarrow \quad \mathbf{X} = \tfrac{2}{3}\mathbf{A}^{-1}\mathbf{CB}^{-1}$$

54 The matrix $\begin{bmatrix} 2 & -1 & 1 \\ m & 2 & 1 \\ 3 & -1 & 2 \end{bmatrix}$ has an inverse if its determinant is $\neq 0$.

and $\begin{vmatrix} 2 & -1 & 1 \\ m & 2 & 1 \\ 3 & -1 & 2 \end{vmatrix} = 2 \begin{vmatrix} 2 & 1 \\ -1 & 2 \end{vmatrix} - -1 \begin{vmatrix} m & 1 \\ 3 & 2 \end{vmatrix} + 1 \begin{vmatrix} m & 2 \\ 3 & -1 \end{vmatrix}$

$$= 2(5) + 1(2m - 3) + (-m - 6)$$
$$= 10 + 2m - 3 - m - 6$$
$$= m + 1$$

i.e., the matrix has an inverse if $m \neq -1$.

55 The equations will have a unique solution if

$$\det \begin{bmatrix} 3 & -a & 2 \\ 1 & 2 & -3 \\ -1 & -1 & 1 \end{bmatrix} \neq 0.$$

$\begin{vmatrix} 3 & -a & 2 \\ 1 & 2 & -3 \\ -1 & -1 & 1 \end{vmatrix} = 3 \begin{vmatrix} 2 & -3 \\ -1 & 1 \end{vmatrix} - -a \begin{vmatrix} 1 & -3 \\ -1 & 1 \end{vmatrix} + 2 \begin{vmatrix} 1 & 2 \\ -1 & -1 \end{vmatrix}$

$$= 3(-1) + a(-2) + 2(1)$$
$$= -1 - 2a$$

which is 0 if $a = -\frac{1}{2}$.

Thus, we have a unique solution if $a \neq -\frac{1}{2}$.

56 $|\mathbf{A}| = \begin{vmatrix} 2 & -1 \\ 1 & 3 \end{vmatrix} = 6 - -1 = 7$ and

$|\mathbf{B}| = \begin{vmatrix} -2 & 5 \\ 1 & 3 \end{vmatrix} = -6 - 5 = -11$

So, $|\mathbf{AB}| = |\mathbf{A}||\mathbf{B}| = 7 \times -11 = -77$.

57 We could get

- no solutions if the two equations were inconsistent
- an infinite number of solutions.

We cannot get a unique solution if there are more unknowns than equations.

58 If there are more unknowns than equations

- check that the equations are consistent
- assign the correct number of parameters: there may be 1 or 2 such parameters.

59 Writing the system in augmented form

$\begin{bmatrix} 1 & 3 & k & | & 2 \\ k & -2 & 3 & | & k \\ 4 & -3 & 10 & | & 5 \end{bmatrix}$

$\sim \begin{bmatrix} 1 & 3 & k & | & 2 \\ 0 & -2-3k & 3-k^2 & | & -k \\ 0 & -15 & 10-4k & | & -3 \end{bmatrix} \begin{matrix} \\ R_2 \rightarrow R_2 - kR_1 \\ R_3 \rightarrow R_3 - 4R_1 \end{matrix}$

$\sim \begin{bmatrix} 1 & 3 & k & | & 2 \\ 0 & -15 & 10-4k & | & -3 \\ 0 & -2-3k & 3-k^2 & | & -k \end{bmatrix} \begin{matrix} \\ R_2 = R_3 \\ R_3 = R_2 \end{matrix}$

$\sim \begin{bmatrix} 1 & 3 & k & | & 2 \\ 0 & -15 & 10-4k & | & -3 \\ 0 & 0 & 25-22k+3k^2 & | & 6-6k \end{bmatrix}$

$R_3 \rightarrow 15R_3 - (2 + 3k)R_2$

$\sim \begin{bmatrix} 1 & 3 & k & | & 2 \\ 0 & -15 & 10-4k & | & -3 \\ 0 & 0 & -(3k+25)(k-1) & | & -6(k-1) \end{bmatrix}$

a If $k = 1$, the last row is $0 \ \ 0 \ \ 0 \ | \ 0$

and the system has an infinite number of solutions.

b If $k = -\frac{25}{3}$, the last line is $0 \ \ 0 \ \ 0 \ | \ -6(1 + \frac{25}{3})$

and the system has no solutions.

c If $k \neq 1$ or $-\frac{25}{3}$, the system has a unique solution.

60 a

$$\begin{bmatrix} a & b & 0 \\ b & 0 & a \\ 0 & 2 & b \end{bmatrix}\begin{bmatrix} 2 & 1 & 1 \\ 1 & 1 & 1 \\ 2 & 2 & 1 \end{bmatrix} = \begin{bmatrix} 2a+b & a+b & a+b \\ 2a+2b & 2a+b & a+b \\ 2+2b & 2+2b & 2+b \end{bmatrix}$$

which is $\begin{bmatrix} 1 & 0 & 0 \\ 0 & 1 & 0 \\ 0 & 0 & 1 \end{bmatrix}$ if $a+b=0$ and $2+2b=0$

$\Rightarrow$ $b=-1$ and $a=1$.

The inverse is $\begin{bmatrix} 1 & -1 & 0 \\ -1 & 0 & 1 \\ 0 & 2 & -1 \end{bmatrix}$.

b Writing the system of equations in matrix form

$$\begin{bmatrix} 2 & 1 & 1 \\ 1 & 1 & 1 \\ 2 & 2 & 1 \end{bmatrix}\begin{bmatrix} x \\ y \\ z \end{bmatrix} = \begin{bmatrix} 1 \\ 6 \\ 5 \end{bmatrix}$$

$$\therefore \begin{bmatrix} 1 & -1 & 0 \\ -1 & 0 & 1 \\ 0 & 2 & -1 \end{bmatrix}\begin{bmatrix} 2 & 1 & 1 \\ 1 & 1 & 1 \\ 2 & 2 & 1 \end{bmatrix}\begin{bmatrix} x \\ y \\ z \end{bmatrix} = \begin{bmatrix} 1 & -1 & 0 \\ -1 & 0 & 1 \\ 0 & 2 & -1 \end{bmatrix}\begin{bmatrix} 1 \\ 6 \\ 5 \end{bmatrix}$$

$$\Rightarrow \begin{bmatrix} x \\ y \\ z \end{bmatrix} = \begin{bmatrix} -5 \\ 4 \\ 7 \end{bmatrix}$$

i.e., $x=-5$, $y=4$, $z=7$.

SOLUTIONS TO TOPIC 5   **VECTORS**

SKILL BUILDER SOLUTIONS

61 The position vector of point A$(1, -2, 3)$ is $\overrightarrow{OA} = \begin{bmatrix} 1 \\ -2 \\ 3 \end{bmatrix}$ and its components are the coordinates of A.

62 a $\overrightarrow{OA} = 1\mathbf{i} - 2\mathbf{j} + 3\mathbf{k}$

b magnitude $= \sqrt{1^2 + (-2)^2 + 3^2} = \sqrt{14}$ units

c The unit vector in the opposite direction is $\dfrac{-1}{\sqrt{14}}\begin{bmatrix} 1 \\ -2 \\ 3 \end{bmatrix}$.

63

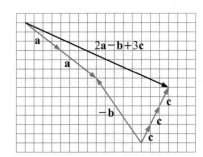

$$2\mathbf{a} - \mathbf{b} + 3\mathbf{c} = 2\begin{bmatrix} 4 \\ -3 \end{bmatrix} - \begin{bmatrix} -5 \\ 7 \end{bmatrix} + 3\begin{bmatrix} 1 \\ 2 \end{bmatrix} = \begin{bmatrix} 8+5+3 \\ -6-7+6 \end{bmatrix}$$

$$= \begin{bmatrix} 16 \\ -7 \end{bmatrix}$$ which checks with the diagram.

64 a

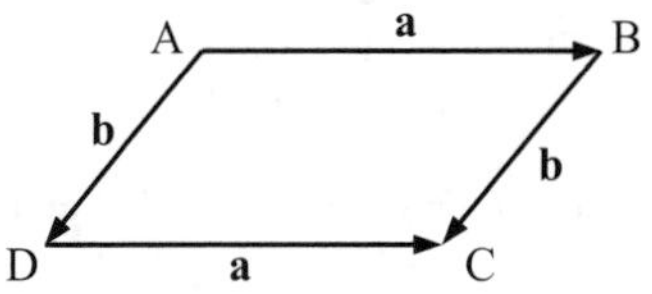

A —— a —— B
(parallelogram with sides labelled a and b)
D —— a —— C
with b on left side AD and b on right side BC

b $\overrightarrow{BC} = \overrightarrow{AD} = \mathbf{b}$ and $\overrightarrow{CD} = -\overrightarrow{AB} = -\mathbf{a}$

$\overrightarrow{AC} = \overrightarrow{AB} + \overrightarrow{BC} = \mathbf{a} + \mathbf{b}$ and $\overrightarrow{BD} = \overrightarrow{BC} + \overrightarrow{CD} = \mathbf{b} - \mathbf{a}$

c $\overrightarrow{AC} \bullet \overrightarrow{BD} = (\mathbf{a} + \mathbf{b})(\mathbf{b} - \mathbf{a})$

$= \mathbf{a} \bullet \mathbf{b} - \mathbf{a} \bullet \mathbf{a} + \mathbf{b} \bullet \mathbf{b} - \mathbf{b} \bullet \mathbf{a}$

$= \mathbf{b} \bullet \mathbf{b} - \mathbf{a} \bullet \mathbf{a}$ {as $\mathbf{a} \bullet \mathbf{b} = \mathbf{b} \bullet \mathbf{a}$}

$= |\mathbf{b}|^2 - |\mathbf{a}|^2$

and, if $|\mathbf{b}| = |\mathbf{a}|$, $\overrightarrow{AC} \bullet \overrightarrow{BD} = 0$

d Since $\overrightarrow{AC} \bullet \overrightarrow{BD} = 0$, $\overrightarrow{AC}$ and $\overrightarrow{BD}$ are perpendicular.

---

65 a $\mathbf{a} \bullet \mathbf{b} = |\mathbf{a}||\mathbf{b}|\cos\theta$ where θ is the angle between $\mathbf{a}$ and $\mathbf{b}$.

If $\mathbf{a} \bullet \mathbf{b} < 0$, then $\cos\theta < 0$ and so $90^o < \theta < 270^o$.

b $\mathbf{a} \bullet \mathbf{b} = \begin{bmatrix} -2 \\ 1 \\ 3 \end{bmatrix} \bullet \begin{bmatrix} 3 \\ -1 \\ 1 \end{bmatrix} = -6 - 1 + 3 = -4$

$|\mathbf{a}| = \sqrt{(-2)^2 + 1^2 + 3^2} = \sqrt{14}$ and

$|\mathbf{b}| = \sqrt{3^2 + (-1)^2 + 1^2} = \sqrt{11}$

and $\cos\theta = \dfrac{-4}{\sqrt{14}\sqrt{11}} \approx -0.3224$ and so $\theta \approx 109^o$

66 a $\begin{bmatrix} k \\ 1 \\ 3 \end{bmatrix}$ and $\begin{bmatrix} 4 \\ k \\ 3k \end{bmatrix}$ are parallel if $\begin{bmatrix} 4 \\ k \\ 3k \end{bmatrix} = a\begin{bmatrix} k \\ 1 \\ 3 \end{bmatrix}$ for some a.

Thus, $4 = ak$ .... (1)

$k = a$ .... (2)

$3k = 3a$ .... (3)

From (1) and (2), $k^2 = 4$ and so $k = \pm 2$.

Hence the vectors are parallel if $k = \pm 2$,

and the vectors are:

- if $k = 2$, $\begin{bmatrix} 2 \\ 1 \\ 3 \end{bmatrix}$ and $\begin{bmatrix} 4 \\ 2 \\ 6 \end{bmatrix}$

- if $k = -2$, $\begin{bmatrix} -2 \\ 1 \\ 3 \end{bmatrix}$ and $\begin{bmatrix} 4 \\ -2 \\ -6 \end{bmatrix}$

b The vectors are perpendicular if $\begin{bmatrix} k \\ 1 \\ 3 \end{bmatrix} \bullet \begin{bmatrix} 4 \\ k \\ 3k \end{bmatrix} = 0$

i.e., $4k + k + 9k = 0 \Rightarrow k = 0$

i.e., the vectors $\begin{bmatrix} 0 \\ 1 \\ 3 \end{bmatrix}$ and $\begin{bmatrix} 4 \\ 0 \\ 0 \end{bmatrix}$ are perpendicular.

67 a The equation can be written as $\dfrac{x-1}{2} = \dfrac{3-y}{3} = z = t$

i.e., $x = 2t + 1$, $y = -3t + 3$, $z = t$

or $\begin{bmatrix} x \\ y \\ z \end{bmatrix} = \begin{bmatrix} 1 \\ 3 \\ 0 \end{bmatrix} + t\begin{bmatrix} 2 \\ -3 \\ 1 \end{bmatrix}$

a vector parallel to the line is $\begin{bmatrix} 2 \\ -3 \\ 1 \end{bmatrix}$.

b A point on the line is $(1, 3, 0)$.

c The point $(7, -3, 2)$ lies on the line if $7 = 2t + 1$ .... (1)

$-3 = -3t + 3$ .... (2)

$2 = t$ .... (3)

So, from (3), $t = 2$ and from (1), $t = 3$ which is not possible. Thus the point $(7, -3, 2)$ does not lie on the line.

68 a There are many possible answers.

Since $\begin{bmatrix} 0 \\ 1 \\ 3 \end{bmatrix}$ is perpendicular to $\begin{bmatrix} 2 \\ -3 \\ 1 \end{bmatrix}$ a possible

line is $\begin{bmatrix} x \\ y \\ z \end{bmatrix} = \begin{bmatrix} 5 \\ -3 \\ 2 \end{bmatrix} + s\begin{bmatrix} 0 \\ 1 \\ 3 \end{bmatrix}$

b If the line were to meet the line of question **67** then

$5 = 2t + 1$ .... (1)

$-3 + s = -3t + 3$ .... (2)

$2 + 3s = t$ .... (3)

and from these we see that $t = 2$ and $s = 0$

So, the lines meet at the point $(5, -3, 2)$.

Note that the given point lies on the line of question **67**.

69 The line of question **67** has direction vector $\begin{bmatrix} 2 \\ -3 \\ 1 \end{bmatrix}$

The line of question **69** has direction vector $\begin{bmatrix} -1 \\ 2 \\ 1 \end{bmatrix}$

If the angle between the lines is θ, then

$$\begin{bmatrix} 2 \\ -3 \\ 1 \end{bmatrix} \bullet \begin{bmatrix} -1 \\ 2 \\ 1 \end{bmatrix} = \sqrt{4+9+1}\sqrt{1+4+1}\cos\theta$$

$$\Rightarrow \quad -2-6+1 = \sqrt{14}\sqrt{6}\cos\theta$$

$$\Rightarrow \quad \cos\theta = \frac{-7}{\sqrt{84}} \quad \text{and so} \quad \theta \approx 139.8°$$

and so the acute angle is $180° - 139.8° = 40.2°$

70 If two lines have two points in common, they coincide. Also, if two lines have the same direction and one point in common they coincide.

71 An equation of a plane through $(3, -1, 2)$ parallel to the vectors $\begin{bmatrix} -2 \\ 1 \\ 3 \end{bmatrix}$ and $\begin{bmatrix} 3 \\ -1 \\ 1 \end{bmatrix}$ is

$$\begin{bmatrix} x \\ y \\ z \end{bmatrix} = \begin{bmatrix} 3 \\ -1 \\ 2 \end{bmatrix} + s\begin{bmatrix} -2 \\ 1 \\ 3 \end{bmatrix} + t\begin{bmatrix} 3 \\ -1 \\ 1 \end{bmatrix}$$

$$\begin{bmatrix} -2 \\ 1 \\ 3 \end{bmatrix} \times \begin{bmatrix} 3 \\ -1 \\ 1 \end{bmatrix} = \begin{vmatrix} \mathbf{i} & \mathbf{j} & \mathbf{k} \\ -2 & 1 & 3 \\ 3 & -1 & 1 \end{vmatrix}$$

$$= \mathbf{i}(1--3) - \mathbf{j}(-2-9) + \mathbf{k}(2-3)$$
$$= 4\mathbf{i} + 11\mathbf{j} - 1\mathbf{k}$$

So, the equation of the plane is

$$\begin{bmatrix} 4 \\ 11 \\ -1 \end{bmatrix} \bullet \begin{bmatrix} x \\ y \\ z \end{bmatrix} = \begin{bmatrix} 4 \\ 11 \\ -1 \end{bmatrix} \bullet \begin{bmatrix} 3 \\ -1 \\ 2 \end{bmatrix}$$

i.e., $4x + 11y - z = 12 - 11 - 2$

i.e., $4x + 11y - z = -1$

72 a $\overrightarrow{AB} = \begin{bmatrix} 2--1 \\ 1-2 \\ 3-1 \end{bmatrix} = \begin{bmatrix} 3 \\ -1 \\ 2 \end{bmatrix}$, $\overrightarrow{AC} = \begin{bmatrix} 4--1 \\ -3-2 \\ 5-1 \end{bmatrix} = \begin{bmatrix} 5 \\ -5 \\ 4 \end{bmatrix}$

An equation of the plane is: $\begin{bmatrix} x \\ y \\ z \end{bmatrix} = \begin{bmatrix} -1 \\ 2 \\ 1 \end{bmatrix} + s\begin{bmatrix} 3 \\ -1 \\ 2 \end{bmatrix} + t\begin{bmatrix} 5 \\ -5 \\ 4 \end{bmatrix}$

b A normal to the plane in **a** is

$$\begin{bmatrix} 3 \\ -1 \\ 2 \end{bmatrix} \times \begin{bmatrix} 5 \\ -5 \\ 4 \end{bmatrix} = \begin{vmatrix} \mathbf{i} & \mathbf{j} & \mathbf{k} \\ 3 & -1 & 2 \\ 5 & -5 & 4 \end{vmatrix}$$

$$= \mathbf{i}(-4+10) - \mathbf{j}(12-10) + \mathbf{k}(-15+5)$$
$$= 6\mathbf{i} - 2\mathbf{j} - 10\mathbf{k}$$

If θ is the acute angle between the normal and the plane,

$$\left| \begin{bmatrix} 6 \\ -2 \\ -10 \end{bmatrix} \bullet \begin{bmatrix} 1 \\ -1 \\ 1 \end{bmatrix} \right| = \sqrt{36+4+100}\sqrt{1+1+1}\cos\theta$$

$$\Rightarrow \quad |6+2-10| = \sqrt{140}\sqrt{3}\cos\theta$$

$$\Rightarrow \quad \cos\theta = \frac{2}{\sqrt{420}} \quad \text{and so} \quad \theta \approx 80.27°$$

So, the angle between the plane and the line is
$(90 - 80.27)° = 9.73°$

73 a A vector normal to $3x - 2y + 7z = 6$ is $\begin{bmatrix} 3 \\ -2 \\ 7 \end{bmatrix}$.

b There are many possible solutions. Letting $y = z = 0$ gives $(2, 0, 0)$ as a point on the plane.

c The shortest distance of $(2, -1, 1)$ to the plane is
$$\frac{|3(2) - 2(-1) + 7(1) - 6|}{\sqrt{9+4+49}} = \frac{9}{\sqrt{62}} \text{ units.}$$

74 a The planes $2x + 4y + z = 1$ and $3x + 5y = 1$ have

normals $\begin{bmatrix} 2 \\ 4 \\ 1 \end{bmatrix}$ and $\begin{bmatrix} 3 \\ 5 \\ 0 \end{bmatrix}$ respectively.

Let θ be the angle between the normals. Then

$$\begin{bmatrix} 2 \\ 4 \\ 1 \end{bmatrix} \bullet \begin{bmatrix} 3 \\ 5 \\ 0 \end{bmatrix} = \sqrt{4+16+1}\sqrt{9+25+0}\cos\theta$$

$$\Rightarrow \quad 6 + 20 - 0 = \sqrt{21}\sqrt{34}\cos\theta$$

$$\Rightarrow \quad \cos\theta = \frac{26}{\sqrt{21}\sqrt{34}} \quad \text{and so} \quad \theta \approx 13.3°$$

b $\quad 2x + 4y + z = 1 \quad$ ...... (1)
$\quad 3x + 5y = 1 \quad$ ...... (2)

Let $x = t$, then in (2), $y = \dfrac{1-3t}{5}$

and so in (1), $\quad 2t + 4\left(\dfrac{1-3t}{5}\right) + z = 1$

$$\Rightarrow \quad 10t + 4 - 12t + 5z = 5$$
$$\Rightarrow \quad 5z = 1 + 2t$$
$$\Rightarrow \quad z = \frac{1+2t}{5}$$

i.e., a solution is $\begin{bmatrix} x \\ y \\ z \end{bmatrix} = \begin{bmatrix} 0 \\ \frac{1}{5} \\ \frac{1}{5} \end{bmatrix} + t\begin{bmatrix} 1 \\ -\frac{3}{5} \\ \frac{2}{5} \end{bmatrix}, \quad t \in \mathbb{R}$

This solution is an equation of the line of intersection of the two planes.

c If the points lie on the plane $5x + 13y + 7z = 4$ then

$$5t + 13\left(\frac{1-3t}{5}\right) + 7\left(\frac{1+2t}{5}\right) = 4$$

$$\Rightarrow \quad 25t + 13 - 39t + 7 + 14t = 20$$
$$\Rightarrow \quad 20 = 20$$

Hence, the line of intersection of the first two planes lies on the third plane. This means that the infinite number of points on the line are the solutions of all three equations.

75

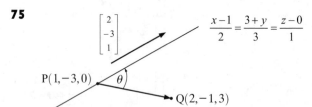

$\begin{bmatrix} 2 \\ -3 \\ 1 \end{bmatrix}$ $\quad \dfrac{x-1}{2} = \dfrac{3+y}{3} = \dfrac{z-0}{1}$

$P(1, -3, 0)$ $\quad \theta$ $\quad Q(2, -1, 3)$

$P(1, -3, 0)$ is a point on the line and $Q(2, -1, 3)$ is the given point.

Then $\overrightarrow{PQ} = \begin{bmatrix} 2-1 \\ -1--3 \\ 3-0 \end{bmatrix} = \begin{bmatrix} 1 \\ 2 \\ 3 \end{bmatrix}$

and if the angle θ is between $\overrightarrow{PQ}$ and the line then

$$\cos\theta = \frac{\begin{bmatrix} 1 \\ 2 \\ 3 \end{bmatrix} \bullet \begin{bmatrix} 2 \\ -3 \\ 1 \end{bmatrix}}{\sqrt{1+4+9}\sqrt{4+9+1}} = \frac{2-6+3}{14} = \frac{-1}{14}$$

and so $\sin\theta = \sqrt{1 - \left(\frac{-1}{14}\right)^2}$

The required distance is $\quad |\overrightarrow{PQ}| \sin\theta$
$$= \sqrt{14} \times \sqrt{1 - \left(\frac{-1}{14}\right)^2}$$
$$\approx 3.73 \text{ units}$$

SKILL BUILDER SOLUTIONS

76 a Sum of frequencies is 30 , and so 30 drivers were chosen.

b

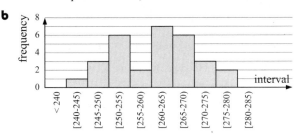

c An estimate of the   mean is 260.5

median is 262

mode is 260

The standard deviation of the sample is ≈ 9.233.

(An unbiased estimate of σ is $\sqrt{\frac{30}{29}} \times 9.233 \approx 9.391$.)

Since the mean, median and mode are about equal the data appears to be symmetric.

d

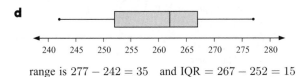

range is $277 - 242 = 35$ and IQR $= 267 - 252 = 15$

e An unbiassed estimate of the mean μ is the sample mean, $\overline{x} = 260.5$. An unbiassed estimate for σ is 9.391.

77 a Cumulative frequency table:

Distance (m)	Frequency	Cumu. Frequ.
240–	1	1
245–	3	4
250–	6	10
255–	2	12
260–	7	19
265–	6	25
270–	3	28
275– but < 280	2	30

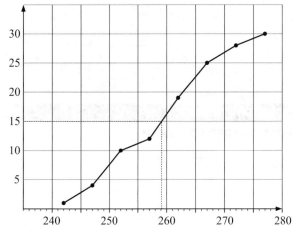

b From the graph,

the median is about 259 and the IQR $= 265 - 250 = 15$

The median is a little different to that found in question **76**. The IQR happens to be the same. The cumulative frequency graph gives some idea of what might happen in between the discrete data values.

c The 10th percentile is about 245, i.e., about 10% of the hits are less than 245 m.

78 $\overline{x} = 80.9$ and $\sum f = 30$

Now $\overline{x} = \dfrac{\sum fx}{\sum f}$, $\therefore$ $\sum fx = 80.9 \times 30 = 2427$

But, $s^2 = \dfrac{\sum (x - \overline{x})^2 f}{\sum f} = \dfrac{\sum x^2 f}{\sum f} - \overline{x}^2$

$296^2 = \dfrac{\sum x^2 f}{30} - 80.9^2$

Thus $\sum x^2 f = 30(296^2 + 80.9^2) \approx 196\,344.3$

79 a The horses in the race do not necessarily have the same chance of winning the race. It is unlikely that a given horse will have a chance of $\frac{1}{10}$ of winning.

b Unless the outcomes are all equally likely, $P(A) = \dfrac{n(A)}{n(U)}$ may not hold.

80 a There are 13 balls in the bucket and so the total number of ways of selecting 5 balls is $\binom{13}{5}$.

2 reds can be selected in $\binom{7}{2}$ ways.

1 blue can be selected in $\binom{3}{1}$ ways.

2 blacks can be selected in $\binom{2}{2}$ ways.

The probability of selecting 2 reds, 1 blue and 2 blacks

is $\dfrac{\binom{7}{2}\binom{3}{1}\binom{2}{2}}{\binom{13}{5}} \approx 0.0490$

b Let X be the number of red balls selected, then

$P(X \geqslant 1) = 1 - P(X = 0)$

$= 1 - \dfrac{\binom{7}{0}\binom{6}{5}}{\binom{13}{5}}$

≈ 0.9953

81 a i Events A and B are mutually exclusive if $A \cap B = \varnothing$. In this case $A \cap B$ contains the numbers 41, 42, 43, 44. The events are not mutually exclusive.

ii $P(A \cup B) = P(A) + P(B) - P(A \cap B)$

$= \frac{44}{100} + \frac{14}{100} - \frac{4}{100}$

$= \frac{54}{100}$

b If the events A and B are *independent*, $P(A \mid B) = P(A)$

If A and B are *mutually exclusive*, $P(A \mid B) = 0$ since if B occurs A cannot occur.

But $P(A) \neq 0$. Hence, the events cannot be independent and mutually exclusive.

82 $P(A \mid B) = \dfrac{P(A \cap B)}{P(B)}$ and if $P(A \mid B) = P(A)$

then $P(A \cap B) = P(A) P(B)$.

83 $P(A \cup B) = P(A) + P(B) - P(A \cap B)$

But A and B are independent, hence $P(A \cap B) = P(A) P(B)$.

Hence, $P(A \cup B) = P(A) + P(B) - P(A) P(B)$

$\Rightarrow$ $0.63 = x + 0.36 - 0.36x$

$\Rightarrow$ $0.27 = 0.64x$

$\Rightarrow$ $x = P(A) \approx 0.422$

84 The tree diagram uses   M   for male   L   for left handed

F   for female   R   for right handed

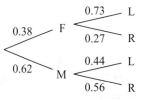

a $P(L) = (0.38)(0.73) + (0.62)(0.44) \approx 0.550$

b $P(F \mid L) = \dfrac{P(F \cap L)}{P(L)} = \dfrac{(0.38)(0.73)}{0.5502} \approx 0.504$

85

die 2							
6	5	4	3	2	1	0	
5	4	3	2	1	0	1	
4	3	2	1	0	1	2	
3	2	1	0	1	2	3	
2	1	0	1	2	3	4	
1	0	1	2	3	4	5	
	1	2	3	4	5	6	die 1

There are 6 outcomes where the difference is 3.

As all outcomes are equally possible, the probability of the difference being 3 is $\frac{6}{36} = \frac{1}{6}$.

86 $P(A \cup B) = 1 - P(A \cup B)' = 1 - \frac{1}{12} = \frac{11}{12}$

$\qquad P(A \cup B) = P(A) + P(B) - P(A \cap B)$

$\qquad \Rightarrow \quad \frac{11}{12} = 0.46 + \frac{5}{7} - P(A \cap B)$

$\Rightarrow \quad P(A \cap B) = 0.46 + \frac{5}{7} - \frac{11}{12}$

$\Rightarrow \quad P(A \cap B) \approx 0.258$

87 a The random variable is discrete.

b $\frac{1}{3} + \frac{1}{6} + k + \frac{1}{12} = 1 \quad \Rightarrow \quad k + \frac{7}{12} = 1 \quad \Rightarrow \quad k = \frac{5}{12}$

c $E(X) = -2(\frac{1}{3}) + 0(\frac{1}{6}) + 3(\frac{5}{12}) + 5(\frac{1}{12}) = 1$ and

$Var(X) = (-2)^2(\frac{1}{3}) + 0^2(\frac{1}{6}) + 3^2(\frac{5}{12}) + 5^2(\frac{1}{12}) - 1^2 = \frac{37}{6}$

$\Rightarrow$ standard deviation $= \sqrt{\frac{37}{6}} \approx 2.48$

d The distribution table is

x	-2	0	3	5
$P(x)$	$\frac{4}{12}$	$\frac{2}{12}$	$\frac{5}{12}$	$\frac{1}{12}$

The median lies between 0 and 3, i.e., $\frac{3}{2}$

3 is the most probable outcome, so mode $= 3$

88 a The random variable is continuous.

b $\displaystyle\int_0^a \sin(\tfrac{1}{2}x)\, dx = 1$

$\Rightarrow \quad \left[-2\cos(\tfrac{1}{2}x)\right]_0^a = 1$

$\Rightarrow \quad -2\cos(\tfrac{a}{2}) + 2 = 1$

$\Rightarrow \quad -2\cos(\tfrac{a}{2}) = -1$

$\Rightarrow \quad \cos(\tfrac{a}{2}) = \tfrac{1}{2}$

$\Rightarrow \quad \tfrac{a}{2} = \tfrac{\pi}{3}$

$\Rightarrow \quad a = \tfrac{2\pi}{3} \quad \{\text{only soln. as } \sin(\tfrac{1}{2}x) \geqslant 0\}$

c $E(X) = \displaystyle\int_0^{\frac{2\pi}{3}} x\sin(\tfrac{1}{2}x)\, dx \approx 1.3697$

$Var(X) = \displaystyle\int_0^{\frac{2\pi}{3}} \left((x - 1.370)^2 \sin(\tfrac{1}{2}x)\right) dx \approx 0.2478$

$\Rightarrow \quad \sigma \approx \sqrt{0.2478} \approx 0.498$

d The median, m, is the solution of $\displaystyle\int_0^m f(x)\, dx = \tfrac{1}{2} \quad \Rightarrow$

$\displaystyle\int_0^m \sin(\tfrac{1}{2}x)\, dx = \tfrac{1}{2}$

$\Rightarrow \quad \left[-2\cos(\tfrac{1}{2}x)\right]_0^m = \tfrac{1}{2}$

$\Rightarrow \quad -2\cos(\tfrac{m}{2}) + 2 = \tfrac{1}{2}$

$\Rightarrow \quad 2\cos(\tfrac{m}{2}) = 1\tfrac{1}{2}$

$\Rightarrow \quad \cos(\tfrac{m}{2}) = \tfrac{3}{4}$

$\Rightarrow \quad \tfrac{m}{2} = 0.7227 \quad \text{and so} \quad m = 1.445$

$\sin(\tfrac{1}{2}x)$ on $0 \leqslant x \leqslant \tfrac{2\pi}{3}$ is a maximum at $x = \tfrac{2\pi}{3}$

$\therefore$ the modal value of X is $\tfrac{2\pi}{3}$

89 a X is Poisson **b** Y is Binomial

90 a i Mean is 12, Variance $=$ mean $= 12$
Standard deviation is $\sqrt{12}$.

ii $P(X = 10) = \dfrac{12^{10}e^{-12}}{10!} \approx 0.105$

iii $P(X \geqslant 10) = 1 - P(X \leqslant 9) \approx 0.758$

b i Y is binomial, with $n = 30$ and $p = \frac{1}{5}$
mean $= np = 30 \times \frac{1}{5} = 6$
variance $= npq = 30 \times \frac{1}{5} \times \frac{4}{5} = 4.8$
standard deviation $= \sqrt{4.8} \approx 2.19$

ii $P(Y = 20) = \binom{30}{20}(\frac{1}{5})^{20}(\frac{4}{5})^{10} \approx 3.38 \times 10^{-8}$
To get a distribution we need to get at least
$6 + 2(2.191) \approx 10.4$ i.e., at least 11 correct answers
for a distinction.
$P(Y \geqslant 11) = 1 - P(Y \leqslant 10) \approx 0.0256$

91 a X is continuous

b Since X is continuous the probability of any specified value is zero, in particular $P(X = 27) = 0$.

c As $\dfrac{33 - 37}{\sqrt{9}} = -\dfrac{4}{3}$, 33 is $\frac{4}{3}$ standard deviations on the left of the mean.

d $P(X \geqslant 33) = P(X \leqslant 33) = \frac{1}{2}$
and since $37 > 33$, $P(X \geqslant 37) < \frac{1}{2}$.

e $P(X \geqslant 39) = 1 - P(X < 39) \approx 0.252$

f $P(31 \leqslant X \leqslant 39) = \text{normalcdf}(31, 39, 37, 3) \approx 0.725$

g $P(|X - 37| \leqslant 2) = P(-2 \leqslant X - 37 \leqslant 2)$
$\qquad\qquad\qquad\quad = P(35 \leqslant X \leqslant 39)$
$\qquad\qquad\qquad\quad = \text{normalcdf}(35, 39, 37, 3)$
$\qquad\qquad\qquad\quad = 0.495$

h $\qquad P(X \geqslant k) = 0.56$
$\Rightarrow \quad P(X \leqslant k) = 0.44$
$\Rightarrow \quad P(\dfrac{X - 37}{3} \leqslant \dfrac{k - 37}{3}) = 0.44$
$\Rightarrow \quad P(Z \leqslant \dfrac{k - 37}{3}) = 0.44$
$\Rightarrow \quad \dfrac{k - 37}{3} = \text{invNorm}(0.44)$
$\Rightarrow \quad k = 37 + 3\,\text{invNorm}(0.44)$
$\Rightarrow \quad k \approx 36.3$

SOLUTIONS TO TOPIC 7   CALCULUS
SKILL BUILDER SOLUTIONS

92 $f(x) = \sqrt{3x^2 + 5x - 2} = (3x^2 + 5x - 2)^{\frac{1}{2}}$

$\therefore \quad f'(x) = \tfrac{1}{2}(3x^2 + 5x - 2)^{-\frac{1}{2}}(6x + 5)$
$\qquad\qquad = \dfrac{(6x + 5)}{2\sqrt{3x^2 + 5x - 2}}$

93 $y = \ln(2x^2 + 8)$, $\therefore \dfrac{dy}{dx} = \dfrac{4x}{2x^2 + 8} = \dfrac{2x}{x^2 + 4}$

94 $f(x) = x^2 e^{2x-3}$
$\therefore \quad f'(x) = 2xe^{2x-3} + x^2 e^{2x-3}(2)$
$\qquad\qquad = 2xe^{2x-3}(1 + x)$

95 $f(x) = 3^{x^2 - x - 2}$, i.e., $y = 3^{x^2 - x - 2}$
$\Rightarrow \quad \ln y = (x^2 - x - 2)\ln 3$
$\Rightarrow \quad \dfrac{1}{y}\dfrac{dy}{dx} = (2x - 1)\ln 3$
$\Rightarrow \quad \dfrac{dy}{dx} = y(2x - 1)\ln 3 = \ln 3\,(2x - 1)\,3^{x^2 - x - 2}$

96 $y = \dfrac{x+2}{x^2+3}$, $\therefore$ $\dfrac{dy}{dx} = \dfrac{1(x^2+3) - (x+2)(2x)}{(x^2+3)^2}$

$$= \dfrac{x^2 + 3 - 2x^2 - 4x}{(x^2+3)^2}$$

$$= \dfrac{-x^2 - 4x + 3}{(x^2+3)^2}$$

97 $f(x) = (\sin x)\, e^{\cos x}$

$\therefore$ $f'(x) = (\cos x)\, e^{\cos x} + (\sin x)\, e^{\cos x}(-\sin x)$

$ = e^{\cos x}(\cos x - \sin^2 x)$

98 $y = \arcsin(2x+3)$ $\therefore$ $\dfrac{dy}{dx} = \dfrac{1}{\sqrt{1 - (2x+3)^2}} \times 2$

$$= \dfrac{2}{\sqrt{1 - 4x^2 - 12x - 9}}$$

$$= \dfrac{2}{\sqrt{-4x^2 - 12x - 8}}$$

$$= \dfrac{2}{2\sqrt{-x^2 - 3x - 2}}$$

$$= \dfrac{1}{\sqrt{-x^2 - 3x - 2}}$$

99 $y = x^2 \sin 2x$

$\Rightarrow$ $\dfrac{dy}{dx} = 2x \sin 2x + x^2 \cos 2x \times (2)$

$\phantom{\Rightarrow \dfrac{dy}{dx}} = 2x \sin 2x + 2x^2 \cos 2x$

$\Rightarrow$ $\dfrac{d^2y}{dx^2} = 2\sin 2x + 2x(2\cos 2x)$
$\phantom{\Rightarrow \dfrac{d^2y}{dx^2} =}+ 4x\cos 2x + 2x^2(-2\sin 2x)$

$\phantom{\Rightarrow \dfrac{d^2y}{dx^2}} = 2\sin 2x + 4x\cos 2x + 4x\cos 2x$
$\phantom{\Rightarrow \dfrac{d^2y}{dx^2} =}- 4x^2 \sin 2x$

$\phantom{\Rightarrow \dfrac{d^2y}{dx^2}} = 2(1 - 2x^2)\sin 2x + 8x\cos 2x$

100 $f(x) = \dfrac{x-4}{x-2}$ has $f(3) = \dfrac{-1}{1} = -1$

$\therefore$ has point of contact $(3, -1)$.

Now $f'(x) = \dfrac{1(x-2) - (x-4)1}{(x-2)^2} = \dfrac{2}{(x-2)^2}$

$\therefore$ $f'(3) = \dfrac{2}{1^2} = 2$

$\therefore$ slope of tangent at $(3, -1)$ is 2.

$\therefore$ equation of tangent is $\quad y - -1 = 2(x - 3)$
$\phantom{\therefore \text{equation of tangent is} \quad} \therefore \quad y + 1 = 2x - 6$
$\phantom{\therefore \text{equation of tangent is} \quad} \therefore \quad y = 2x - 7$

101 $y = x^2 - 2x - 1$ $\Rightarrow$ $\dfrac{dy}{dx} = 2x - 2$ and when $x = -1$

$y = 1 + 2 - 1 = 2$ and $\dfrac{dy}{dx} = -2 - 2 = -4$

$\therefore$ at $(-1, 2)$, the normal has slope $\frac{1}{4}$.

$\therefore$ equation of normal is $\quad y - 2 = \frac{1}{4}(x - -1)$
$\phantom{\therefore \text{equation of normal is} \quad} \therefore \quad 4y - 8 = x + 1$
$\phantom{\therefore \text{equation of normal is} \quad} \therefore \quad x - 4y = -9$

102 $f(x) = \dfrac{x}{x^2 - 2}$ $\Rightarrow$ $\dfrac{dy}{dx} = \dfrac{1(x^2-2) - x(2x)}{(x^2-2)^2} = \dfrac{-x^2 - 2}{(x^2-2)^2}$

and $\dfrac{d^2y}{dx^2} = \dfrac{-2x(x^2-2)^2 - (-x^2-2)2(x^2-2)(2x)}{(x^2-2)^4}$

$\phantom{\text{and} \dfrac{d^2y}{dx^2}} = \dfrac{-2x(x^2-2) - 4x(-x^2-2)}{(x^2-2)^3}$

$\phantom{\text{and} \dfrac{d^2y}{dx^2}} = \dfrac{-2x^3 + 4x + 4x^3 + 8x}{(x^2-2)^3}$

$\phantom{\text{and} \dfrac{d^2y}{dx^2}} = \dfrac{2x^3 + 12x}{(x^2-2)^3}$

$\phantom{\text{and} \dfrac{d^2y}{dx^2}} = \dfrac{2x(x^2 + 6)}{(x^2-2)^3}$

which has sign diagram

$\therefore$ is concave down for
$$x \in \;]-\infty, -\sqrt{2}\,[\; \cup \; [\,0, \sqrt{2}\,[$$

103 $\qquad f(x) = 2x^3 - 3x^2 - 12x + 7$
$\therefore$ $f'(x) = 6x^2 - 6x - 12$
$ = 6(x^2 - x - 2)$
$ = 6(x+1)(x-2)$

which is 0 when $x = -1$ or 2

$\qquad f(-1) = -2 - 3 + 12 + 7 = 14$
$\qquad f(2) = 16 - 12 - 24 + 7 = -13$

$\therefore$ stationary points are at $(-1, 14)$ and at $(2, -13)$

104 $f(x) = \dfrac{x-3}{x^2-5}$, $\therefore$ $f'(x) = \dfrac{1(x^2-5) - (x-3)2x}{(x^2-5)^2}$

$ = \dfrac{x^2 - 5 - 2x^2 + 6x}{(x^2-5)^2}$

$ = \dfrac{-x^2 + 6x - 5}{(x^2-5)^2}$

$ = \dfrac{-(x^2 - 6x + 5)}{(x^2-5)^2}$

$ = \dfrac{-(x-1)(x-5)}{(x^2-5)^2}$

which is 0 when $x = 1$ or 5

and $f(1) = \dfrac{-2}{-4} = \frac{1}{2}$, $f(5) = \dfrac{2}{20} = \frac{1}{10}$

$\therefore$ stationary points are at $(1, \frac{1}{2})$ and at $(5, \frac{1}{10})$.

105 $f(x) = \dfrac{2x^2 - 3x + 6}{x^2 - x - 6}$ has VAs when

$\qquad x^2 - x - 6 = 0$
$\Rightarrow$ $(x - 3)(x + 2) = 0$
$ \Rightarrow \quad x = 3$ or -2

i.e., they are $x = 3$ and $x = -2$

also $f(x) = \dfrac{2 - \dfrac{3}{x} + \dfrac{6}{x^2}}{1 - \dfrac{1}{x} - \dfrac{6}{x^2}}$ which $\to 2$ as $x \to \pm\infty$

$\therefore$ $y = 2$ is the HA

106 $\qquad\qquad x^2 - xy^2 + y = 21$

$\therefore$ $2x - [1y^2 + x\,2y\dfrac{dy}{dx}] + \dfrac{dy}{dx} = 0$

$\therefore$ $2x - y^2 - 2xy\dfrac{dy}{dx} + \dfrac{dy}{dx} = 0$

$\therefore$ $\dfrac{dy}{dx}(1 - 2xy) = y^2 - 2x$

$\therefore$ $\dfrac{dy}{dx} = \dfrac{y^2 - 2x}{1 - 2xy}$

107 $\displaystyle\int \dfrac{2x^2 - x - 3}{x^2}\,dx$

$\displaystyle= \int 2 - \dfrac{1}{x} - 3x^{-2}\,dx$

$= 2x - \ln|x| - \dfrac{3x^{-1}}{-1} + c$

$= 2x - \ln|x| + \dfrac{3}{x} + c$

108 $\displaystyle\int_3^5 \dfrac{x}{x^2 - 8}\,dx$

$\displaystyle= \frac{1}{2}\int_3^5 \dfrac{2x}{x^2 - 8}\,dx$

$= \frac{1}{2}\Big[\ln|x^2 - 8|\Big]_3^5$

$= \frac{1}{2}\{\ln 17 - \ln 1\}$

$= \frac{1}{2}\ln 17$

109 $\displaystyle\int \sin^2 3x\,dx$

$\displaystyle= \int \frac{1}{2} - \frac{1}{2}\cos 6x\,dx$

$= \frac{1}{2}x - \frac{1}{2}(\frac{1}{6})\sin 6x + c$

$= \frac{1}{2}x - \frac{1}{12}\sin 6x + x$

110 $\displaystyle\int \tan^2 2x\,dx$

$\displaystyle= \int \sec^2 2x - 1\,dx$

$= \frac{1}{2}\tan 2x - x + c$

111

$$\int_0^k \frac{x}{\sqrt{x^2+4}}\,dx = 1$$

$$\Rightarrow \quad \frac{1}{2}\int_0^k (x^2+4)^{-\frac{1}{2}}(2x)\,dx = 1$$

$$\Rightarrow \quad \frac{1}{2}\left[\frac{(x^2+4)^{\frac{1}{2}}}{\frac{1}{2}}\right]_0^k = 1$$

$$\Rightarrow \quad \left[\sqrt{x^2+4}\right]_0^k = 1$$

$$\Rightarrow \quad \sqrt{k^2+4} - 2 = 1$$

$$\Rightarrow \quad \sqrt{k^2+4} = 3$$

$$\Rightarrow \quad k^2+4 = 9$$

$$\Rightarrow \quad k^2 = 5$$

$$\Rightarrow \quad k = \pm\sqrt{5}$$

But $k > 0$, $\therefore$ $k = \sqrt{5}$.

112 $\int x \ln x \, dx$ $\quad \begin{cases} u = \ln x & v' = x \\ u' = \dfrac{1}{x} & v = \dfrac{x^2}{2} \end{cases}$

$$= (\ln x)(\frac{x^2}{2}) - \int(\frac{1}{x})(\frac{x^2}{2})\,dx$$

$$= \frac{1}{2}x^2 \ln x - \frac{1}{2}\int x\,dx$$

$$= \frac{1}{2}x^2 \ln x - \frac{1}{4}x^2 + c$$

113 $\int \arctan x \, dx$ $\quad \begin{cases} u = \arctan x & v' = 1 \\ u' = \dfrac{1}{1+x^2} & v = x \end{cases}$

$$= x \arctan x - \int \frac{x}{1+x^2}\,dx$$

$$= x \arctan x - \frac{1}{2}\int \frac{2x}{1+x^2}\,dx$$

$$= x \arctan x - \frac{1}{2}\ln|1+x^2| + c$$

But $1 + x^2 > 0$, for all x

$$= x \arctan x - \frac{1}{2}\ln(1+x^2) + c$$

114 $\displaystyle\int_0^4 \frac{1}{\sqrt{x+4}}\,dx = \int_0^4 (x+4)^{-\frac{1}{2}}\,dx$

$$= \left[\frac{(x+4)^{\frac{1}{2}}}{\frac{1}{2}}\right]_0^4$$

$$= \left[2\sqrt{x+4}\right]_0^4$$

$$= 2\sqrt{8} - 2\sqrt{4}$$

$$= 4\sqrt{2} - 4$$

115 $v = t^3 - 3t^2 e^{0.05t}$

$\therefore$ the distance travelled in the first 5 seconds

$$= \int_0^5 |v|\,dt$$

$$= \int_0^5 |t^3 - 3t^2 e^{0.05t}|\,dt \approx 28.2 \text{ units} \quad \{\text{gcalc}\}$$

116 $y = 8x - x^2 = x(8-x)$ cuts the x-axis at 0 and 8

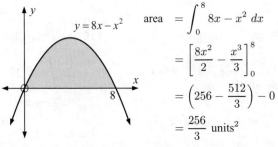

area $= \displaystyle\int_0^8 8x - x^2\,dx$

$$= \left[\frac{8x^2}{2} - \frac{x^3}{3}\right]_0^8$$

$$= \left(256 - \frac{512}{3}\right) - 0$$

$$= \frac{256}{3} \text{ units}^2$$

117 $y = x^2 - 3x$ meets $y = x$ where

$$x^2 - 3x = x$$
$$\Rightarrow \quad x^2 - 4x = 0$$
$$\Rightarrow \quad x(x-4) = 0$$
$$\Rightarrow \quad x = 0 \text{ or } 4$$

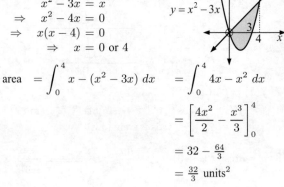

area $= \displaystyle\int_0^4 x - (x^2 - 3x)\,dx = \int_0^4 4x - x^2\,dx$

$$= \left[\frac{4x^2}{2} - \frac{x^3}{3}\right]_0^4$$

$$= 32 - \frac{64}{3}$$

$$= \frac{32}{3} \text{ units}^2$$

118

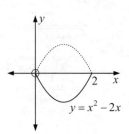

$y = x^2 - 2x$

$V = \pi \displaystyle\int_0^2 y^2\,dx$

$$= \pi\int_0^2 (x^2 - 2x)^2\,dx$$

$$= \pi\int_0^2 x^4 - 4x^3 + 4x^2\,dx$$

$$= \pi\left[\frac{x^5}{5} - \frac{4x^4}{4} + \frac{4x^3}{3}\right]_0^2$$

$$= \pi(\frac{32}{5} - 16 + \frac{32}{3})$$

$$= \frac{16}{15}\pi \text{ units}^3$$

119

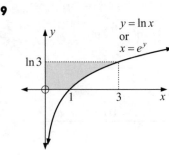

$y = \ln x$ or $x = e^y$

$V = \pi \displaystyle\int_0^{\ln 3} x^2\,dy$

$$= \pi\int_0^{\ln 3} e^{2y}\,dy$$

$$= \pi\left[\frac{1}{2}e^{2y}\right]_0^{\ln 3}$$

$$= \frac{1}{2}\pi(e^{2\ln 3} - e^0)$$

$$= \frac{1}{2}\pi(e^{\ln 3^2} - 1)$$

$$= \frac{1}{2}\pi(9 - 1)$$

$$= 4\pi \text{ units}^3$$

120

$$y\frac{dy}{dx} = 2x - 3$$

$$\Rightarrow \quad \int y\frac{dy}{dx}\,dx = \int 2x - 3\,dx$$

$$\Rightarrow \quad \int y\,dy = \int 2x - 3\,dx$$

$$\Rightarrow \quad \frac{y^2}{2} = \frac{2x^2}{2} - 3x + c_1$$

$$\Rightarrow \quad y^2 = 2x^2 - 6x + c$$

But, when $x = 0$, $y = 4$ $\therefore$ $c = 16$

So, $y^2 = 2x^2 - 6x + 16$

$$\Rightarrow \quad y = \pm\sqrt{2x^2 - 6x + 16}$$

But $x = 0$, $y = 4$ does not satisfy $y = -\sqrt{2x^2 - 6x + 16}$

$\Rightarrow$ solution is $y = \sqrt{2x^2 - 6x + 16}$

121

$$\frac{dy}{dx} = 3x^2 y + y = y(3x^2 + 1)$$

$$\Rightarrow \quad \int \frac{1}{y}\frac{dy}{dx}\,dx = \int 3x^2 + 1\,dx$$

$$\Rightarrow \quad \ln|y| = \frac{3x^3}{3} + x + c$$

$$\Rightarrow \quad \ln|y| = x^3 + x + c$$

$$\Rightarrow \quad |y| = e^{x^3 + x + c}$$

$$\Rightarrow \quad y = \pm e^c e^{x^3 + x} \text{ and so } y = Ae^{x^3 + x}$$

But, when $x = 0$, $y = 2$

$$\therefore \quad 2 = Ae^0 = A \quad \Rightarrow \quad y = 2e^{x^3 + x}$$

122 a $S_8 = -4$ and $S_{16} = 188 - 4 = 184$

But $S_n = \frac{n}{2}[2u_1 + (n-1)d]$

$\therefore \quad \frac{8}{2}[2u_1 + 7d] = -4$

$\therefore \quad 2u_1 + 7d = -1 \quad \text{...... (1)}$

and $\frac{16}{2}[2u_1 + 15d] = 184$

$\therefore \quad 8[2u_1 + 15d] = 184$

$\therefore \quad 2u_1 + 15d = 23 \quad \text{...... (2)}$

(2) $-$ (1) gives $8d = 23 - -1 = 24 \quad \therefore \quad d = 3$

and in (1), $2u_1 + 21 = -1 \quad \Rightarrow \quad u_1 = -11$

Now $u_n = u_1 + (n-1)d$

$\Rightarrow \quad u_n = -11 + (n-1)3$

$\Rightarrow \quad u_n = 3n - 14$

b $9, x, y$ are geometric $\Rightarrow \quad \frac{x}{9} = \frac{y}{x} \quad \text{...... (1)}$

x, y, z are arithmetic $\Rightarrow \quad y - x = 2 - y \quad \text{....... (2)}$

From (2) $2y = x + 2 \quad \therefore \quad y = \frac{x+2}{2}$

So in (1) $\frac{x}{9} = \frac{x+2}{2x}$

$\Rightarrow \quad 2x^2 = 9x + 18$

$\Rightarrow \quad 2x^2 - 9x - 18 = 0$

$\Rightarrow \quad (2x+3)(x-6) = 0$

$\Rightarrow \quad x = -\frac{3}{2} \text{ or } 6$

$\Rightarrow \quad x = 6 \qquad \{x \in \mathbb{Z}\}$

and so $y = \frac{6+2}{2} = 4$

123 a With no restrictions, there are $8! = 40\,320$ different orderings.

b The mathematics books can be in one block in 3! ways.

This block plus the other 5 blocks can be ordered in 6! ways. $\therefore$ total number is $3!6! = 4320$ ways.

c

3	◄──────────►	2

3 Ma books   other 6 books   other 2 Ma books

i.e., $3 \times 2 \times 6! = 4320$ ways

124
$\begin{bmatrix} y_1 \\ y_2 \\ y_3 \end{bmatrix} = \begin{bmatrix} 1 & 1 & -1 \\ 2 & -1 & 5 \\ 3 & -2 & 1 \end{bmatrix} \begin{bmatrix} x_1 \\ x_2 \\ x_3 \end{bmatrix}$

and $\begin{bmatrix} x_1 \\ x_2 \\ x_3 \end{bmatrix} = \begin{bmatrix} 2 & 3 & -1 \\ 4 & -2 & 1 \\ 1 & -6 & 7 \end{bmatrix} \begin{bmatrix} z_1 \\ z_2 \\ z_3 \end{bmatrix}$

So, $\begin{bmatrix} y_1 \\ y_2 \\ y_3 \end{bmatrix} = \begin{bmatrix} 1 & 1 & -1 \\ 2 & -1 & 5 \\ 3 & -2 & 1 \end{bmatrix} \begin{bmatrix} 2 & 3 & -1 \\ 4 & -2 & 1 \\ 1 & -6 & 7 \end{bmatrix} \begin{bmatrix} z_1 \\ z_2 \\ z_3 \end{bmatrix}$

$\Rightarrow \begin{bmatrix} y_1 \\ y_2 \\ y_3 \end{bmatrix} = \begin{bmatrix} 5 & 7 & -7 \\ 5 & -22 & 32 \\ -1 & 7 & 2 \end{bmatrix} \begin{bmatrix} z_1 \\ z_2 \\ z_3 \end{bmatrix}$

i.e., $y_1 = 5z_1 + 7z_2 - 7z_3$

$y_2 = 5z_1 - 22z_2 + 32z_3$

$y_3 = -1z_1 + 7z_2 + 2z_3$

125 $\overrightarrow{OX}$ is perpendicular to $\overrightarrow{OY}$ if $\overrightarrow{OX} \bullet \overrightarrow{OY} = 0$

i.e., $\begin{bmatrix} 3\mu \\ 2 \\ 1 \end{bmatrix} \bullet \begin{bmatrix} \mu \\ 1 - 3\mu \\ 2\mu - 1 \end{bmatrix} = 0$

i.e., $3\mu^2 + 2(1 - 3\mu) + (2\mu - 1) = 0$

i.e., $3\mu^2 - 4\mu + 1 = 0$

i.e., $(3\mu - 1)(\mu - 1) = 0$

i.e., if $\mu = \frac{1}{3}$ or $\mu = 1$

126 a f is $y = x^2 + 4x \quad -\infty < x \leqslant -2$

so f^{-1} is $x = y^2 + 4y, \quad -\infty < x \leqslant -2$

i.e., $y^2 + 4y - x = 0$

i.e., $y = \frac{-4 \pm \sqrt{16 + 4x}}{2} = -2 \pm \sqrt{4 + x}$

But $y \leqslant -2$, Hence $y = -2 - \sqrt{4 + x}$

b $(g \circ f)(-3) = g(f(-3))$

$= g\left((-3)^2 + 4(-3)\right)$

$= g(-3)$

$= \sqrt{3 - 2(-3)}$

$= \sqrt{3 + 6}$

$= 3$

127 Let $P(x) = x^n + ax^2 - 6$. From the remainder theorem

$P(1) = -3 \Rightarrow 1 + a - 6 = -3$ Hence $a = 2$

and $P(-3) = (-3)^n + a(-3)^2 - 6$

$= (-3)^n + 2 \times 9 - 6$

$= (-3)^n + 12$

$\therefore \quad (-3)^n + 12 = -15 \quad \{\text{given}\}$

i.e., $(-3)^n = -27$ and so $n = 3$

i.e., $P(x) = x^3 + 2x^2 - 6$

128 a

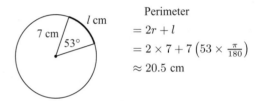

Perimeter

$= 2r + l$

$= 2 \times 7 + 7\left(53 \times \frac{\pi}{180}\right)$

≈ 20.5 cm

b Area $= \frac{1}{2}r^2\theta = \frac{1}{2} \times 7^2 \times \left(53 \times \frac{\pi}{180}\right) \approx 22.7$ cm^2

129

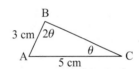

By the Sine Rule, $\frac{\sin 2\theta}{5} = \frac{\sin \theta}{3}$

$\therefore \quad 3\sin 2\theta = 5\sin \theta$

$\Rightarrow \quad 6\sin \theta \cos \theta = 5\sin \theta$

$\Rightarrow \quad \sin \theta(6\cos \theta - 5) = 0$

$\Rightarrow \quad \cos \theta = \frac{5}{6}$ as $\sin \theta \neq 0$

as $3\theta < 180°$, $\theta < 60°$.

So θ is acute.

$\therefore \quad \sin \theta = \frac{\sqrt{11}}{6}$

Let angle BAC $= \alpha°$ then $\alpha + 3\theta = \pi$

$\Rightarrow \quad \alpha = \pi - 3\theta$

$\sin \alpha = \sin(\pi - 3\theta)$

$= \sin \pi \cos 3\theta - \cos \pi \sin 3\theta$

$= (0)\cos 3\theta - (-1)\sin 3\theta$

$= \sin 3\theta$

$= \sin(2\theta + \theta)$

$= \sin 2\theta \cos \theta + \cos 2\theta \sin \theta$

$= 2\sin \theta \cos^2 \theta + (\cos^2 \theta - \sin^2 \theta)\sin \theta$

$= 2\left(\frac{\sqrt{11}}{6}\right)\left(\frac{25}{36}\right) + \left(\frac{25}{36} - \frac{11}{36}\right)\left(\frac{\sqrt{11}}{6}\right)$

$= \frac{8}{27}\sqrt{11}$

So, area $\triangle ABC = \frac{1}{2} \times 3 \times 5 \times \sin \alpha$

$= \frac{15}{2}\left(\frac{8}{27}\sqrt{11}\right)$ cm^2

$= \left(\frac{60}{27}\sqrt{11}\right)$ cm^2

130

$$\sin^2 x + \cos x = \tfrac{5}{4}, \quad -\pi \leqslant x \leqslant \pi$$

$$\Rightarrow \quad 1 - \cos^2 x + \cos x - \tfrac{5}{4} = 0$$

$$\Rightarrow \quad \cos^2 x - \cos x + \tfrac{1}{4} = 0$$

$$\Rightarrow \quad 4\cos^2 x - 4\cos x + 1 = 0$$

$$\Rightarrow \quad (2\cos x - 1)^2 = 0$$

$$\Rightarrow \quad \cos x = \tfrac{1}{2}$$

$$\Rightarrow \quad x = \pm\tfrac{\pi}{3}$$

131 $\arccos(\sin 3x + \cos 2x)$ is defined where

$$-1 \leqslant \sin 3x + \cos 2x \leqslant 1$$

The graph of $y = \sin 3x + \cos 2x$ is obtained from a gcalc:

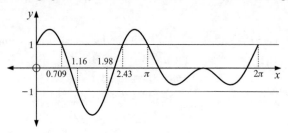

$$\therefore \quad x = 0, \quad 0.709 \leqslant x \leqslant 1.16,$$
$$1.98 \leqslant x \leqslant 2.43, \quad \pi \leqslant x \leqslant 2\pi$$

132 Consider the tree diagram:

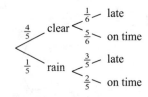

$$P(\text{Raining} \mid \text{Late}) = \frac{P(\text{Raining} \cap \text{Late})}{P(\text{Late})}$$

$$= \frac{\tfrac{1}{5} \times \tfrac{3}{5}}{\tfrac{4}{5} \times \tfrac{1}{6} + \tfrac{1}{5} \times \tfrac{3}{5}}$$

$$= \tfrac{9}{19}$$

133 a Since p is a probability function

then $\qquad \sum P(X = x) = 1$

$$\Rightarrow \quad \tfrac{1}{6} + 2k + \tfrac{1}{5}k + \tfrac{1}{3} + \tfrac{2}{5}k = 1$$

$$\Rightarrow \quad \tfrac{1}{6} + \tfrac{1}{3} + \left(2 + \tfrac{1}{5} + \tfrac{2}{5}\right)k = 1$$

$$\Rightarrow \quad \tfrac{1}{2} + \tfrac{13}{5}k = 1$$

$$\Rightarrow \quad k = \tfrac{5}{26}$$

b $P(0 < X < 4) = P(X = 1, 2, 3)$

$$= 2k + \tfrac{1}{5}k + \tfrac{1}{3}$$

$$= \left(2 + \tfrac{1}{5}\right)\tfrac{5}{26} + \tfrac{1}{3}$$

$$= \left(\tfrac{11}{5}\right)\left(\tfrac{5}{26}\right) + \tfrac{1}{3}$$

$$= \tfrac{59}{78}$$

134 $X \sim B(7, p)$

If $P(X = 4) = 0.25$ then $\binom{7}{4} p^4 (1 - p)^3 = 0.25$

Using technology $p \approx 0.464$ or 0.674

135 $y = \sin x$ has $\dfrac{dy}{dx} = \cos x$

when $x = \tfrac{\pi}{6}$, $\dfrac{dy}{dx} = \cos\left(\tfrac{\pi}{6}\right) = \tfrac{\sqrt{3}}{2}$

$\therefore$ normal has slope $\tfrac{-2}{\sqrt{3}}$ and so the equation of the normal

is $y - \tfrac{1}{2} = \tfrac{-2}{\sqrt{3}}\left(x - \tfrac{\pi}{6}\right)$ and meets the x-axis when $y = 0$

$$\therefore \quad -\tfrac{1}{2} = \tfrac{-2}{\sqrt{3}}\left(x - \tfrac{\pi}{6}\right)$$

$$\therefore \quad x - \tfrac{\pi}{6} = \tfrac{\sqrt{3}}{4}$$

i.e., $x = \tfrac{\sqrt{3}}{4} + \tfrac{\pi}{6}$ $\therefore$ coords are $\left(\tfrac{\sqrt{3}}{4} + \tfrac{\pi}{6}, 0\right)$.

136 $f(x) = ax^3 + bx^2 + cx + d$ $\therefore$ $f'(x) = 3ax^2 + 2bx + c$

Now $f(0) = 1$, $\qquad f'(0) = 0$

$\qquad f(-2) = -2$, $\qquad f'(-2) = 0$

Using $f(0) = 1$ we have $d = 1$.

Using $f'(0) = 0$ we have $3a(0) + 2b(0) + c = 0$

So, $c = 0$, $d = 1$

$f(-2) = -2 \Rightarrow a(-8) + b(4) + 0(-2) + 1 = -2$

$$\Rightarrow \quad -8a + 4b + 1 = -2$$

$$\Rightarrow \quad -8a + 4b = -3 \quad \ldots\ldots \text{(1)}$$

and $f'(-2) = 0 \Rightarrow 3a(4) + 2b(-2) + 0 = 0$

$$\Rightarrow \quad 12a - 4b = 0$$

$$\Rightarrow \quad b = 3a \quad \ldots\ldots \text{(2)}$$

Substituting (2) into (1) $\quad -8a + 12a = -3$

$$\Rightarrow \quad 4a = -3$$

$$\Rightarrow \quad a = -\tfrac{3}{4} \quad \text{and so} \quad b = -\tfrac{9}{4}$$

Thus $a = -\tfrac{3}{4}$, $b = -\tfrac{9}{4}$, $c = 0$, $d = 1$.

137

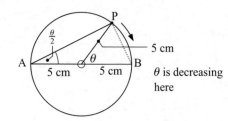

θ is decreasing here

$$\frac{d\theta}{dt} = \frac{-1 \text{ rev}}{10\pi \text{ sec}} = \frac{-2\pi^c}{10\pi \text{ sec}} = -\tfrac{1}{5} \, {}^c/\text{sec}$$

$$\angle PAB = \tfrac{\theta}{2} \quad \{\text{angle at centre theorem}\}$$

$$A = \tfrac{1}{2}(AP)(PB)$$

$$\Rightarrow \quad A = \tfrac{1}{2}\left[10\cos\left(\tfrac{\theta}{2}\right)\right]\left[10\sin\left(\tfrac{\theta}{2}\right)\right]$$

$$\Rightarrow \quad A = 50\sin\left(\tfrac{\theta}{2}\right)\cos\left(\tfrac{\theta}{2}\right)$$

$$\Rightarrow \quad A = 25\sin\theta$$

$$\Rightarrow \quad \frac{dA}{dt} = 25\cos\theta\,\frac{d\theta}{dt}$$

Particular case: $\tfrac{\theta}{2} = \tfrac{\pi}{3}$ i.e., $\theta = \tfrac{2\pi}{3}$

$$\frac{dA}{dt} = 25\cos\left(\tfrac{2\pi}{3}\right)\left(-\tfrac{1}{5}\right) = -5\left(-\tfrac{1}{2}\right) = 2.5$$

$\therefore$ at this instant the area is increasing at 2.5 cm^2 per second.

138

$$\int_0^{\frac{\pi}{6}} (\sin 3x \cos 2x + \cos 3x \sin 2x) \, dx$$

$$= \int_0^{\frac{\pi}{6}} \sin(5x) \, dx$$

$$= \tfrac{1}{5}\left[-\cos(5x)\right]_0^{\frac{\pi}{6}}$$

$$= -\tfrac{1}{5}\left(\cos\left(\tfrac{5\pi}{6}\right) - \cos 0\right)$$

$$= -\tfrac{1}{5}\left(\tfrac{-\sqrt{3}}{2} - 1\right)$$

$$= \tfrac{\sqrt{3}}{10} + \tfrac{1}{5}$$

139

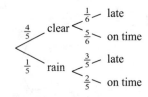

$y = \arccos x$

$\therefore x = \cos y$

$$V = \pi \int_{\frac{\pi}{6}}^{\frac{\pi}{3}} x^2 \, dy$$

$$= \pi \int_{\frac{\pi}{6}}^{\frac{\pi}{3}} \cos^2 y \, dy$$

$$= \pi \int_{\frac{\pi}{6}}^{\frac{\pi}{3}} \tfrac{1}{2} + \tfrac{1}{2}\cos 2y \, dy$$

$$= \pi \left[\tfrac{1}{2}y + \tfrac{1}{4}\sin 2y\right]_{\frac{\pi}{6}}^{\frac{\pi}{3}}$$

$$= \pi \left(\tfrac{\pi}{6} + \tfrac{1}{4} \sin \left(\tfrac{2\pi}{3} \right) - \tfrac{\pi}{12} - \tfrac{1}{4} \sin \left(\tfrac{\pi}{3} \right) \right)$$

$$= \pi \left(\tfrac{\pi}{12} \right)$$

$$= \tfrac{\pi^2}{12} \text{ units}^3$$

140
$$\int_0^{\frac{1}{2}} \sqrt{1 - x^2}\, dx \qquad \text{Let } x = \sin u$$
$$\frac{dx}{du} = \cos u$$

$$= \int_0^{\frac{\pi}{6}} \sqrt{1 - \sin^2 u}\, \cos u\, du$$

$$= \int_0^{\frac{\pi}{6}} \cos^2 u\, du$$

$$= \int_0^{\frac{\pi}{6}} \tfrac{1}{2} + \tfrac{1}{2} \cos 2u\, du$$

$$= \left[\tfrac{1}{2} u + \tfrac{1}{4} \sin 2u \right]_0^{\frac{\pi}{6}}$$

$$= \tfrac{\pi}{12} + \tfrac{1}{4} \sin \left(\tfrac{\pi}{3} \right) - 0 - 0$$

$$= \tfrac{\pi}{12} + \tfrac{1}{4} \tfrac{\sqrt{3}}{2}$$

$$= \tfrac{\pi}{12} + \tfrac{\sqrt{3}}{8}$$

141
$$\int_0^p \left(x^3 + x \right) dx = \tfrac{15}{4}, \quad p > 0$$

$$\Rightarrow \quad \left[\frac{x^4}{4} + \frac{x^2}{2} \right]_0^p = \tfrac{15}{4}$$

$$\Rightarrow \quad \frac{p^4}{4} + \frac{p^2}{2} - 0 = \tfrac{15}{4}$$

$$\Rightarrow \quad p^4 + 2p^2 = 15$$

$$\Rightarrow \quad p^4 + 2p^2 - 15 = 0$$

$$\Rightarrow \quad (p^2 + 5)(p^2 - 3) = 0$$

$$\Rightarrow \quad p^2 = -5 \quad \text{or} \quad 3$$

But p is real and > 0 $\;\therefore\;$ $p = \sqrt{3}$

142 a

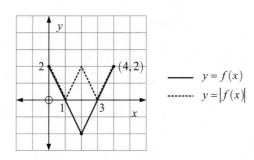

Note that $f(x)$ and $|f(x)|$ coincide for $f(x) > 0$

b Since $f(0) = 2$ is the y-intercept of $f(x)$
$\dfrac{1}{f(0)} = 0.5$ is the y-intercept of $\dfrac{1}{f(x)}$.

c

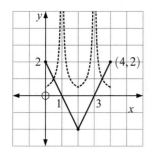

143 a The two lines will be coplanar if they have a point in common.

$$l_2: \quad x + 1 = \frac{y - k}{2} = \frac{z - 1}{-2} = \mu$$

Thus, $\quad x = \mu - 1, \quad y = 2\mu + k, \quad z = -2\mu + 1$

---

and the lines have a point in common if

$$3\lambda + 4 = \mu - 1 \qquad \text{...... (1)}$$
$$\lambda + 4 = 2\mu + k \qquad \text{...... (2)}$$
$$2\lambda - 1 = -2\mu + 1 \qquad \text{...... (3)}$$
$$3\lambda - \mu = -5 \qquad \text{...... (1)}$$
$$\lambda - 2\mu - k = -4 \qquad \text{...... (2)}$$
$$2\lambda + 2\mu = 2 \qquad \text{...... (3)}$$

This has solution $\lambda = -1, \quad \mu = 2, \quad k = -1$.

The lines are coplanar if $k = -1$ and the point of intersection is $(1, 3, -3)$.

b A direction of l_1 is $\begin{bmatrix} 3 \\ 1 \\ 2 \end{bmatrix}$ and a direction of l_2 is $\begin{bmatrix} 1 \\ 2 \\ -2 \end{bmatrix}$

$$\mathbf{p} = \begin{bmatrix} 3 \\ 1 \\ 2 \end{bmatrix} \times \begin{bmatrix} 1 \\ 2 \\ -2 \end{bmatrix} \text{ is perpendicular to both } l_1 \text{ and } l_2.$$

$$\text{and} \quad \mathbf{p} = \begin{vmatrix} \mathbf{i} & \mathbf{j} & \mathbf{k} \\ 3 & 1 & 2 \\ 1 & 2 & -2 \end{vmatrix} = -6\mathbf{i} + 8\mathbf{j} + 5\mathbf{k}$$

c Since the point $(1, 3, -3)$ is on the line l_1, an equation of the plane normal to $\mathbf{p}$ is $\begin{bmatrix} -6 \\ 8 \\ 5 \end{bmatrix} \bullet \begin{bmatrix} x \\ y \\ z \end{bmatrix} = \begin{bmatrix} -6 \\ 8 \\ 5 \end{bmatrix} \bullet \begin{bmatrix} 1 \\ 3 \\ -3 \end{bmatrix}$

i.e., $\quad -6x + 8y + 5z = 3$

144 a Let X be the measured speed of a car travelling at 60 kmph. Then $X - 60$ is the error in reading the speed which is E.
So $X - 60 = E$ or $X = 60 + E$.

b Since $E \sim N(0, \sigma^2)$ $\qquad X \sim N(60, \sigma^2)$

$$P(X \geqslant 65) = 0.01$$
$$\Rightarrow P(X \leqslant 65) = 0.99$$
$$\Rightarrow P\left(\frac{X - 60}{\sigma} \leqslant \frac{65 - 60}{\sigma} \right) = 0.99$$
$$\Rightarrow P\left(Z \leqslant \frac{5}{\sigma} \right) = 0.99$$
$$\Rightarrow \frac{5}{\sigma} = \text{invNorm}(0.99)$$
$$\Rightarrow \sigma = \frac{5}{\text{invNorm}(0.99)} \approx 2.15$$

145 $f(x) = \dfrac{k \ln x}{x}, \quad k > 0, \quad x > 0$

a $f'(x) = \dfrac{\left(\dfrac{k}{x} \right) x - k \ln x(1)}{x^2} = \dfrac{k - k \ln x}{x^2}$

$$= \dfrac{k(1 - \ln x)}{x^2}$$

$f'(x) = 0$ when $\ln x = 1 \Rightarrow x = e$

Sign diag. of $f'(x)$:

$\therefore$ max. turning point $\left(e, \dfrac{k}{e} \right)$

b $f''(x) = \dfrac{k \left(\dfrac{-1}{x} \right) x^2 - k(1 - \ln x) 2x}{x^4}$

$$= \dfrac{-kx - 2kx + 2kx \ln x}{x^4}$$

$$= \dfrac{-3k + 2k \ln x}{x^3}$$

$$= \dfrac{k(-3 + 2 \ln x)}{x^3}$$

which is 0 when $2 \ln x = 3 \Rightarrow x = e^{\frac{3}{2}}$

$\therefore$ point of inflection $\left(e^{\frac{3}{2}}, \dfrac{3k}{2e^{\frac{3}{2}}} \right)$

c $\displaystyle\int_1^{e^2} \frac{k\ln x}{x}\, dx = 10 \qquad \Rightarrow \quad k\int_1^{e^2} \frac{\ln x}{x}\, dx = 10$

$$\Rightarrow \quad k\int_1^{e^2} (\ln x)\frac{1}{x}\, dx = 10$$
$$\uparrow \quad \uparrow$$
$$[f(x)]^1 \quad f'(x)$$

$$\Rightarrow \quad k\left[\frac{(\ln x)^2}{2}\right]_1^{e^2} = 10$$

$$\Rightarrow \quad k\{2-0\} = 10$$
$$\Rightarrow \quad 2k = 10$$
$$\Rightarrow \quad k = 5$$

d $\displaystyle\int \frac{(\ln x)^2}{x^2}\, dx$ $\qquad \begin{cases} u = (\ln x)^2 & v' = x^{-2} \\ u' = \dfrac{2\ln x}{x} & v = \dfrac{x^{-1}}{-1} \end{cases}$

$= (\ln x)^2\left(-\dfrac{1}{x}\right) - \displaystyle\int -\dfrac{2\ln x}{x}\left(\dfrac{1}{x}\right) dx$

$= \dfrac{-(\ln x)^2}{x} + 2\displaystyle\int \dfrac{\ln x}{x^2}\, dx \qquad \begin{cases} u = \ln x & v' = x^{-2} \\ u' = \dfrac{1}{x} & v = -x^{-1} \end{cases}$

$= \dfrac{-(\ln x)^2}{x} + 2\left[-\dfrac{\ln x}{x} - \displaystyle\int \dfrac{1}{x}\left(-\dfrac{1}{x}\right) dx\right]$

$= \dfrac{-(\ln x)^2}{x} - \dfrac{2\ln x}{x} + 2\displaystyle\int x^{-2}\, dx$

$= \dfrac{-(\ln x)^2}{x} - \dfrac{2\ln x}{x} + \dfrac{2x^{-1}}{-1} + c$

$= \dfrac{-(\ln x)^2}{x} - \dfrac{2\ln x}{x} - \dfrac{2}{x} + c$

e Volume

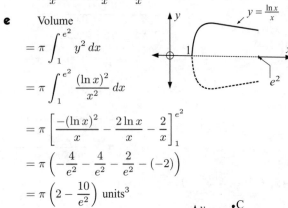

$= \pi \displaystyle\int_1^{e^2} y^2\, dx$

$= \pi \displaystyle\int_1^{e^2} \dfrac{(\ln x)^2}{x^2}\, dx$

$= \pi\left[\dfrac{-(\ln x)^2}{x} - \dfrac{2\ln x}{x} - \dfrac{2}{x}\right]_1^{e^2}$

$= \pi\left(-\dfrac{4}{e^2} - \dfrac{4}{e^2} - \dfrac{2}{e^2} - (-2)\right)$

$= \pi\left(2 - \dfrac{10}{e^2}\right)$ units^3

146

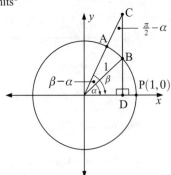

a In $\triangle ODB$,

$\cos\beta = \dfrac{OD}{OB} = \dfrac{OD}{1} \quad \Rightarrow \quad OD = \cos\beta$

$\sin\beta = \dfrac{BD}{OB} = \dfrac{BD}{1} \quad \Rightarrow \quad BD = \sin\beta$

b In $\triangle ODC$, $\cos\alpha = \dfrac{OD}{OC} \quad \Rightarrow \quad OC = \dfrac{OD}{\cos\alpha}$

$\Rightarrow \quad OC = \dfrac{\cos\beta}{\cos\alpha}$ {from **a**}

c $\tan\alpha = \dfrac{DC}{OD} \quad \therefore \quad DC = OD\tan\alpha = \cos\beta\tan\alpha$

Thus $BC = DC - BD = \cos\beta\tan\alpha - \sin\beta$

d By the Sine Rule in $\triangle OBC$,

$$\dfrac{\sin(\beta - \alpha)}{BC} = \dfrac{\sin\left(\frac{\pi}{2} - \alpha\right)}{1}$$

$\Rightarrow \quad \sin(\beta - \alpha) = BC\sin\left(\dfrac{\pi}{2} - \alpha\right)$

$\qquad\qquad\qquad = BC\cos\alpha$

$\qquad\qquad\qquad = (\cos\beta\tan\alpha - \sin\beta)\cos\alpha$ {from **c**}

$\qquad\qquad\qquad = \left(\cos\beta\dfrac{\sin\alpha}{\cos\alpha} - \sin\beta\right)\cos\alpha$

$\qquad\qquad\qquad = \cos\beta\sin\alpha - \sin\beta\cos\alpha$

$\qquad\qquad\qquad = \sin\alpha\cos\beta - \cos\alpha\sin\beta$

e $\sin 15°$

$= \sin(45° - 30°)$

$= \sin 45°\cos 30° - \cos 45°\sin 30°$ {from **d**}

$= \left(\dfrac{1}{\sqrt{2}}\right)\left(\dfrac{\sqrt{3}}{2}\right) - \left(\dfrac{1}{\sqrt{2}}\right)\left(\dfrac{1}{2}\right)$

$= \dfrac{\sqrt{3} - 1}{2\sqrt{2}}$

$= \left(\dfrac{\sqrt{3} - 1}{2\sqrt{2}}\right)\dfrac{\sqrt{2}}{\sqrt{2}}$

$= \dfrac{\sqrt{6} - \sqrt{2}}{4}$

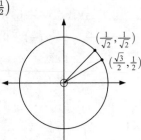

147 a $\mathbf{A}$ is non-singular if $\det\mathbf{A} \neq 0$, and

$\det\mathbf{A} = \begin{vmatrix} 1-k & -2 & -1 \\ 1 & -1 & -2 \\ 1 & k & -1 \end{vmatrix}$

$= (1-k)\begin{vmatrix} -1 & -2 \\ k & -1 \end{vmatrix} - -2\begin{vmatrix} 1 & -2 \\ 1 & -1 \end{vmatrix} + -1\begin{vmatrix} 1 & -1 \\ 1 & k \end{vmatrix}$

$= (1-k)(1+2k) + 2(1) - 1(k+1)$

$= 1 + 2k - k - 2k^2 + 2 - k - 1$

$= 2 - 2k^2$

$= 2(1+k)(1-k)$

So, $\mathbf{A}$ is non-singular for $k \neq \pm 1$.

b If $k = 0$, $\qquad \mathbf{A} = \begin{bmatrix} 1 & -2 & -1 \\ 1 & -1 & -2 \\ 1 & 0 & -1 \end{bmatrix}$

$\mathbf{A}^{-1} = \begin{bmatrix} \frac{1}{2} & -1 & \frac{3}{2} \\ -\frac{1}{2} & 0 & \frac{1}{2} \\ \frac{1}{2} & -1 & \frac{1}{2} \end{bmatrix}$ {using a gcalc}

c If $\begin{array}{l} x - 2y - z = 2 \\ x - y - 2z = -1 \\ x - z = 2 \end{array}$ then $\mathbf{A}\begin{bmatrix} x \\ y \\ z \end{bmatrix} = \begin{bmatrix} 2 \\ -1 \\ 2 \end{bmatrix}$

Thus $\begin{bmatrix} x \\ y \\ z \end{bmatrix} = \mathbf{A}^{-1}\begin{bmatrix} 2 \\ -1 \\ 2 \end{bmatrix} = \begin{bmatrix} \frac{1}{2} & -1 & \frac{3}{2} \\ -\frac{1}{2} & 0 & \frac{1}{2} \\ \frac{1}{2} & -1 & \frac{1}{2} \end{bmatrix}\begin{bmatrix} 2 \\ -1 \\ 2 \end{bmatrix}$

$\Rightarrow \begin{bmatrix} x \\ y \\ z \end{bmatrix} = \begin{bmatrix} 5 \\ 0 \\ 3 \end{bmatrix}$ Thus, the point of intersection is $(5, 0, 3)$.

d The line has equations: $\dfrac{x+3}{2} = y + 4 = \dfrac{z-7}{-1}$

If $x = 5$, $\dfrac{x+3}{2} = \dfrac{5+3}{2} = 4$

If $y = 0$, $y + 4 = 4$

If $z = 3$, $\dfrac{z-7}{-1} = \dfrac{-4}{-1} = 4$

So, $(5, 0, 3)$ lies on the line.

e Let θ be the acute angle between the line and the normal to the plane.

Now the direction vector of the line is $\begin{bmatrix} 2 \\ 1 \\ -1 \end{bmatrix}$

and the direction vector of the plane's normal is $\begin{bmatrix} 1 \\ -2 \\ 1 \end{bmatrix}$

$\therefore \quad \cos\theta = \dfrac{|2-2-1|}{\sqrt{6}\sqrt{6}} = \frac{1}{6}$ and so $\theta \approx 80.41°$

The required angle is $90° - 80.41°$ i.e., $9.59°$.

SOLUTIONS TO EXAMINATION PRACTICE SET 2

148 a $\frac{1}{2} < r < 1 \quad \therefore$ converges

$$u_2 = u_1 r = 6 \quad \text{and} \quad S_\infty = 49$$

$$\Rightarrow \quad \frac{u_1}{1-r} = 49$$

$$\Rightarrow \quad \frac{6}{r} = 49(1-r)$$

$$\Rightarrow \quad 6 = 49r - 49r^2$$

$$\Rightarrow \quad 49r^2 - 49r + 6 = 0$$

$$\Rightarrow \quad (7r-1)(7r-6) = 0$$

$$\Rightarrow \quad r = \frac{1}{7} \text{ or } \frac{6}{7}$$

But $\frac{1}{2} < r < 1$, $\therefore \quad r = \frac{6}{7}$

b But $u_1 r = 6 \quad \therefore \quad u_1\left(\frac{6}{7}\right) = 6 \quad \Rightarrow \quad u_1 = 7$

and $u_n = u_1 r^{n-1} \quad \Rightarrow \quad u_n = 7\left(\frac{6}{7}\right)^{n-1}$

149 $2^{2x} + 2^{x+1} - 15 = 0$

Let $m = 2^x \quad \therefore \quad m^2 = (2^x)^2 = 2^{2x}$

So, $m^2 + 2m - 15 = 0$

$\Rightarrow \quad (m-3)(m+5) = 0$

$\Rightarrow \quad m = 3 \text{ or } -5$

$\Rightarrow \quad 2^x = 3 \text{ or } -5$

$\Rightarrow \quad 2^x = 3 \quad \{2^x > 0 \text{ for all } x\}$

$\Rightarrow \quad \log 2^x = \log 3$

$\Rightarrow \quad x\log 2 = \log 3$

$\Rightarrow \quad x = \dfrac{\log 3}{\log 2} \quad$ (or $\log_2 3$)

150 For $\left(2x^2 + \dfrac{1}{x}\right)^9$, $T_{r+1} = \binom{9}{r}(2x^2)^{9-r}\left(\dfrac{1}{x}\right)^r$

$$= \binom{9}{r} 2^{9-r} x^{18-2r} x^{-r}$$

$$= \binom{9}{r} 2^{9-r} x^{18-3r}$$

So, if we let $r = 6$, $T_7 = \binom{9}{6} 2^3 x^0$

$\therefore$ constant term is $\binom{9}{6} \times 8 = 672$.

151 $(f \circ g)(x) = f(g(x)) = f(3x-2) = x+2$ (given)

and $f(9x-8) = f(3(3x-2)-2)$

$= f(3y-2)$ letting $y = 3x-2$

$= y+2$

$= 3x$

152 $x^2 y = 4 + x \quad \Rightarrow \quad y = \dfrac{4+x}{x^2}$ providing $x \neq 0$

The graph of $y = \dfrac{4+x}{x^2}$ and $y = e^x - 3x + 1$ is shown.

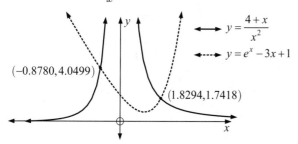

The graph shows there are two real roots at $(-0.8780, 4.0499)$ and $(1.8294, 1.7418)$

153 a $\dfrac{p(x)}{x(2x-3)} = (ax+b) + \dfrac{ax+b}{x(2x-3)}$

$$= \dfrac{(ax+b)x(2x-3) + (ax+b)}{x(2x-3)}$$

i.e., $p(x) = (ax+b)x(2x-3) + (ax+b)$

$\Rightarrow \quad p(x) = (ax+b)\left[x(2x-3) + 1\right]$

$\Rightarrow \quad p(x) = (ax+b)(2x^2 - 3x + 1)$

$\Rightarrow \quad p(x) = (ax+b)(2x-1)(x-1)$

b Since $p\left(\frac{1}{2}\right) = 0$ and $p(1) = 0$

both $(2x-1)$ and $(x-1)$ are factors of $p(x)$.

c $p(0) = 7 \quad \Rightarrow \quad b(-1)(-1) = 7$ i.e., $b = 7$

$p(2) = 39 \quad \Rightarrow \quad (2a+7)(4-1)(2-1) = 39$

$\Rightarrow \quad (2a+7)3 = 39$

$\Rightarrow \quad 2a+7 = 13$

$\Rightarrow \quad 2a = 6$

$\Rightarrow \quad a = 3$

i.e., $p(x) = (3x+7)(2x-1)(x-1)$

$= 6x^3 + 5x^2 - 18x + 7$

154

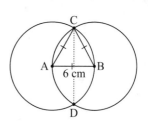

A 6 cm B

$\triangle ABC$ and ABD are equilateral

$\therefore$ angle $CBD = 120° = \frac{2\pi}{3}^c$

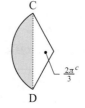

Thus, total area $= 2 \times$ shaded area

Area of segment $= \frac{1}{2}(r^2\theta - \frac{1}{2}r^2 \sin\theta)$

$\therefore$ required area $= r^2\theta - r^2 \sin\theta$

$= 6^2\left(\frac{2\pi}{3} - \sin\left(\frac{2\pi}{3}\right)\right)$

$= 36\left(\frac{2\pi}{3} - \left(\frac{\sqrt{3}}{2}\right)\right)$

$= 24\pi - 18\sqrt{3} \text{ cm}^2$

155 By the Cosine Rule, $7^2 = x^2 + 5^2 - 2 \times x \times 5 \times \cos 60°$

$\Rightarrow \quad 49 = x^2 + 25 - 10x\left(\frac{1}{2}\right)$

$\Rightarrow \quad x^2 - 5x - 24 = 0$

$\Rightarrow \quad (x-8)(x+3) = 0$

$\Rightarrow \quad x = 8 \text{ or } -3$

But $x > 0$, $\therefore \quad x = 8$

156

$$2\sin\left(x + \frac{\pi}{6}\right) = \sin x$$

$\Rightarrow \quad 2\left[\sin x \cos\frac{\pi}{6} + \cos x \sin\frac{\pi}{6}\right] = \sin x$

$\Rightarrow \quad 2\sin x\left(\frac{\sqrt{3}}{2}\right) + 2\cos x\left(\frac{1}{2}\right) = \sin x$

$\Rightarrow \quad \sqrt{3}\sin x + \cos x = \sin x$

$\Rightarrow \quad \sin x(\sqrt{3} - 1) = -\cos x$

$\Rightarrow \quad \dfrac{\sin x}{\cos x} = \dfrac{-1}{\sqrt{3} - 1}$

$\Rightarrow \quad \tan x = \left(\dfrac{-1}{\sqrt{3}-1}\right)\left(\dfrac{\sqrt{3}+1}{\sqrt{3}+1}\right) = \dfrac{-\sqrt{3}-1}{3-1}$

$= -\frac{1}{2}(1 + \sqrt{3})$

157 Consider $\sin(\arcsin a + \arcsin b)$

Let $\arcsin a = \theta$, $\arcsin b = \phi$

$\therefore$ $\sin\theta = a$ and $\sin\phi = b$

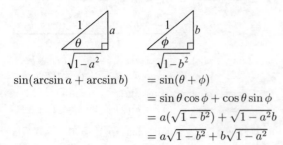

$$\sin(\arcsin a + \arcsin b) = \sin(\theta + \phi)$$
$$= \sin\theta\cos\phi + \cos\theta\sin\phi$$
$$= a(\sqrt{1-b^2}) + \sqrt{1-a^2}\,b$$
$$= a\sqrt{1-b^2} + b\sqrt{1-a^2}$$

158 a
$$\begin{bmatrix} -1 & k \\ k & 1 \end{bmatrix}^{-1} = \frac{1}{-1-k^2}\begin{bmatrix} 1 & -k \\ -k & -1 \end{bmatrix}$$

b $-x + ky = 2k$

$kx + y = 1 - k^2$ can be written in matrix form as:

$$\begin{bmatrix} -1 & k \\ k & 1 \end{bmatrix}\begin{bmatrix} x \\ y \end{bmatrix} = \begin{bmatrix} 2k \\ 1-k^2 \end{bmatrix}$$

$$\begin{bmatrix} x \\ y \end{bmatrix} = \frac{1}{-(1+k^2)}\begin{bmatrix} 1 & -k \\ -k & -1 \end{bmatrix}\begin{bmatrix} 2k \\ 1-k^2 \end{bmatrix}$$

$$\begin{bmatrix} x \\ y \end{bmatrix} = \frac{1}{-(1+k^2)}\begin{bmatrix} 2k - k + k^3 \\ -2k^2 - 1 + k^2 \end{bmatrix}$$

$$\begin{bmatrix} x \\ y \end{bmatrix} = \frac{1}{-(1+k^2)}\begin{bmatrix} k + k^3 \\ -1 - k^2 \end{bmatrix}$$

$$\begin{bmatrix} x \\ y \end{bmatrix} = \frac{1}{-(1+k^2)}\begin{bmatrix} k(1+k^2) \\ -(1+k^2) \end{bmatrix} = \begin{bmatrix} -k \\ 1 \end{bmatrix}$$

i.e., $x = -k$, $y = 1$

159 Since the vectors are perpendicular

$$(\lambda\mathbf{i} + \mathbf{j} - \lambda\mathbf{k})\bullet(3\mathbf{i} - 4\mathbf{j} + \mathbf{k}) = 0$$
$$\text{i.e.,}\quad 3\lambda - 4 - \lambda = 0\quad\text{or}\quad \lambda = 2$$

The vector $2\mathbf{i} + \mathbf{j} - 2\mathbf{k}$ has length $\sqrt{2^2 + 1^2 + 2^2} = 3$

A vector of unit length parallel to

$2\mathbf{i} + \mathbf{j} - 2\mathbf{k}$ is $\frac{2}{3}\mathbf{i} + \frac{1}{3}\mathbf{j} - \frac{2}{3}\mathbf{k}$.

160 We assume the number of students in the school is large enough to use the Binomial distribution.

If X is the number of students who travel by bike, then

$X \sim B(7, \frac{2}{7})$ and $P(x = 4) = \binom{7}{4}(\frac{2}{7})^4(\frac{5}{7})^3$
$$= \text{binompdf}(7, \tfrac{2}{7}, 4)$$
$$\approx 0.0850$$

161 Let X be the number of fish suitable for sale in 20 chosen from the box. As these are selected from a box of 1000 (a large number), we assume that $X \sim B(20, 0.963)$

a $P(X = 20) = \binom{20}{20}(0.963)^{20}$
$$= \text{binompdf}(20, 0.963, 20)$$
$$\approx 0.470$$

b If exactly one is not suitable for sale, 19 are.

$P(X = 19) = \binom{20}{19}(0.963)^{19}(0.037)$
$$= \text{binompdf}(20, 0.963, 19)$$
$$\approx 0.362$$

162 $f(x) = e^{x\ln x}$ $\therefore$ $f'(x) = e^{x\ln x}\left(1\ln x + x(\frac{1}{x})\right)$
$$= e^{x\ln x}(\ln x + 1)$$

which is 0 when $\ln x = -1$ {as $e^{x\ln x} > 0$ for all x}

i.e., $f'(x) = 0$ when $x = e^{-1}$

So, the x-coordinate of the stationary point is $\dfrac{1}{e}$.

163
$$y = \sin x(1 + \cos x), \quad 0 \leqslant x \leqslant 2\pi$$
$$\therefore\quad \frac{dy}{dx} = \cos x(1 + \cos x) + \sin x(-\sin x)$$
$$= \cos x + \cos^2 x - \sin^2 x$$
$$= \cos x + \cos^2 x - (1 - \cos^2 x)$$
$$= 2\cos^2 x + \cos x - 1$$
$$= (2\cos x - 1)(\cos x + 1)$$

which is 0 $\Leftrightarrow$ $\cos x = \frac{1}{2}$ or -1

$\Leftrightarrow$ $x = \frac{\pi}{3}, \pi, \frac{5\pi}{3}$

164

Surface area,
$$A = 2\pi r^2 + 2\pi rh$$
$$\Rightarrow\quad A = 2\pi r^2 + 2\pi r(2r)$$
$$\text{i.e.,}\quad A = 6\pi r^2$$

Thus, $\dfrac{dA}{dt} = 12\pi r\dfrac{dr}{dt}$ ...... (1)

Volume, $V = \pi r^2 h$
$$\Rightarrow\quad V = \pi r^2(2r)$$
$$\Rightarrow\quad V = 2\pi r^3 \quad\text{and so}\quad \frac{dV}{dt} = 6\pi r^2\frac{dr}{dt} \quad ...... (2)$$

Particular case: $r = 5$, $\dfrac{dV}{dt} = 5\pi$

$$\therefore\quad 5\pi = 6\pi(5)^2\frac{dr}{dt}$$
$$\Rightarrow\quad \frac{5\pi}{6\pi\times 25} = \frac{dr}{dt}$$
$$\Rightarrow\quad \frac{dr}{dt} = \tfrac{1}{30}\text{ cms}^{-1}$$

Hence, $\dfrac{dA}{dt} = 12\pi(5)(\frac{1}{30}) = 2\pi$ cm^{2}s^{-1}

i.e., the surface area is increasing at a rate of 2π cm^2 each second at that instant.

165
$$\int_{\frac{\pi}{6}}^{\frac{\pi}{3}} \cos^2 x + \tan^2 x\, dx$$
$$= \int_{\frac{\pi}{6}}^{\frac{\pi}{3}} \tfrac{1}{2} + \tfrac{1}{2}\cos(2x) + \sec^2 x - 1\, dx$$
$$= \int_{\frac{\pi}{6}}^{\frac{\pi}{3}} \tfrac{1}{2}\cos(2x) + \sec^2 x - \tfrac{1}{2}\, dx$$
$$= \left[\tfrac{1}{4}\sin(2x) + \tan x - \tfrac{1}{2}x\right]_{\frac{\pi}{6}}^{\frac{\pi}{3}}$$
$$= \tfrac{1}{4}\sin\left(\tfrac{2\pi}{3}\right) + \tan\left(\tfrac{\pi}{3}\right) - \tfrac{\pi}{6} - \tfrac{1}{4}\sin\left(\tfrac{\pi}{3}\right) - \tan\left(\tfrac{\pi}{6}\right) + \tfrac{\pi}{12}$$
$$= \tfrac{1}{4}\left(\tfrac{\sqrt{3}}{2}\right) + \sqrt{3} - \tfrac{\pi}{6} - \tfrac{1}{4}\left(\tfrac{\sqrt{3}}{2}\right) - \tfrac{1}{\sqrt{3}} + \tfrac{\pi}{12}$$
$$= \sqrt{3} - \tfrac{1}{\sqrt{3}} - \tfrac{\pi}{12}$$

166 $y = \dfrac{1}{\sqrt{4 - x^2}}$

$y = \dfrac{1}{\sqrt{4-x^2}}$

a Area $= \displaystyle\int_0^1 \dfrac{1}{\sqrt{4 - x^2}}\, dx$
$$= \left[\tfrac{1}{2}\arcsin\left(\tfrac{x}{2}\right)\right]_0^1$$
$$= \tfrac{1}{2}\arcsin\left(\tfrac{1}{2}\right) - \tfrac{1}{2}\arcsin(0)$$
$$= \tfrac{1}{2}\left(\tfrac{\pi}{6}\right) - \tfrac{1}{2}(0)$$
$$= \tfrac{\pi}{12}\text{ units}^2$$

b Volume $= \pi \displaystyle\int_0^1 \frac{1}{4 - x^2}\, dx$

≈ 0.863 units^3 (gcalc)

For the exact value

Let $\dfrac{1}{4 - x^2} = \dfrac{A}{2 + x} + \dfrac{B}{2 - x}$

$\therefore \quad A(2 - x) + B(2 + x) = 1$

If $x = 2$, $\quad 4B = 1 \quad \therefore \quad B = \frac{1}{4}$

If $x = -2$, $\quad 4A = 1 \quad \therefore \quad A = \frac{1}{4}$

$\therefore$ Volume $= \pi \displaystyle\int_0^1 \left(\dfrac{\frac{1}{4}}{x + 2} + \dfrac{\frac{1}{4}}{2 - x} \right) dx$

$= \frac{1}{4}\pi \left[\ln|x + 2| - \ln|2 - x| \right]_0^1$

$= \frac{\pi}{4} \{ \ln 3 - \ln 1 - \ln 2 + \ln 2 \}$

$= \dfrac{\pi \ln 3}{4}$ units^3

167 $\displaystyle\int \frac{x^2}{\sqrt{x + 2}}\, dx \qquad$ Let $u = x + 2$

$= \displaystyle\int \frac{(u - 2)^2}{\sqrt{u}}\, du \qquad$ then $\dfrac{du}{dx} = 1$

$= \displaystyle\int \frac{u^2 - 4u + 4}{u^{\frac{1}{2}}}\, du \qquad$ and $x = u - 2$

$= \displaystyle\int u^{\frac{3}{2}} - 4u^{\frac{1}{2}} + 4u^{-\frac{1}{2}}\, du$

$= \dfrac{u^{\frac{5}{2}}}{\frac{5}{2}} - \dfrac{4u^{\frac{3}{2}}}{\frac{3}{2}} + \dfrac{4u^{\frac{1}{2}}}{\frac{1}{2}} + c$

$= \frac{2}{5}(x + 2)^{\frac{5}{2}} - \frac{8}{3}(x + 2)^{\frac{3}{2}} + 8\sqrt{x + 2} + c$

168 $\displaystyle\int_1^k 3\sqrt{10 - x}\, dx = 38$

$\Rightarrow \displaystyle\int_1^k (10 - x)^{\frac{1}{2}}\, dx = \frac{38}{3}$

$\Rightarrow \left[\dfrac{1}{-1} \dfrac{(10 - x)^{\frac{3}{2}}}{\frac{3}{2}} \right]_1^k = \frac{38}{3}$

$\Rightarrow -\frac{2}{3}\left((10 - k)^{\frac{3}{2}} - 9^{\frac{3}{2}} \right) = \frac{38}{3}$

$\Rightarrow (10 - k)^{\frac{3}{2}} - 27 = -19$

$\Rightarrow (10 - k)^{\frac{3}{2}} = 8$

$\Rightarrow 10 - k = 8^{\frac{2}{3}} = 4$

$\Rightarrow k = 6$

169 a Since $\quad \frac{2}{7} + \frac{1}{7} + \frac{3}{14} + \frac{1}{14} + \frac{1}{7} + y = 1$

So, $\frac{6}{7} + y = 1 \quad \therefore \quad y = \frac{1}{7}$

b $E(X)$

$= 1 \times \frac{2}{7} + 2 \times \frac{1}{7} + 3 \times \frac{3}{14} + 4 \times \frac{1}{14} + 5 \times \frac{1}{7} + 6 \times \frac{1}{7}$

$= \frac{1}{14}(4 + 4 + 9 + 4 + 10 + 12)$

$= \frac{43}{14}$

$\mathrm{Var}(X)$

$= E(X^2) - (E(X))^2$

$= 1^2(\frac{2}{7}) + 2^2(\frac{1}{7}) + 3^2(\frac{3}{14}) + 4^2(\frac{1}{14}) + 5^2(\frac{1}{7}) + 6^2(\frac{1}{7}) - \left(\frac{43}{14}\right)^2$

$= \frac{159}{14} - \left(\frac{43}{14}\right)^2$

$= \frac{377}{196}$

c If the die is tossed many times we expect the mean value of the tosses to be $\frac{43}{14}$ with standard deviation of $\sqrt{\frac{377}{196}}$.

170 a i $\sin(A + B) = \sin A \cos B + \cos A \sin B$

$\sin(A - B) = \sin A \cos B - \cos A \sin B$

adding them gives:

$\sin(A + B) + \sin(A - B) = 2 \sin A \cos B$

ii $f(x) = \sin 5x \cos 2x$

$= \frac{1}{2}(2 \sin 5x \cos 2x)$

$= \frac{1}{2}(\sin 7x + \sin 3x)$

$= \frac{1}{2}\sin 7x + \frac{1}{2}\sin 3x$

$\qquad\qquad \uparrow \qquad\qquad\quad \uparrow$

period $\frac{2\pi}{7} \qquad$ period $\frac{2\pi}{3}$

$= \frac{6\pi}{21} \qquad\qquad = \frac{14\pi}{21}$

$\sin 7x$ repeats after $\frac{6\pi}{21}, \frac{12\pi}{21}, \frac{18\pi}{21}, \frac{24\pi}{21}, \ldots\ldots$

$\sin 3x$ repeats after $\frac{14\pi}{21}, \frac{28\pi}{21}, \frac{42\pi}{21}, \ldots\ldots$

LCM of 6 and 14 is 42 $\quad \therefore \quad$ period $= \frac{42\pi}{21} = 2\pi$

iii $\displaystyle\int \sin 5x \cos 2x\, dx$

$= \displaystyle\int \frac{1}{2}\sin 7x + \frac{1}{2}\sin 3x\, dx$

$= \left(\frac{1}{2}\right)\left(\frac{1}{7}\right)(-\cos 7x) + \frac{1}{2}\left(\frac{1}{3}\right)(-\cos 3x) + c$

$= -\frac{1}{14}\cos 7x - \frac{1}{6}\cos 3x + c$

iv $\displaystyle\int_0^{\frac{\pi}{3}} \sin 5x \cos 2x\, dx$

$= \left[-\frac{1}{14}\cos 7x - \frac{1}{6}\cos 3x \right]_0^{\frac{\pi}{3}}$

$= -\frac{1}{14}\cos\left(\frac{7\pi}{3}\right) - \frac{1}{6}\cos \pi + \frac{1}{14}\cos 0 + \frac{1}{6}\cos 0$

$= -\frac{1}{28} + \frac{1}{6} + \frac{1}{14} + \frac{1}{6}$

$= \frac{31}{84}$

b i $\cos(A + B) - \cos(A - B)$

$= \cos A \cos B - \sin A \sin B - (\cos A \cos B + \sin A \sin B)$

$= -2 \sin A \sin B$

ii $P(n)$ is

$\sin x + \sin 3x + \sin 5x + \ldots\ldots + \sin(2n - 1)x = \dfrac{\sin^2 nx}{\sin x}$

for all $n \in \mathbb{Z}^+$.

Proof: (By the Principle of Math Induction)

(1) If $n = 1$, LHS $= \sin x \quad$ RHS $= \dfrac{\sin^2 x}{\sin x} = \sin x$

$\therefore \quad P(1)$ is true.

(2) If $P(k)$ is true then

$\sin x + \sin 3x + \sin 5x + \ldots\ldots + \sin(2k - 1)x = \dfrac{\sin^2 kx}{\sin x}$

$\therefore \quad \sin x + \sin 3x + \ldots\ldots + \sin(2k - 1)x + \sin(2k + 1)x$

$= \dfrac{\sin^2 kx}{\sin x} + \sin(2k + 1)x$

$= \dfrac{\sin^2 kx + \sin(2k + 1)x \sin x}{\sin x}$

$= \dfrac{\sin^2 kx + (-\frac{1}{2})[\cos(2k + 2)x - \cos 2kx]}{\sin x} \quad$ {using **b i**}

$= \dfrac{\sin^2 kx - \frac{1}{2}\cos 2(k + 1)x + \frac{1}{2}\cos 2kx}{\sin x}$

$= \dfrac{\frac{1}{2} - \frac{1}{2}\cos 2kx - \frac{1}{2}\cos 2(k + 1)x + \frac{1}{2}\cos 2kx}{\sin x}$

$= \dfrac{\frac{1}{2} - \frac{1}{2}\cos 2(k + 1)x}{\sin x}$

$= \dfrac{\sin^2(k + 1)x}{\sin x} \qquad \{\cos 2\theta = 2\cos^2 \theta - 1$

$\qquad\qquad\qquad\qquad = 1 - 2\sin^2 \theta\}$

Thus $P(k + 1)$ is true whenever $P(k)$ is true and $P(1)$ is true. $\Rightarrow P(n)$ is true. {P of MI}

171 a By the Sine Rule

$$\frac{\sin 2\theta}{a} = \frac{\sin \theta}{b}$$

$$\Rightarrow \quad \frac{2\sin\theta\cos\theta}{a} = \frac{\sin\theta}{b}$$

$$\Rightarrow \quad \cos\theta = \frac{a}{2b} \ \ldots\ldots (1)$$

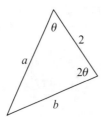

By the Cosine Rule,

$$b^2 = a^2 + 2^2 - 2(a)(2)\cos\theta$$

$$\Rightarrow \quad b^2 = a^2 + 4 - 4a\left(\frac{a}{2b}\right)$$

$$\Rightarrow \quad b^2 = a^2 + 4 - \frac{2a^2}{b}$$

$$\Rightarrow \quad b^3 = a^2 b + 4b - 2a^2$$

$$\Rightarrow \quad b^3 - 4b = a^2(b-2)$$

$$\Rightarrow \quad b(b^2 - 4) = a^2(b-2)$$

$$\Rightarrow \quad b(b+2)(b-2) = a^2(b-2)$$

$$\Rightarrow \quad b(b+2) = a^2 \quad \{\text{as } b \neq 2\}$$

$$\Rightarrow \quad a = \sqrt{b(b+2)}$$

In the special case when $b = 2$
the triangle is isosceles and
$\theta + \theta + 2\theta = 180°$

$$\Rightarrow \quad \theta = 45° \text{ and } 2\theta = 90°$$

$$\Rightarrow \text{ the triangle is right angled.}$$

In this case, $a^2 = 2^2 + 2^2 = 8 = 2 \times (2 + 2)$
i.e., $a = \sqrt{b(b+2)}$ again.

b

$$\int_0^{\frac{\pi}{4}} \tan^n x\, dx + \int_0^{\frac{\pi}{4}} \tan^{n-2} x\, dx$$

$$= \int_0^{\frac{\pi}{4}} [\tan x]^{n-2}(\tan^2 x + 1)\, dx$$

$$= \int_0^{\frac{\pi}{4}} [\tan x]^{n-2} \sec^2 x\, dx$$

$$= \left[\frac{[\tan x]^{n-1}}{n-1}\right]_0^{\frac{\pi}{4}}$$

$$= \frac{1}{n-1}\left(\left(\tan\tfrac{\pi}{4}\right)^{n-1} - (\tan 0)^{n-1}\right)$$

$$= \frac{1}{n-1}(1 - 0)$$

$$= \frac{1}{n-1}$$

172 a $\mathbf{r} = \begin{bmatrix} 2t+5 \\ -2t-1 \\ t \end{bmatrix}$.

If $t = 2$, $\mathbf{r} = \begin{bmatrix} 9 \\ -5 \\ 2 \end{bmatrix}$ so that B(9, −5, 2) lies on line L.

b An equation of the plane P is

$$\begin{bmatrix} 3 \\ -4 \\ -1 \end{bmatrix} \bullet \begin{bmatrix} x \\ y \\ z \end{bmatrix} = \begin{bmatrix} 3 \\ -4 \\ -1 \end{bmatrix} \bullet \begin{bmatrix} -1 \\ 0 \\ 4 \end{bmatrix}$$

i.e., $3x - 4y - z = -7$.

c If $t = -2$, $\mathbf{r} = \begin{bmatrix} 2(-2)+5 \\ -2(-2)-1 \\ -2 \end{bmatrix} = \begin{bmatrix} 1 \\ 3 \\ -2 \end{bmatrix}$

So C (1, 3, −2) lies on the line.

Also $3(1) - 4(3) - 1(-2) = -7$

Hence C (1, 3, −2) also lies on the plane.

d Since a normal to the plane has direction $\begin{bmatrix} 3 \\ -4 \\ -1 \end{bmatrix}$
an equation of the line is

$$\mathbf{r} = \begin{bmatrix} 9 \\ -5 \\ 2 \end{bmatrix} + s\begin{bmatrix} 3 \\ -4 \\ -1 \end{bmatrix} = \begin{bmatrix} 9+3s \\ -5-4s \\ 2-s \end{bmatrix}$$

e The line meets the plane if

$$3(9 + 3s) - 4(-5 - 4s) - (2 - s) = -7$$

$$\text{i.e., } \quad 26s + 45 = -7$$

$$\text{or } \quad s = -2$$

Hence the line and plane intersect at D (3, 3, 4)

or note if $s = -2$, $\mathbf{r} = \begin{bmatrix} 9+3(-2) \\ -5-4(-2) \\ 2-(-2) \end{bmatrix} = \begin{bmatrix} 3 \\ 3 \\ 4 \end{bmatrix}$.

Hence (3, 3, 4) is on the line and
$3(3) - 4(3) - (4) = -7$ and so also lies on the plane.

f

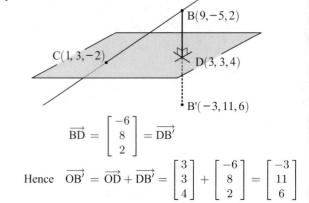

$$\overrightarrow{BD} = \begin{bmatrix} -6 \\ 8 \\ 2 \end{bmatrix} = \overrightarrow{DB'}$$

Hence $\overrightarrow{OB'} = \overrightarrow{OD} + \overrightarrow{DB'} = \begin{bmatrix} 3 \\ 3 \\ 4 \end{bmatrix} + \begin{bmatrix} -6 \\ 8 \\ 2 \end{bmatrix} = \begin{bmatrix} -3 \\ 11 \\ 6 \end{bmatrix}$

So, B′ is (−3, 11, 6).

g $\overrightarrow{CB'} = \begin{bmatrix} -4 \\ 8 \\ 8 \end{bmatrix} = -4\begin{bmatrix} 1 \\ -2 \\ -2 \end{bmatrix} = -4(\mathbf{i} - 2\mathbf{j} - 2\mathbf{k})$

and the line CB′ is parallel to $\mathbf{i} - 2\mathbf{j} - 2\mathbf{k}$.

173 a mean $= 27.5$ median $= 25.5$ mode $= 25.5$
$Q_1 = 15.5$ $Q_2 = 35.5$ range $= 50$

b

Travelling time	frequency	mid-point	cumulative frequency
1 - 10	11	5.5	11
11 - 20	19	15.5	30
21 - 30	32	25.5	62
31 - 40	22	35.5	84
41 - 50	9	45.5	93
51 - 60	7	55.5	100

c

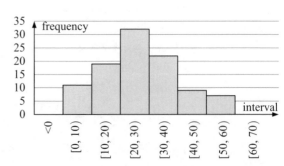

The data is roughly symmetric. From **a** median, mean and mode are about the same.

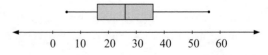

The box plot again shows symmetry with perhaps a few travelling times a little on the long side.

d

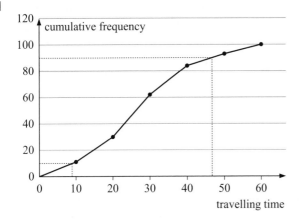

The 10th percentile is 9, the 90th percentile is about 47.

About 10% of the sample take less than 9 minutes to go to work.

About 90% of the sample take less than 47 minutes to go to work.

e Y is $B(n, p)$ and its mean $= np = 3$ and its

standard deviation $= \sqrt{npq} = \frac{3}{2}$

Thus, $npq = \frac{9}{4} \Rightarrow 3q = \frac{9}{4} \Rightarrow q = \frac{3}{4}$

Hence, $p = \frac{1}{4}$ and $n = 12$

So, $P(Y \leqslant 4) = $ binomcdf$(12, 0.25, 4) \approx 0.842$

SOLUTIONS TO EXAMINATION PRACTICE SET 3

174 a $\displaystyle\sum_{r=1}^{3}(2r + 2^r) = (2 + 2) + (4 + 4) + (6 + 8) = 26$

b $\displaystyle\sum_{r=1}^{n}(2r + 2^r)$

$= 2 + 2^1 + 4 + 2^2 + 6 + 2^3 + 8 + 2^4 + \ldots\ldots + 2n + 2^n$

$= (2 + 4 + 6 + 8 + \ldots\ldots + 2n) + (2 + 2^2 + 2^4 + \ldots\ldots + 2^n)$

$= \underbrace{\frac{n}{2}(2 + 2n)}_{\text{arithmetic sum}} + \underbrace{\frac{2(2^n - 1)}{2 - 1}}_{\text{geometric sum}}$

$= n(n + 1) + 2(2^n - 1)$

175 $\log_a \sqrt{72} = \log_a (2^3 3^2)^{\frac{1}{2}}$

$= \log_a (2^{\frac{3}{2}} 3^1)$

$= \frac{3}{2}\log_a 2 + \log_a 3$

$= \frac{3}{2}b + c$

176 For $(ax+3)^5$, $T_{r+1} = \binom{5}{r}(ax)^{5-r}3^r = \binom{5}{r}a^{5-r}3^r x^{5-r}$

$\therefore$ coefficient of x^4 is $\binom{5}{1}a^4 3^1$

For $(ax+3)^7$, $T_{r+1} = \binom{7}{r}(ax)^{7-r}3^r = \binom{7}{r}a^{7-r}3^r x^{7-r}$

$\therefore$ coefficient of x^5 is $\binom{7}{2}a^5 3^2$

Thus $\binom{5}{1}a^4 3^1 = \binom{7}{2}a^5 3^2$ and so $15a^4 = 21 \times 9a^5$

$\therefore$ as $a \neq 0$, $a = \dfrac{15}{21 \times 9} = \dfrac{5}{63}$

177 a $(g \circ f)(4)$

$= g(f(4))$

$= g\left(\dfrac{1}{4+5}\right)$

$= g\left(\dfrac{1}{9}\right)$

$= 3\left(\dfrac{1}{9}\right)$

$= \dfrac{1}{3}$

b g is $y = 3x$

g^{-1} is $x = 3y$

i.e., $y = \dfrac{x}{3}$

$g^{-1}(x) = \dfrac{x}{3}$

c Domain of g^{-1} is all $x \in \mathbb{R}$

---

178 a

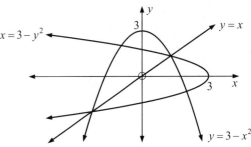

b The inverse of $y = f(x)$ is not a function since for one value of x there may be more than 1 value of y. For example, when $x = 0$, y has two values, $y = -3$ as well as $y = 3$.

c The function f is $y = -x^2 + 3$, $x \leqslant 0$, and so the function f^{-1} is $x = -y^2 + 3$, $y \leqslant 0$

$\Rightarrow y^2 = 3 - x$

$\Rightarrow y = \pm\sqrt{3-x}$

But $y \leqslant 0$ and so $y = -\sqrt{3-x}$

Graph of $y = -\sqrt{3-x}$

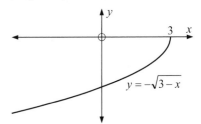

179 $f(x) = 2x^3 - x^2 - 8x - 5$

$f(-1) = 0$ hence $(x + 1)$ is a factor.

$$
\begin{array}{r|rrrr}
-1 & 2 & -1 & -8 & -5 \\
 & 0 & -2 & 3 & 5 \\
\hline
 & 2 & -3 & -5 & 0
\end{array}
$$

So $2x^3 - x^2 - 8x - 5$

$= (x + 1)(2x^2 - 3x - 5)$

$= (x + 1)(x + 1)(2x - 5)$

$= (x + 1)^2(2x - 5)$

$f(x) \geqslant 0$ if $2x - 5 \geqslant 0$ {since $(x + 1)^2 \geqslant 0$ for all x}

i.e., $f(x) \geqslant 0$ if $x \geqslant \frac{5}{2}$.

180

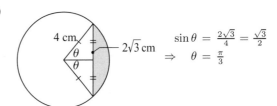

$\sin\theta = \frac{2\sqrt{3}}{4} = \frac{\sqrt{3}}{2}$

$\Rightarrow \theta = \frac{\pi}{3}$

Area $= \frac{1}{2}r^2 2\theta - \frac{1}{2}r^2\sin(2\theta)$

$= \frac{1}{2} \times r^2\left(\frac{2\pi}{3} - \sin\frac{2\pi}{3}\right)$

$= 8\left(\frac{2\pi}{3} - \frac{\sqrt{3}}{2}\right)$ cm^2

$= \left(\frac{16\pi}{3} - 4\sqrt{3}\right)$ cm^2

181

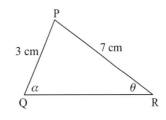

By the Sine Rule:

$\dfrac{\sin\alpha}{7} = \dfrac{\sin\theta}{3}$

$\Rightarrow \dfrac{\sin\alpha}{7} = \dfrac{\sqrt{3}}{14}$

$\Rightarrow \sin\alpha = \dfrac{\sqrt{3}}{14} \times 7 = \dfrac{\sqrt{3}}{2}$

$\therefore \alpha = 60^\circ$ or 120°

182
$$3\cos 2\theta + 2 = 7\sin\theta$$
$$\Rightarrow \quad 3(1 - 2\sin^2\theta) + 2 - 7\sin\theta = 0$$
$$\Rightarrow \quad 3 - 6\sin^2\theta + 2 - 7\sin\theta = 0$$
$$\Rightarrow \quad 6\sin^2\theta + 7\sin\theta - 5 = 0$$
$$\Rightarrow \quad (2\sin\theta - 1)(3\sin\theta + 5) = 0$$
$$\Rightarrow \quad \sin\theta = \tfrac{1}{2} \text{ or } -\tfrac{5}{3}$$

But $-1 < \sin\theta < 1$ for all θ $\therefore$ $\sin\theta = \tfrac{1}{2}$

183 Let $\arcsin\left(\tfrac{3}{5}\right) = a$ and $\arccos\left(\tfrac{2}{3}\right) = b$
$$\Rightarrow \quad \sin a = \tfrac{3}{5} \quad \text{and} \quad \cos b = \tfrac{2}{3}$$

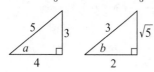

$$\Rightarrow \quad \cos a = \tfrac{4}{5} \quad \text{and} \quad \sin b = \tfrac{\sqrt{5}}{3}$$

Now $\cos\left(\arcsin\tfrac{3}{5} + \arccos\tfrac{2}{3}\right)$
$$= \cos(a + b)$$
$$= \cos a\cos b - \sin a\sin b$$
$$= \left(\tfrac{4}{5}\right)\left(\tfrac{2}{3}\right) - \left(\tfrac{3}{5}\right)\left(\tfrac{\sqrt{5}}{3}\right)$$
$$= \frac{8 - 3\sqrt{5}}{15}$$

184 a If **A** is the inverse of **B** then
$$\begin{bmatrix} 2 & 1 & a \\ a & 2 & 1 \\ 0 & 6 & 1 \end{bmatrix}\begin{bmatrix} -2b & 7 & -3 \\ a & b & 1 \\ 6 & -6b & -5 \end{bmatrix} = \begin{bmatrix} 1 & 0 & 0 \\ 0 & 1 & 0 \\ 0 & 0 & 1 \end{bmatrix}$$

i.e., $\begin{bmatrix} -4b + 7a & 14 + b - 6ab & -5 - 5a \\ -2ab + 2a + 6 & 7a - 4b & -3a - 3 \\ 6a + 6 & 6b - 6b & 1 \end{bmatrix} = \begin{bmatrix} 1 & 0 & 0 \\ 0 & 1 & 0 \\ 0 & 0 & 1 \end{bmatrix}$

Equating the elements in the first row:
$$-4b + 7a = 1 \quad \dots\dots \text{(1)}$$
$$14 + b - 6ab = 0 \quad \dots\dots \text{(2)}$$
$$-5 - 5a = 0 \quad \dots\dots \text{(3)}$$
From (3) $a = -1$
From (1) $-4b - 7 = 1$ and so $b = -2$
These values of a and b check for other entries.

b In matrix form
$$\begin{bmatrix} 4 & 7 & -3 \\ -1 & -2 & 1 \\ 6 & 12 & -5 \end{bmatrix}\begin{bmatrix} u \\ v \\ w \end{bmatrix} = \begin{bmatrix} -8 \\ 3 \\ -15 \end{bmatrix}$$
$$\begin{bmatrix} u \\ v \\ w \end{bmatrix} = \begin{bmatrix} 4 & 7 & -3 \\ -1 & -2 & 1 \\ 6 & 12 & -5 \end{bmatrix}^{-1}\begin{bmatrix} -8 \\ 3 \\ -15 \end{bmatrix}$$
$$\begin{bmatrix} u \\ v \\ w \end{bmatrix} = \begin{bmatrix} 2 & 1 & -1 \\ -1 & 2 & 1 \\ 0 & 6 & 1 \end{bmatrix}\begin{bmatrix} -8 \\ 3 \\ -15 \end{bmatrix} = \begin{bmatrix} 2 \\ -1 \\ 3 \end{bmatrix}$$
i.e., $u = 2$, $v = -1$, $w = 3$

185 Since $\mathbf{a} + \mathbf{b} + \mathbf{c} = \mathbf{0}$
$$\mathbf{a} \times (\mathbf{a} + \mathbf{b} + \mathbf{c}) = \mathbf{0}$$
i.e., $\mathbf{a} \times \mathbf{b} + \mathbf{a} \times \mathbf{c} = \mathbf{0}$ {since $\mathbf{a} \times \mathbf{a} = \mathbf{0}$}
i.e., $\mathbf{a} \times \mathbf{b} = -(\mathbf{a} \times \mathbf{c})$ ......(1)
Also $(\mathbf{a} + \mathbf{b} + \mathbf{c}) \times \mathbf{c} = \mathbf{0}$
i.e., $\mathbf{a} \times \mathbf{c} + \mathbf{b} \times \mathbf{c} = \mathbf{0}$ {since $\mathbf{c} \times \mathbf{c} = \mathbf{0}$}
i.e., $\mathbf{b} \times \mathbf{c} = -(\mathbf{a} \times \mathbf{c})$ ......(2)
From (1) and (2) $\mathbf{a} \times \mathbf{b} = \mathbf{b} \times \mathbf{c}$.

186 Let X be the diameter of a disc, then $X \sim N(73, 1.1^2)$
Hence, $P(X > 75) = \text{normalcdf}(75, \text{E99}, 73, 1.1)$
$$\approx 0.0345$$

187 $P(A \cup B) = P(A) + P(B) - P(A \cap B)$
Since A and B are independent $P(A \cap B) = P(A) \times P(B)$
Hence, letting $P(B) = p$, $\quad 0.75 = 0.35 + p - 0.35p$
i.e., $0.65p = 0.40$
$$p = \frac{40}{65} = \frac{8}{13}$$

188 Let X be the number of blonde children. Then, $X \sim B(5, \tfrac{1}{7})$.
a $E(X) = np = 5 \times \tfrac{1}{7} = \tfrac{5}{7}$
Expected number of blonde children is $\tfrac{5}{7}$.
(**Note:** this does **not** mean they will have $\tfrac{5}{7}$ of a child blonde!)

b $P(X = 3)$
$$= \binom{5}{3}\left(\tfrac{1}{7}\right)^3\left(\tfrac{6}{7}\right)^2$$
$$= \text{binompdf}(5, \tfrac{1}{7}, 3)$$
$$\approx 0.0214$$

c $P(X > 3)$
$$= 1 - P(X \leqslant 3)$$
$$= 1 - \text{binompdf}(5, \tfrac{1}{7}, 3)$$
$$\approx 0.00184$$

189 A tree diagram shows the situation.

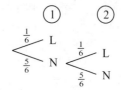

Probability she leaves it in shop 1 given it is missing is
$$= \frac{P(\text{shop 1 and left it})}{P(\text{left it})} = \frac{\tfrac{1}{6}}{\tfrac{5}{36} + \tfrac{1}{6}} = \tfrac{6}{11}$$

190 $y = \ln(x^2 - 3)$ has $\dfrac{dy}{dx} = \dfrac{2x}{x^2 - 3}$ and
$$\frac{d^2y}{dx^2}$$
$$= \frac{2(x^2 - 3) - 2x(2x)}{(x^2 - 3)^2}$$
$$= \frac{2x^2 - 6 - 4x^2}{(x^2 - 3)^2}$$
$$= \frac{-2x^2 - 6}{(x^2 - 3)^2}$$

Thus
$$\frac{d^2y}{dx^2} + \left(\frac{dy}{dx}\right)^2$$
$$= \frac{-2x^2 - 6}{(x^2 - 3)^2} + \frac{4x^2}{(x^2 - 3)^2}$$
$$= \frac{2x^2 - 6}{(x^2 - 3)^2}$$
$$= \frac{2(x^2 - 3)}{(x^2 - 3)^2}$$
$$= \frac{2}{x^2 - 3}$$

191 $f(x) = \dfrac{e^{x^2}}{e^x - 1}$

a i The VA's occur when $e^x - 1 = 0 \quad \Rightarrow \quad e^x = 1$
$$\Rightarrow \quad x = 0$$
$\therefore$ VA is $x = 0$
ii From a gcalc
the max. turning point is $(-0.604, -3.18)$
the min. turning point is $(0.864, 1.54)$

b

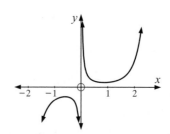

192 $\tan x - \dfrac{\tan x - 1}{\tan x + 1} = \dfrac{\tan x(\tan x + 1) - (\tan x - 1)}{\tan x + 1}$
$$= \frac{\tan^2 x + \tan x - \tan x + 1}{\tan x + 1}$$
$$= \frac{\sec^2 x}{\tan x + 1}$$

$$\therefore \int \tan x - \frac{\tan x - 1}{\tan x + 1}\, dx$$

$$= \int \frac{\sec^2 x}{\tan x + 1}\, dx \qquad \left\{ \begin{array}{l} u = \tan x + 1 \\ \dfrac{du}{dx} = \sec^2 x \end{array} \right.$$

$$= \int \frac{1}{u}\frac{du}{dx}\, dx$$

$$= \int \frac{1}{u}\, du$$

$$= \ln |u| + c$$

$$\therefore \int_0^{\frac{\pi}{4}} \left(\tan x - \frac{\tan x - 1}{\tan x + 1} \right) dx = [\ln(\tan x + 1)]_0^{\frac{\pi}{4}}$$
$$= \ln 2 - \ln 1$$
$$= \ln 2$$

193

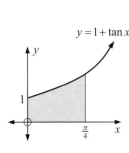

$y = 1 + \tan x$

Volume

$$= \pi \int_0^{\frac{\pi}{4}} y^2\, dx$$

$$= \pi \int_0^{\frac{\pi}{4}} \left(1 + 2\tan x + \tan^2 x \right) dx$$

$$= \pi \int_0^{\frac{\pi}{4}} \sec^2 x - 2\frac{-\sin x}{\cos x}\, dx$$

$$= \pi \left[\tan x - 2 \ln |\cos x| \right]_0^{\frac{\pi}{4}}$$

$$= \pi \left[(1 - 2\ln\tfrac{1}{\sqrt{2}}) - (0 - 0) \right]$$

$$= \pi (1 - 2(\ln 2^{-\frac{1}{2}}))$$

$$= \pi (1 + \ln 2) \text{ units}^3$$

194 $v = t^3 - 3t^2 + 2t$
$= t(t^2 - 3t + 2)$
$= t(t-1)(t-2)$ So, $v = 0$ at $t = 0, 1, 2$ sec

Sign diagram of v:

$$s = \frac{t^4}{4} - \frac{3t^3}{3} + \frac{2t^2}{2} + c$$

i.e., $s = \frac{1}{4}t^4 - t^3 + t^2 + c$ metres

$s(0) = c$
$s(1) = \frac{1}{4} - 1 + 1 + c = c + \frac{1}{4}$
$s(2) = 4 - 8 + 4 + c = c$
$s(3) = \frac{81}{4} - 27 + 9 + c = 20\frac{1}{4} - 27 + 9 + c = 2\frac{1}{4} + c$

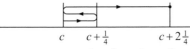

Total distance travelled $= \frac{1}{4} + \frac{1}{4} + 2\frac{1}{4} = 2\frac{3}{4}$ m $= 2.75$ m

195 $xy\frac{dy}{dx} + 1 = x^2 \qquad \Rightarrow \quad xy\frac{dy}{dx} = x^2 - 1$

$$\Rightarrow \quad y\frac{dy}{dx} = \frac{x^2 - 1}{x} = x - \frac{1}{x}$$

$$\Rightarrow \quad \int y\frac{dy}{dx}\, dx = \int x - \frac{1}{x}\, dx$$

$$\Rightarrow \quad \int y\, dy = \int x - \frac{1}{x}\, dx$$

$$\Rightarrow \quad \frac{y^2}{2} = \frac{x^2}{2} - \ln |x| + c$$

Now when $x = 1$, $y = 2$ $\therefore$ $2 = \frac{1}{2} + c$ i.e., $c = \frac{3}{2}$

Thus, $\frac{y^2}{2} = \frac{x^2}{2} - \ln |x| + \frac{3}{2}$

So, $y^2 = x^2 - 2\ln |x| + 3$

$\Rightarrow y = \sqrt{x^2 - 2\ln |x| + 3}$ {as $y > 0$}

196

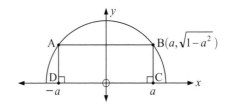

$B(a, \sqrt{1-a^2})$

a Area, $A = 2a\sqrt{1-a^2}$ $\therefore$ $A^2 = 4a^2(1-a^2)$
$= 4a^2 - 4a^4$

b $2A\frac{dA}{da} = 8a - 16a^3 \Rightarrow \frac{dA}{dt} = \frac{8a(1-2a^2)}{2A}$

$$\Rightarrow \frac{dA}{dt} = \frac{4a(1+\sqrt{2}a)(1-\sqrt{2}a)}{A}$$

and has sign diagram:

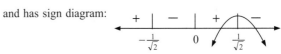

But $a > 0$, $\therefore$ we have a local max. at $a = \frac{1}{\sqrt{2}}$

i.e., $x = \frac{1}{\sqrt{2}}$ where the area is a maximum.

c $A_{\max} = 2\left(\frac{1}{\sqrt{2}}\right)\sqrt{(1-\frac{1}{2})} = \frac{2}{\sqrt{2}}\sqrt{\left(\frac{1}{2}\right)} = 1$ unit^2

197 a $\overrightarrow{AB} = \begin{bmatrix} -2 \\ 0 \\ 1 \end{bmatrix}$ $\overrightarrow{AC} = \begin{bmatrix} -1 \\ -3 \\ 3 \end{bmatrix}$ and

$$\overrightarrow{AB} \times \overrightarrow{AC} = \begin{vmatrix} \mathbf{i} & \mathbf{j} & \mathbf{k} \\ -2 & 0 & 1 \\ -1 & -3 & 3 \end{vmatrix}$$

$$= \mathbf{i}\,(0+3) - \mathbf{j}\,(-6+1) + \mathbf{k}\,(6)$$
$$= 3\mathbf{i} + 5\mathbf{j} + 6\mathbf{k} \qquad \text{i.e., } \begin{bmatrix} 3 \\ 5 \\ 6 \end{bmatrix}$$

b i The first plane has normal vector $\begin{bmatrix} 3 \\ 5 \\ 6 \end{bmatrix}$.

$\therefore$ its equation is is $\begin{bmatrix} 3 \\ 5 \\ 6 \end{bmatrix} \bullet \begin{bmatrix} x \\ y \\ z \end{bmatrix} = \begin{bmatrix} 3 \\ 5 \\ 6 \end{bmatrix} \bullet \begin{bmatrix} 1 \\ 0 \\ 3 \end{bmatrix}$

i.e., $3x + 5y + 6z = 21$

Sub. the coordinates of A in $3x + 5y + 6z$
$= 3(3) + 5(0) + 6(2)$
$= 21$

So A lies on plane $3x + 5y + 6z = 21$

Also $2(3) - 1(0) + 4(2) = 14$

So A lies on the plane $2x - y + 4z = 14$.

Similarly for B(1, 0, 3), $3(1) + 5(0) + 6(3) = 21$

and $2(1) - 1(0) + 4(3) = 14$

So B lies on both planes. Thus A and B are points on the river.

ii $\overrightarrow{AB} = \begin{bmatrix} -2 \\ 0 \\ 1 \end{bmatrix}$ Since A(3, 0, 2) lies on the line, an equation is

$$\mathbf{r} = \begin{bmatrix} 3 \\ 0 \\ 2 \end{bmatrix} + \lambda \begin{bmatrix} -2 \\ 0 \\ 1 \end{bmatrix} = \begin{bmatrix} 3 - 2\lambda \\ 0 \\ 2 + \lambda \end{bmatrix}$$

iii $\overrightarrow{BC} = \begin{bmatrix} 1 \\ -3 \\ 2 \end{bmatrix}$ and $\overrightarrow{BC} \bullet \overrightarrow{AB} = \begin{bmatrix} 1 \\ -3 \\ 2 \end{bmatrix} \bullet \begin{bmatrix} -2 \\ 0 \\ 1 \end{bmatrix} = 0$

So $\overrightarrow{BC}$ is perpendicular to $\overrightarrow{AB}$.

Hence B is the closest point on the river to C.

iv The shortest distance is $|BC| = \sqrt{1^2 + (-3)^2 + 2^2}$
$= \sqrt{14}$ units

198 a

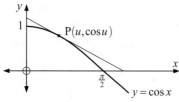

P$(u, \cos u)$

$y = \cos x$

i $\dfrac{dy}{dx} = -\sin x = -\sin u$ at $(u, \cos u)$

∴ tangent has equation

$y - \cos u = -\sin u(x - u)$

i.e., $y = (-\sin u)x + u\sin u + \cos u$

ii Cuts x-axis when $y = 0$

$\Rightarrow (\sin u)x = u\sin u + \cos u$

$\Rightarrow x = u + \cot u$

∴ A is at $(u + \cot u, 0)$

Cuts y-axis when $x = 0$

$\Rightarrow y = u\sin u + \cos u$ ∴ B is at $(0, u\sin u + \cos u)$

iii Area $= \frac{1}{2}(AO)(OB)$

$= \frac{1}{2}\left(u + \dfrac{\cos u}{\sin u}\right)(u\sin u + \cos u)$

$= \frac{1}{2}\left(\dfrac{u\sin u + \cos u}{\sin u}\right)(u\sin u + \cos u)$

$= \dfrac{(u\sin u + \cos u)^2}{2\sin u}$ units^2

iv Using a gcalc

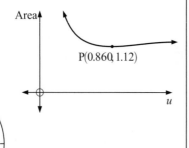

Area

P(0.860, 1.12)

u

b

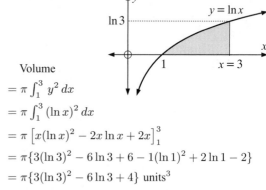

3 m

x m

θ

2 m

Hour hand moves at 1 rev/12 hours $= \dfrac{2\pi^c}{12\text{ h}} = \frac{\pi}{6}{}^c/\text{h}$

Minute hand moves at 1 rev/1 hour $= \dfrac{2\pi^c}{1\text{ h}} = 2\pi^c/\text{h}$

∴ $\dfrac{d\theta}{dt} = \frac{\pi}{6} - 2\pi = \dfrac{-11\pi}{6}{}^c/\text{h}$

Now by the Cosine Rule

$x^2 = 2^2 + 3^2 - 2 \times 2 \times 3 \times \cos\theta$

∴ $x^2 = 13 - 12\cos\theta$

∴ $2x\dfrac{dx}{dt} = -12(-\sin\theta)\dfrac{d\theta}{dt}$

∴ $x\dfrac{dx}{dt} = 6\sin\theta\dfrac{d\theta}{dt}$

Particular case at 4 pm, $\theta = \frac{2\pi}{3}$

and $x^2 = 13 - 12(-\frac{1}{2}) = 19$

∴ $\sqrt{19}\dfrac{dx}{dt} = 6\left(\frac{\sqrt{3}}{2}\right)\left(\frac{-11\pi}{6}\right)$

∴ $\dfrac{dx}{dt} = -\dfrac{11\pi\sqrt{3}}{2\sqrt{19}}$ mh^{-1} ≈ -6.87 mh^{-1}

∴ distance is decreasing at 6.87 mh^{-1}

199 a $P(n)$ is

$\begin{bmatrix} 1 & 1 \\ 1 & 0 \end{bmatrix}^n = \begin{bmatrix} u_{n+1} & u_n \\ u_n & u_{n-1} \end{bmatrix}$ for all $n \geqslant 2$, $n \in \mathbb{Z}$

Proof: (By the Principle of Math Induction)

---

(1) If $n = 2$, $\begin{bmatrix} 1 & 1 \\ 1 & 0 \end{bmatrix}^2 = \begin{bmatrix} 1 & 1 \\ 1 & 0 \end{bmatrix}\begin{bmatrix} 1 & 1 \\ 1 & 0 \end{bmatrix} = \begin{bmatrix} 2 & 1 \\ 1 & 1 \end{bmatrix}$

$= \begin{bmatrix} u_3 & u_2 \\ u_2 & u_1 \end{bmatrix}$ So, $P(2)$ is true.

(2) If $P(k)$ is true.

$\begin{bmatrix} 1 & 1 \\ 1 & 0 \end{bmatrix}^k = \begin{bmatrix} u_{k+1} & u_k \\ u_k & u_{k-1} \end{bmatrix}$

∴ $\begin{bmatrix} 1 & 1 \\ 1 & 0 \end{bmatrix}^{k+1} = \begin{bmatrix} u_{k+1} & u_k \\ u_k & u_{k-1} \end{bmatrix}\begin{bmatrix} 1 & 1 \\ 1 & 0 \end{bmatrix}$

$= \begin{bmatrix} u_{k+1} + u_k & u_{k+1} \\ u_k + u_{k-1} & u_k \end{bmatrix}$

$= \begin{bmatrix} u_{k+2} & u_{k+1} \\ u_{k+1} & u_k \end{bmatrix}$

i.e., $P(k+1)$ is true whenever $P(k)$ is true and $P(2)$ is true $\Rightarrow$ $P(n)$ is true {P of MI}

b i $\displaystyle\int (\ln x)^2\, dx$ $\quad \begin{cases} u = (\ln x)^2 & v' = 1 \\ u' = \dfrac{2\ln x}{x} & v = x \end{cases}$

$= \int 1(\ln x)^2\, dx$

$= x(\ln x)^2 - \displaystyle\int \left(\dfrac{2\ln x}{x}\right)x\, dx$

$= x(\ln x)^2 - \int 2\ln x\, dx$ $\quad \begin{cases} u = \ln x & v' = 2 \\ u' = \dfrac{1}{x} & v = 2x \end{cases}$

$= x(\ln x)^2 - \left[2x\ln x - \displaystyle\int \left(\dfrac{1}{x}\right)2x\, dx\right]$

$= x(\ln x)^2 - 2x\ln x + \int 2\, dx$

$= x(\ln x)^2 - 2x\ln x + 2x + c$

ii

$y = \ln x$

ln 3

1

$x = 3$

Volume

$= \pi \displaystyle\int_1^3 y^2\, dx$

$= \pi \displaystyle\int_1^3 (\ln x)^2\, dx$

$= \pi \left[x(\ln x)^2 - 2x\ln x + 2x\right]_1^3$

$= \pi\{3(\ln 3)^2 - 6\ln 3 + 6 - 1(\ln 1)^2 + 2\ln 1 - 2\}$

$= \pi\{3(\ln 3)^2 - 6\ln 3 + 4\}$ units^3

iii $V = \displaystyle\int_0^{\ln 3} (x_1^2 - x_2^2)\, dy$

$= \displaystyle\int_0^{\ln 3} 3^2 - (e^y)^2\, dy$

$= \displaystyle\int_0^{\ln 3} 9 - e^{2y}\, dy$

$= \pi\left[9y - \frac{1}{2}e^{2y}\right]_0^{\ln 3}$

$= \pi\left[9\ln 3 - \frac{1}{2}e^{2\ln 3} - 0 + \frac{1}{2}\right]$

$= \pi\left[9\ln 3 - \frac{1}{2}(9) + \frac{1}{2}\right]$

$= \pi[9\ln 3 - 4]$ units^3

SOLUTIONS TO EXAMINATION PRACTICE SET 4

200 a $3 + 8 + 13 + \ldots\ldots$ is arithmetic with $u_1 = 3$ and $d = 5$

Thus $S_n = \dfrac{n}{2}[2u_1 + (n-1)d]$

$= \dfrac{n}{2}[6 + 5(n-1)]$

$= \dfrac{n}{2}[5n + 1]$

$= \dfrac{n(5n+1)}{2}$

b For $S_n > 1000$

$$n(5n+1) > 2000$$

Using a gcalc, $n > 19.9.....$
and so the smallest n is $n = 20$.

201 $\log_2 27 \times \log_3 16 \quad = \log_2 3^3 \times \log_3 2^4$

$$= 3\log_2 3 \times 4\log_3 2$$

$$= \frac{3\log 3}{\log 2} \times \frac{4\log 2}{\log 3}$$

$$= 12$$

202 $(1+ax)^n$

$$= 1^n + \binom{n}{1}1^{n-1}(ax) + \binom{n}{2}1^{n-2}(ax)^2 + ...$$

$$= 1 + nax + \frac{n(n-1)}{2}a^2x^2 + ...$$

Thus $na = 35$ and $\frac{n(n-1)}{2}a^2 = 525$

$$\therefore \quad (n^2 - n)a^2 = 1050$$

$$\Rightarrow \quad n^2a^2 - a(na) = 1050$$

$$\Rightarrow \quad 1225 - 35a = 1050$$

$$\Rightarrow \quad 35a = 175$$

$$\Rightarrow \quad a = 5$$

Consequently $n = 7$, Thus $a = 5$, $n = 7$.

203 a $f : x \mapsto a + \dfrac{b}{x+c}$

Since f has an asymptote at $x = -2$

$x + c = 0$ at $x = -c$ $\therefore$ $c = 2$

Since f has an asymptote at $y = 3$, as x becomes large f will be close to 3 i.e., $a = 3$.

Since the graph passes through $(2, 4)$

$$4 = a + \frac{b}{2+c} \quad \Rightarrow \quad 4 = 3 + \frac{b}{4} \quad \text{i.e.,} \quad b = 4$$

i.e., $f : \quad x \mapsto 3 + \dfrac{4}{x+2}$ and $a = 3$, $b = 4$, $c = 2$.

b Domain of f is $x \in \mathbb{R}$, $x \neq -2$.
Range of f is $y \in \mathbb{R}$, $y \neq 3$.

c f is $y = 3 + \dfrac{4}{x+2}$ so f^{-1} is $x = 3 + \dfrac{4}{y+2}$

$$\text{i.e.,} \quad x - 3 = \frac{4}{y+2}$$

$$\Rightarrow \quad y + 2 = \frac{4}{x-3}$$

$$\Rightarrow \quad f^{-1}(x) = \frac{4}{x-3} - 2$$

Domain of f is $x \in \mathbb{R}$, $x \neq 3$.
Range of f is $y \in \mathbb{R}$, $y \neq -2$.
(Compare this answer with part **b**.)

204 $y = kx^2 - 3x + (k+2)$ cuts the x-axis in two distinct points if $\Delta > 0$.

Now $\Delta = 9 - 4k(k+2)$

$$= 9 - 4k^2 - 8k$$

$$= -\left(4k^2 + 8k - 9\right)$$

which is 0 if $k = \dfrac{-8 \pm \sqrt{64 - 4(4)(-9)}}{8} = \dfrac{-8 \pm \sqrt{208}}{8}$

i.e., $k = -1 \pm \frac{1}{2}\sqrt{13}$

Thus Δ has sign diag:

$$\xleftarrow{\quad - \quad | \quad + \quad | \quad - \quad}$$
$$\qquad\qquad -1-\tfrac{1}{2}\sqrt{13} \quad -1+\tfrac{1}{2}\sqrt{13}$$

$\Delta > 0$ if $-1 - \frac{1}{2}\sqrt{13} < k < -1 + \frac{1}{2}\sqrt{13}$

205 Since $1 - 2i$ is a zero of $p(z) = 2z^3 - 9z^2 + 20z - 25$

$1 + 2i$ is also a zero and $p(z)$ has factor

These two roots have a sum of 2 and a product of $1 + 4 = 5$ and so come from the quadratic factor $z^2 - 2z + 5$

Thus, $p(z) = (z^2 - 2z + 5)(2z - 5)$

other zeros are $z = \frac{5}{2}$ and $z = 1 + 2i$

206

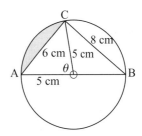

$AB = \sqrt{6^2 + 8^2} = \sqrt{100} = 10$ cm

$\therefore$ $AO = OB = 5$ cm

By the Cosine Rule, $\cos\theta = \dfrac{5^2 + 5^2 - 6^2}{2 \times 5 \times 5} = \dfrac{14}{50} = \dfrac{7}{25}$

So, $\sin\theta = \frac{24}{25}$

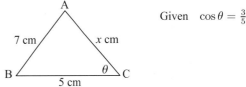

$$\begin{aligned} \sqrt{625 - 49} &= \sqrt{576} \\ &= 24 \end{aligned}$$

$\therefore$ area of segment $= \frac{1}{2}r^2(\theta - \sin\theta)$

$$= \frac{1}{2} \times 25\left(\arccos\left(\frac{7}{25}\right) - \frac{24}{25}\right)$$

$$\approx 909 \text{ cm}^2$$

207

Given $\cos\theta = \frac{3}{5}$

By the Cosine Rule, $7^2 = x^2 + 5^2 - 2(x)(5)\cos\theta$

$$\Rightarrow \quad 49 = x^2 + 25 - 10x\left(\frac{3}{5}\right)$$

$$\Rightarrow \quad x^2 - 6x - 24 = 0$$

$$\Rightarrow \quad x = \frac{6 \pm \sqrt{36 - 4(1)(-24)}}{2}$$

$$\Rightarrow \quad x = \frac{6 \pm \sqrt{132}}{2}$$

$$\Rightarrow \quad x = 3 \pm \sqrt{33}$$

But $x > 0$ $\therefore$ $AC = (3 + \sqrt{33})$ cm.

208 $\cot 2A = \frac{3}{5} \quad \Rightarrow \quad \tan 2A = \frac{5}{3}$

$$\Rightarrow \quad \frac{2\tan A}{1 - \tan^2 A} = \frac{5}{3}$$

$$\Rightarrow \quad 6\tan A = 5 - 5\tan^2 A$$

$$\Rightarrow \quad 5\tan^2 A + 6\tan A - 5 = 0$$

Thus $\tan A = \dfrac{-6 \pm \sqrt{36 - 4(5)(-5)}}{10} = \dfrac{-6 \pm \sqrt{136}}{10}$

$$= \frac{-3 \pm \sqrt{34}}{5}$$

But A is obtuse $\therefore$ $\tan A = \dfrac{-3 - \sqrt{34}}{5}$

$\therefore$ $\cot A = \left(\dfrac{5}{-3 - \sqrt{34}}\right)\left(\dfrac{-3 + \sqrt{34}}{-3 + \sqrt{34}}\right)$

$$= \frac{-15 + 5\sqrt{34}}{9 - 34}$$

$$= \frac{-15 + 5\sqrt{34}}{-25}$$

$$= \frac{3}{5} - \frac{1}{5}\sqrt{34}$$

209 Let $\arcsin\left(\frac{3}{5}\right) = \theta$

$\therefore$ $\sin\theta = \frac{3}{5}$

and so $\cos\theta = \frac{4}{5}$

Now $\sin 2\left(\arcsin\frac{3}{5}\right) = \sin 2\theta$

$= 2\sin\theta\cos\theta$

$= 2\left(\frac{3}{5}\right)\left(\frac{4}{5}\right)$

$= \frac{24}{25}$

210 $|\mathbf{A} - \lambda\mathbf{I}| = \left|\begin{bmatrix} 0 & 4 \\ 1 & 3 \end{bmatrix} - \begin{bmatrix} \lambda & 0 \\ 0 & \lambda \end{bmatrix}\right| = \left|\begin{matrix} -\lambda & 4 \\ 1 & 3-\lambda \end{matrix}\right|$

$\therefore$ $|\mathbf{A} - \lambda\mathbf{I}| = (-3\lambda + \lambda^2) - 4 = \lambda^2 - 3\lambda - 4$

$|\mathbf{A} - \lambda\mathbf{I}| = -2$ if $\lambda^2 - 3\lambda - 4 = -2$

$\lambda^2 - 3\lambda - 2 = 0$

i.e., $\lambda = \dfrac{3 \pm \sqrt{9+8}}{2}$

i.e., $\lambda = \frac{3}{2} + \frac{\sqrt{17}}{2}$ or $\lambda = \frac{3}{2} - \frac{\sqrt{17}}{2}$

211 Writing the system of equations in augmented matrix form

$$\begin{bmatrix} 2 & -2 & k & | & 0 \\ 1 & 0 & 4 & | & 0 \\ k & 1 & 1 & | & 0 \end{bmatrix}$$

$\sim \begin{bmatrix} 1 & 0 & 4 & | & 0 \\ 2 & -2 & k & | & 0 \\ k & 1 & 1 & | & 0 \end{bmatrix} \begin{matrix} R_1 \to R_2 \\ R_2 \to R_1 \end{matrix}$

$\sim \begin{bmatrix} 1 & 0 & 4 & | & 0 \\ 0 & -2 & k-8 & | & 0 \\ 0 & 1 & 1-4k & | & 0 \end{bmatrix} \begin{matrix} R_2 \to R_2 - 2R_1 \\ R_3 \to R_3 - kR_1 \end{matrix}$

$\sim \begin{bmatrix} 1 & 0 & 4 & | & 0 \\ 0 & 1 & 1-4k & | & 0 \\ 0 & -2 & k-8 & | & 0 \end{bmatrix} \begin{matrix} R_2 \to R_3 \\ R_3 \to R_2 \end{matrix}$

$\sim \begin{bmatrix} 1 & 0 & 4 & | & 0 \\ 0 & 1 & 1-4k & | & 0 \\ 0 & 0 & -7k-6 & | & 0 \end{bmatrix} R_3 \to R_3 + 2R_2$

and this has a non-zero solution if $-7k - 6 = 0$ or $k = -\frac{6}{7}$.

212 a Since $\frac{1}{4} + \frac{3}{7} + k = 1$,

$k = 1 - \left(\frac{1}{4} + \frac{3}{7}\right)$

$= \frac{9}{28}$

x	0	2	7
$P(x)$	$\frac{7}{28}$	$\frac{12}{28}$	$\frac{9}{28}$

b Mean $\mu = 0 \times \frac{7}{28} + 2 \times \frac{12}{28} + 7 \times \frac{9}{28} = \frac{87}{28} = 3\frac{3}{28}$

median is 2, mode is 2

c Variance, $\sigma^2 = 0^2\left(\frac{7}{28}\right) + 2^2\left(\frac{12}{28}\right) + 7^2\left(\frac{9}{28}\right) - \left(\frac{87}{28}\right)^2$

≈ 7.810

and standard deviation $\sigma \approx \sqrt{7.810} \approx 2.795$

213 $X \sim N(\mu, \sigma^2)$

$P(X \geqslant 20) = 0.386$

$\Rightarrow P\left(Z \geqslant \dfrac{20-\mu}{\sigma}\right) = 0.386$

$\Rightarrow P\left(Z \leqslant \dfrac{20-\mu}{\sigma}\right) = 1 - 0.386 = 0.614$

$\Rightarrow \dfrac{20-\mu}{\sigma} = \text{invNorm}(0.614, 0, 1)$

$\Rightarrow 20 - \mu \approx 0.289\,75\sigma$ ...... (1)

Also $P(X \geqslant 25) = 0.183$

$\Rightarrow P\left(Z \geqslant \dfrac{25-\mu}{\sigma}\right) = 0.183$

$\Rightarrow P\left(Z \leqslant \dfrac{25-\mu}{\sigma}\right) = 0.817$

$\Rightarrow \dfrac{25-\mu}{\sigma} = \text{invNorm}(0.817, 0, 1)$

$\Rightarrow 25 - \mu \approx 0.903\,99\sigma$ ...... (2)

Solving (1) and (2) simultaneously gives

$\mu \approx 17.64$ and $\sigma \approx 8.143$

214 As $f(x) = \dfrac{ax+2}{x^2+1}$, $f'(x) = \dfrac{a(x^2+1) - (ax+2)2x}{(x^2+1)^2}$

$= \dfrac{ax^2 + a - 2ax^2 - 4x}{(x^2+1)^2}$

$= \dfrac{-ax^2 - 4x + a}{(x^2+1)^2}$

Now $f(x)$ has stationary points where $f'(x) = 0$

$\Rightarrow -ax^2 - 4x + a = 0$

$\Rightarrow ax^2 + 4x - a = 0$

which has real solutions when $\Delta = 16 - 4(a)(-a) > 0$

i.e., $16 + 4a^2 > 0$

which is true for all $a \in \mathbb{R}$.

215 $y = xe^{2x} - 3e^{2x} = (x-3)e^{2x}$

$\therefore \dfrac{dy}{dx} = 1e^{2x} + (x-3)e^{2x}(2) = e^{2x}(1 + 2x - 6)$

$= e^{2x}(2x - 5)$

which is $0 \Leftrightarrow 2x - 5 = 0 \Leftrightarrow x = \frac{5}{2}$

$\therefore$ at $x = \frac{5}{2}$ we have a stationary point.

216 $\int \sec x \tan x\, dx$

$= \int \dfrac{1}{\cos x}\dfrac{\sin x}{\cos x}\, dx$

$= \int [\cos x]^{-2} \sin x\, dx$

$= \int u^{-2}\left(-\dfrac{du}{dx}\right) dx \qquad \begin{bmatrix} u = \cos x \\ \dfrac{du}{dx} = -\sin x \end{bmatrix}$

$= -\int u^{-2}\, du$

$= -\dfrac{u^{-1}}{-1} + c$

$= \dfrac{1}{u} + c$

$= \sec x + c$

217 $\displaystyle\int_0^{\frac{1}{2}} \dfrac{1}{\sqrt{1-x^2}}\, dx = [\arcsin x]_0^{\frac{1}{2}}$

$= \arcsin\left(\frac{1}{2}\right) - \arcsin(0)$

$= \dfrac{\pi}{6} - 0$

$= \dfrac{\pi}{6}$

218 a

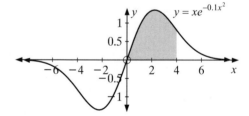

Area $= \displaystyle\int_0^4 xe^{-0.1x^2}\, dx$

$= \displaystyle\int_0^4 e^u\left(-5\dfrac{du}{dx}\right) dx \qquad \begin{cases} u = -0.1x^2 \\ \dfrac{du}{dx} = -0.2x \\ u(0) = 0 \\ u(4) = -1.6 \end{cases}$

$= -5\displaystyle\int_0^{-1.6} e^u\, du$

$= -5[e^u]_0^{-1.6}$

$= -5e^{-1.6} + 5e^0$

$= 5 - 5e^{-1.6}$ units^2

b Volume $= \pi \int_0^4 y^2 \, dx = \pi \int_0^4 x^2 e^{-0.02x^2} \, dx$

≈ 14.1 units^3 (gcalc)

219

$$a = 3t^2 - 2t + 1$$

$$v = \int a \, dt = \frac{3t^3}{3} - \frac{2t^2}{2} + t + c$$

i.e., $v = t^3 - t^2 + t + c$

But $v(0) = 5 \Rightarrow 5 = c$

Thus $v = t^3 - t^2 + t + 5 \text{ ms}^{-1}$

Hence $s = \int v \, dt$

i.e., $s = \frac{t^4}{4} - \frac{t^3}{3} + \frac{t^2}{2} + 5t + d$

220

$$\frac{dy}{dx} = x \sec y$$

$$\therefore \quad \frac{1}{\sec y} \frac{dy}{dx} = x$$

$$\Rightarrow \quad \cos y \frac{dy}{dx} = x$$

$$\Rightarrow \quad \int \cos y \frac{dy}{dx} \, dx = \int x \, dx$$

$$\Rightarrow \quad \int \cos y \, dy = \int x \, dx$$

$$\Rightarrow \quad \sin y = \frac{x^2}{2} + c$$

But when $x = 0$, $y = \frac{\pi}{6}$ $\therefore \frac{1}{2} = c$

i.e., $\sin y = \frac{x^2}{2} + \frac{1}{2} = \frac{x^2 + 1}{2}$

$$\Rightarrow \quad y = \arcsin\left(\frac{x^2 + 1}{2}\right)$$

221 a i $\overrightarrow{BA}$

$= \overrightarrow{BO} + \overrightarrow{OA}$

$= -\mathbf{b} + \mathbf{a}$

ii $\overrightarrow{OD} = \overrightarrow{OB} + \overrightarrow{BC} + \overrightarrow{CD}$

$= \mathbf{b} + 2\mathbf{a} + k\overrightarrow{BA}$

$= \mathbf{b} + 2\mathbf{a} + k(-\mathbf{b} + \mathbf{a})$

$= (1 - k)\mathbf{b} + (2 + k)\mathbf{a}$

b If $\overrightarrow{OD}$ is perpendicular to $\overrightarrow{AB}$ then $\overrightarrow{OD} \bullet \overrightarrow{AB} = 0$

i.e., $[(2 + k)\mathbf{a} + (1 - k)\mathbf{b}] \bullet [\mathbf{a} - \mathbf{b}] = 0$

i.e., $(2 + k)\mathbf{a} \bullet \mathbf{a} - (2 + k)\mathbf{a} \bullet \mathbf{b}$

$+ (1 - k)\mathbf{b} \bullet \mathbf{a} - (1 - k)\mathbf{b} \bullet \mathbf{b} = 0$

But $\mathbf{a} \bullet \mathbf{b} = |\mathbf{a}||\mathbf{b}|\cos(60^o) = \frac{1}{2}|\mathbf{a}||\mathbf{b}|$

i.e., $(2 + k)|\mathbf{a}|^2 - \frac{1}{2}(1 + 2k)|\mathbf{a}||\mathbf{b}| - (1 - k)|\mathbf{b}|^2 = 0$

But $|\mathbf{b}| = 3|\mathbf{a}|$

i.e., $(2 + k)|\mathbf{a}|^2 - \frac{1}{2}(1 + 2k)3|\mathbf{a}|^2 - (1 - k)9|\mathbf{a}|^2 = 0$

$\Rightarrow \left(2 + k - \frac{3}{2} - 3k - 9 + 9k\right)|\mathbf{a}|^2 = 0$

$\Rightarrow \left(-\frac{17}{2} + 7k\right)|\mathbf{a}|^2 = 0$

$\Rightarrow -\frac{17}{2} + 7k = 0$ or $k = \frac{17}{14}$

222 The information is displayed in the tree diagram.

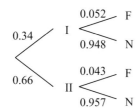

a Probability a compound is faulty is

$0.34 \times 0.052 + 0.66 \times 0.043 = 0.0461$

b Let II be the event of machine II, F be the event of faulty

Then $P(\text{II} \mid F) = \dfrac{P(\text{II} \cap F)}{P(F)}$

$= \dfrac{0.66 \times 0.043}{0.34 \times 0.052 + 0.66 \times 0.043}$

$= 0.6165$

223 Let X be the weight, then $X \sim N(120, 1.063^2)$

a Hence, $P(X < 118) = \text{normalcdf}(-E99, 118, 120, 1.063)$

≈ 0.0300

So, 3.00% of the bags are rejected.

b We now have $X \sim N(120, \sigma^2)$

Since $P(X < 118) = 0.06$

$\Rightarrow P\left(\dfrac{X - 120}{\sigma} < \dfrac{118 - 120}{\sigma}\right) = 0.06$

$\Rightarrow P\left(Z < \dfrac{-2}{\sigma}\right) = 0.06$

$\Rightarrow \dfrac{-2}{\sigma} = \text{invNorm}(0.06)$

$\Rightarrow \sigma = \dfrac{-2}{\text{invNorm}(0.06)}$

$\Rightarrow \sigma \approx 1.286$

c X is now $\sim N(\mu, 1.286^2)$

and since $P(X < 118) = 0.03$

$\Rightarrow P\left(\dfrac{X - \mu}{1.286} < \dfrac{118 - \mu}{1.286}\right) = 0.03$

$\Rightarrow P\left(Z < \dfrac{118 - \mu}{1.286}\right) = 0.03$

$\Rightarrow \dfrac{118 - \mu}{1.286} = -1.8808 \Rightarrow \mu \approx 120.42$

d

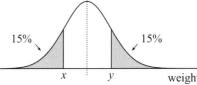

Since $P(x \leqslant X \leqslant y) = 0.70$, by symmetry,

$P(X \leqslant x) = P(X \geqslant y) = 0.15$.

But $X \sim N(120.4, 1.286^2)$

For $P(X \leqslant x) = 0.15$, $P\left(Z < \dfrac{x - 120.4}{1.286}\right) = 0.15$

$\Rightarrow \dfrac{x - 120.4}{1.286} = \text{invNorm}(0.15)$

$\Rightarrow x = 120.4 + 1.286 \times \text{invNorm}(0.15)$

$\Rightarrow x \approx 119.1$

and using the symmetry, $\dfrac{x + y}{2} = 120.4$

$\Rightarrow y \approx 240.8 - 119.1 = 121.75$

224 a $f(0) = \frac{-2}{-6} = \frac{1}{3}$ $\therefore$ y-intercept is $\frac{1}{3}$

when $y = 0$, $x - 2 = 0$

$\therefore x = 2$ $\therefore$ x-intercept is 2

b $f(x) = \dfrac{\dfrac{1}{x} - \dfrac{2}{x^2}}{1 + \dfrac{c}{x} - \dfrac{6}{x^2}}$ $\therefore$ as $x \to \pm\infty$, $f(x) \to 0$

So, $y = 0$ is the HA.

c VAs exist where $x^2 + cx - 6 = 0$ and $\Delta \geqslant 0$

i.e., $c^2 - 4(1)(-6) \geqslant 0$

i.e., $c^2 + 24 > 0$ which is true for all $c \in \mathbb{R}$

d $f'(x) = \dfrac{1(x^2 + cx - 6) - (x - 2)(2x + c)}{(x^2 + cx - 6)^2}$

$= \dfrac{x^2 + cx - 6 - 2x^2 + 4x - cx + 2c}{(x^2 + cx - 6)^2}$

$= \dfrac{-x^2 + 4x + 2c - 6}{(x^2 + cx - 6)^2}$

e It has at least one stationary point when

$-x^2 + 4x + 2c - 6 = 0$ has real roots

$\Rightarrow \Delta \geqslant 0$

$\Rightarrow 16 - 4(-1)(2c - 6) \geqslant 0$

$\Rightarrow 16 + 8c - 24 \geqslant 0$

$\Rightarrow 8c \geqslant 8$ and so $c \geqslant 1$

f When $c = 0$, $f'(x) = \dfrac{-x^2 + 4x - 6}{(x^2 - 6)^2}$

Using a gcalc $f''(x) = 0$ when $x \approx 0.893$

$\Rightarrow$ a point of inflection at $(0.893, 0.213)$

g
$$\int_{-1}^{1} \frac{x - 2}{x^2 - 4x - 6}\, dx \quad = \tfrac{1}{2} \int_{-1}^{1} \frac{2x - 4}{x^2 - 4x - 6}\, dx$$
$$= \tfrac{1}{2}\left[\ln\left|x^2 - 4x - 6\right|\right]_{-1}^{1}$$
$$= \tfrac{1}{2}\left[\ln 9 - \ln 1\right]$$
$$= \tfrac{1}{2}\ln 3^2$$
$$= \ln 3$$

225 a i $(\cos\theta + i\sin\theta)^5$

$= (c + is)^5$ where $c = \cos\theta$ and $s = \sin\theta$

$= c^5 + 5c^4(is) + 10c^3(is)^2 + 10c^2(is)^3 + 5c(is)^4 + (is)^5$

$= \left[c^5 - 10c^3 s^2 + 5cs^4\right] + i\left[5c^4 s - 10c^2 s^3 + s^5\right]$

But $(\cos\theta + i\sin\theta)^5 \quad = (\text{cis }\theta)^5$

$\qquad\qquad\qquad\qquad\qquad = \text{cis } 5\theta$ {De Moivre}

$\qquad\qquad\qquad\qquad\qquad = \cos 5\theta + i\sin 5\theta$

Equating imaginary parts

$\sin 5\theta = 5c^4 s - 10c^2 s^3 + s^5$

$\qquad = 5s(1 - s^2)^2 - 10s^3(1 - s^2) + s^5$

$\qquad = 5s(1 - 2s^2 + s^4) - 10s^3 + 10s^5 + s^5$

$\qquad = 16s^5 - 20s^3 + 5s$

$\qquad = 16\sin^5\theta - 20\sin^3\theta + 5\sin\theta$

ii If $\theta = 36^\circ$, $5\theta = 180^\circ$

$\Rightarrow \sin 36^\circ$ is a solution of

$\qquad 16s^5 - 20s^3 + 5s = \sin 180^\circ = 0$

$\Rightarrow s(16s^4 - 20s^2 + 5) = 0$

$\qquad \Rightarrow 16s^4 - 20s^2 + 5 = 0$, as $s \neq 0$

$$\Rightarrow s^2 = \frac{20 \pm \sqrt{400 - 4(16)(5)}}{32}$$
$$\Rightarrow s^2 = \frac{20 \pm \sqrt{80}}{32}$$
$$\Rightarrow s^2 = \frac{10 \pm 2\sqrt{5}}{16}$$
$$\Rightarrow s = \pm\frac{\sqrt{10 \pm 2\sqrt{5}}}{4}$$

So, $\sin 36^\circ = \tfrac{1}{4}\sqrt{10 - 2\sqrt{5}}$ (which is ≈ 0.588)

b i

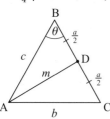

Let $\angle ABC = \theta$, by the Cosine Rule:

$$\cos\theta = \frac{c^2 + \left(\frac{a}{2}\right)^2 - m^2}{2c\left(\frac{a}{2}\right)} = \frac{a^2 + c^2 - b^2}{2ac}$$

$\qquad\qquad\qquad\qquad$ {using $\triangle ABD$ and $\triangle ABC$}

$$\Rightarrow \frac{c^2 + \frac{a^2}{4} - m^2}{ac} = \frac{a^2 + c^2 - b^2}{2ac}$$
$$\Rightarrow 2\left(c^2 + \frac{a^2}{4} - m^2\right) = a^2 + c^2 - b^2$$
$$\Rightarrow 2c^2 + \frac{a^2}{2} - 2m^2 = a^2 + c^2 - b^2$$
$$\Rightarrow 4c^2 + a^2 - 4m^2 = 2a^2 + 2c^2 - 2b^2$$
$$\Rightarrow 4m^2 = 2c^2 + 2b^2 - a^2$$
$$\Rightarrow m^2 = \tfrac{1}{4}(2c^2 + 2b^2 - a^2)$$

ii If $x = b = c$

$\qquad m^2 = \tfrac{1}{4}(4x^2 - a^2)$

$\Rightarrow 4m^2 = 4x^2 - a^2$

$$\Rightarrow m^2 = \frac{4x^2 - a^2}{4}$$

$\Rightarrow m = \tfrac{1}{2}\sqrt{4x^2 - a^2}$ {since $m > 0$}

and area $= \tfrac{1}{2}(a)(m) \quad = \tfrac{1}{2}a \times \tfrac{1}{2}\sqrt{4x^2 - a^2}$

$\qquad\qquad\qquad\qquad = \dfrac{a}{4}\sqrt{4x^2 - a^2}$ units^2

SOLUTIONS TO EXAMINATION PRACTICE SET 5

226 $\ln\sqrt{2} + \ln 2 + \ln\sqrt{8} + \ldots\ldots$

$= \ln 2^{\frac{1}{2}} + \ln 2 + \ln 2^{\frac{3}{2}} + \ldots\ldots$

$= \tfrac{1}{2}\ln 2 + \ln 2 + \tfrac{3}{2}\ln 2 + \ldots\ldots$

$= \ln 2\left[\tfrac{1}{2} + 1 + \tfrac{3}{2} + \ldots\ldots\right]$

arithmetic with $u_1 = \tfrac{1}{2}$, $d = \tfrac{1}{2}$

$\qquad S_n = \ln 2\left(\tfrac{n}{2}[2u_1 + (n-1)d]\right)$

$\qquad\quad = \ln 2\left(\tfrac{n}{2}[1 + (n-1)\tfrac{1}{2}]\right)$

$\therefore \quad S_{100} = \ln 2\left(50[1 + \tfrac{99}{2}]\right)$

$\qquad\qquad = \ln 2\left(50 \times \tfrac{101}{2}\right)$

$\qquad\qquad = 2525\ln 2$

227 a $\quad\log_a 27$

$\qquad = \log_a 3^3$

$\qquad = 3\log_a 3$

$\qquad = 3 \times 7$

$\qquad = 21$

b Let $\log_{\sqrt{a}} 3 = x$

$\therefore \quad 3 = (\sqrt{a})^x = a^{\frac{x}{2}}$

$\log_a 3 = \dfrac{x}{2}$

$\therefore \quad x = 2\log_a 3$

$\therefore \quad x = 2 \times 7 = 14$

c $\quad\log_a 3 = 7 \Rightarrow 3 = a^7$

$\qquad\qquad \Rightarrow a = 3^{\frac{1}{7}} \approx 1.17$

228 $\dfrac{z}{w} = \left(\dfrac{5 - 3i}{b + 2i}\right)\left(\dfrac{b - 2i}{b - 2i}\right)$

$\qquad = \dfrac{5b - 6 + (-3b - 10)i}{b^2 + 4}$

$\qquad = \left(\dfrac{5b - 6}{b^2 + 4}\right) + \left(\dfrac{-3b - 10}{b^2 + 4}\right)i$

which is real $\Leftrightarrow \left(\dfrac{-3b - 10}{b^2 + 4}\right) = 0 \Leftrightarrow b = -\dfrac{10}{3}$

229 a $f(x)$ is real and finite if $0 \leqslant \dfrac{1}{x^2} - 4 < \infty$

$\qquad\qquad$ i.e., $0 \leqslant \dfrac{1 - 4x^2}{x^2} < \infty$

$\qquad\qquad$ i.e., $0 \leqslant \dfrac{(1 - 2x)(1 + 2x)}{x^2} < \infty$

Sign diag. of $\dfrac{(1 - 2x)(1 + 2x)}{x^2}$:

$\qquad\quad \begin{array}{ccccc} - & | & + & | & + & | & - \\ \hline & -\frac{1}{2} & & 0 & & \frac{1}{2} & \end{array}$

i.e., $-\tfrac{1}{2} \leqslant x < 0$ or $0 < x \leqslant \tfrac{1}{2}$

b Range of f is $y \geqslant 0$.

230 $y = mx + 16$ will meet the parabola $y = x^2 + 25$

$\qquad\qquad$ where $mx + 16 = x^2 + 25$

$\qquad\qquad$ i.e., $x^2 - mx + 9 = 0$

The line will be a tangent if $\qquad\qquad \Delta = 0$

$\qquad\qquad\qquad\qquad \Rightarrow m^2 - 4 \times 9 = 0$

$\qquad\qquad\qquad\qquad\qquad \Rightarrow m^2 = 36$

$\qquad\qquad\qquad\qquad\qquad \Rightarrow m = \pm 6$

231 $\log_3\left(4x^2 - 5x - 6\right) = 1 + 2\log_3 x$

For this to be a valid equation in real numbers, we must have $(4x + 3)(x - 2) > 0$ **and** $x > 0$.

Sign diagram of the quadratic is:

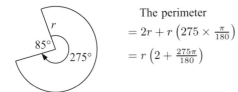

i.e., $x < -\frac{3}{4}$ or $x > 2$. But $x > 0$ $\therefore$ $x > 2$.

$$\log_3\left(4x^2 - 5x - 6\right) = 1 + 2\log_3(x)$$
$$\Rightarrow \log_3(4x^2 - 5x - 6) - 2\log_3(x) = 1$$
$$\Rightarrow \log_3(4x^2 - 5x - 6) - \log_3(x^2) = 1$$
$$\Rightarrow \log_3\left(\frac{4x^2 - 5x - 6}{x^2}\right) = 1$$
$$\Rightarrow \frac{4x^2 - 5x - 6}{x^2} = 3$$
$$\Rightarrow 4x^2 - 5x - 6 = 3x^2$$
$$\Rightarrow x^2 - 5x - 6 = 0$$
$$\Rightarrow (x+1)(x-6) = 0$$

i.e., $x = -1$ or $x = 6$

But $x > 2$ $\therefore$ $x = 6$ is the only solution.

232

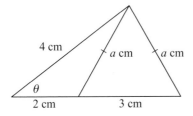

The perimeter
$$= 2r + r\left(275 \times \frac{\pi}{180}\right)$$
$$= r\left(2 + \frac{275\pi}{180}\right)$$

Thus $r\left(2 + \frac{275\pi}{180}\right) = 100$

$$r = \frac{100}{\left(2 + \frac{275\pi}{180}\right)} \approx 14.7066......$$

$$\text{Area} = \tfrac{1}{2}r^2\theta \approx \tfrac{1}{2}(14.7066......)^2\left(\frac{275\pi}{180}\right)$$
$$\approx 519 \text{ cm}^2$$

233

By the Cosine Rule,

$$\cos\theta = \frac{4^2 + 5^2 - a^2}{2 \times 4 \times 5} = \frac{41 - a^2}{40} \quad ...... (1)$$

and $\cos\theta = \frac{2^2 + 4^2 - a^2}{2 \times 2 \times 4} = \frac{20 - a^2}{16} \quad ...... (2)$

Thus $\frac{41 - a^2}{40} = \frac{20 - a^2}{16}$
$$\Rightarrow 82 - 2a^2 = 100 - 5a^2$$
$$\Rightarrow 3a^2 = 18$$
$$\Rightarrow a^2 = 6$$
$$\Rightarrow a = \sqrt{6} \quad \{\text{as } a > 0\}$$

234
$$\cos\theta + \sin\theta = \sqrt{2}, \quad 0 \leqslant \theta \leqslant 2\pi$$
$$\Rightarrow (\cos\theta + \sin\theta)^2 = 2$$
$$\Rightarrow \cos^2\theta + 2\sin\theta\cos\theta + \sin^2\theta = 2$$
$$\Rightarrow 1 + \sin 2\theta = 2$$
$$\Rightarrow \sin 2\theta = 1$$

where $0 \leqslant 2\theta \leqslant 4\pi$
$\therefore$ $2\theta = \frac{\pi}{2}, \frac{5\pi}{2}$ $\Rightarrow$ $\theta = \frac{\pi}{4}, \frac{5\pi}{4}$

But $\theta = \frac{5\pi}{4}$ gives $\cos\theta + \sin\theta = -\sqrt{2}$ $\therefore$ $\theta = \frac{\pi}{4}$

Note: Squaring equations can produce incorrect solutions, so all solutions must be checked.

235 $\arctan\frac{x}{3} + \arctan 6 = \arctan 3$

$\therefore$ $\tan\left(\arctan\frac{x}{3} + \arctan 6\right) = \tan(\arctan 3)$

$$\Rightarrow \frac{\tan(\arctan\frac{x}{3}) + \tan(\arctan 6)}{1 - \tan(\arctan\frac{x}{3})\tan(\arctan 6)} = 3$$

$$\Rightarrow \frac{\frac{x}{3} + 6}{1 - \left(\frac{x}{3}\right)6} = 3$$

$$\Rightarrow \frac{x}{3} + 6 = 3 - 6x$$
$$\Rightarrow x + 18 = 9 - 18x$$
$$\Rightarrow 19x = -9$$
$$\Rightarrow x = -\frac{9}{19}$$

236 a i $\quad \mathbf{MN} = \begin{bmatrix} 2 & 3 \\ 1 & 0 \end{bmatrix}\begin{bmatrix} 1 & 6 \\ 2 & -3 \end{bmatrix} = \begin{bmatrix} 8 & 3 \\ 1 & 6 \end{bmatrix}$

$\quad \mathbf{NM} = \begin{bmatrix} 1 & 6 \\ 2 & -3 \end{bmatrix}\begin{bmatrix} 2 & 3 \\ 1 & 0 \end{bmatrix} = \begin{bmatrix} 8 & 3 \\ 1 & 6 \end{bmatrix}$

Hence $\mathbf{MN} = \mathbf{NM}$.

ii $\quad (\mathbf{MN})^{-1} \qquad\qquad \mathbf{N}^{-1}$

$= \begin{bmatrix} 8 & 3 \\ 1 & 6 \end{bmatrix}^{-1} \qquad = \begin{bmatrix} 1 & 6 \\ 2 & -3 \end{bmatrix}^{-1}$

$= \frac{1}{48 - 3}\begin{bmatrix} 6 & -3 \\ -1 & 8 \end{bmatrix} \quad = \frac{1}{-3 - 12}\begin{bmatrix} -3 & -6 \\ -2 & 1 \end{bmatrix}$

$= \begin{bmatrix} \frac{6}{45} & \frac{-3}{45} \\ \frac{-1}{45} & \frac{8}{45} \end{bmatrix} \qquad = \begin{bmatrix} \frac{3}{15} & \frac{6}{15} \\ \frac{2}{15} & \frac{-1}{15} \end{bmatrix}$

$\mathbf{M}^{-1} = \begin{bmatrix} 2 & 3 \\ 1 & 0 \end{bmatrix}^{-1} = \frac{1}{0-3}\begin{bmatrix} 0 & -3 \\ -1 & 2 \end{bmatrix} = \begin{bmatrix} 0 & \frac{3}{3} \\ \frac{1}{3} & -\frac{2}{3} \end{bmatrix}$

and $\mathbf{N}^{-1}\mathbf{M}^{-1} = \begin{bmatrix} \frac{3}{15} & \frac{6}{15} \\ \frac{2}{15} & -\frac{1}{15} \end{bmatrix}\begin{bmatrix} 0 & \frac{3}{3} \\ \frac{1}{3} & -\frac{2}{3} \end{bmatrix}$

$= \begin{bmatrix} \frac{6}{45} & -\frac{3}{45} \\ \frac{-1}{45} & \frac{8}{45} \end{bmatrix}$ which is $(\mathbf{MN})^{-1}$

b $\quad (\mathbf{M} - \mathbf{N})(\mathbf{M} + \mathbf{N}) = \mathbf{M}^2 + \mathbf{MN} - \mathbf{NM} - \mathbf{N}^2$
But $\mathbf{MN} = \mathbf{NM}$ {from **a i**}
$\mathbf{M}^2 + \mathbf{MN} - \mathbf{NM} - \mathbf{N}^2 = \mathbf{M}^2 + \mathbf{MN} - \mathbf{MN} - \mathbf{N}^2$
$= \mathbf{M}^2 - \mathbf{N}^2$

$\mathbf{M}^2 - \mathbf{N}^2 = (\mathbf{M} - \mathbf{N})(\mathbf{M} + \mathbf{N}) = \begin{bmatrix} 1 & -3 \\ -1 & 3 \end{bmatrix}\begin{bmatrix} 3 & 9 \\ 3 & -3 \end{bmatrix}$

$= \begin{bmatrix} -6 & 18 \\ 6 & -18 \end{bmatrix}$

237 a is perpendicular to **b** if $\mathbf{a} \bullet \mathbf{b} = 0$

i.e., if $(-2\mathbf{i} + p\mathbf{j} - \mathbf{k}) \bullet (\mathbf{i} + 3(p+4)\mathbf{j} + (2p-5)\mathbf{k}) = 0$

i.e., $-2 + p(3p + 12) - (2p - 5) = 0$

i.e., $3p^2 + 10p + 3 = 0$

i.e., $(3p + 1)(p + 3) = 0$

i.e., if $p = -\frac{1}{3}$ or $p = -3$

238 The possible outcomes when two dice are rolled are shown on the grid:

There are 5 outcomes where a 4 is scored.

Assuming fair dice are used, the probability if this occurence is $\frac{5}{36}$.

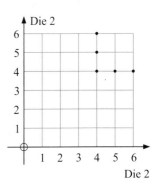

Die 2

59

239 From the binomial theorem, for $\left(\frac{5}{2}x^2 - \frac{2}{5x}\right)^{12}$

$$T_{r+1} = \binom{12}{r}\left(\frac{5}{2}x^2\right)^r \left(\frac{-2}{5x}\right)^{12-r}$$

$$= \binom{12}{r}\left(\frac{5}{2}\right)^r x^{2r}\left(-\frac{5}{2}\right)^{-(12-r)} x^{-(12-r)}$$

$$= \binom{12}{r}(-1)^{r-12}\left(\frac{5}{2}\right)^{2r-12} x^{3r-12}$$

The term independent of x will have $\quad 3r - 12 = 0$

$$\text{i.e.,} \quad r = 4$$

Coefficient of x^0 is $\quad \binom{12}{4}(-1)^{-8}\left(\frac{5}{2}\right)^{-4} = \binom{12}{4}\left(\frac{2}{5}\right)^4$

$$= \frac{1584}{125}$$

240 a Since f is a density function

$$\int_0^2 \left(\frac{x}{8} + c\right) dx = 1 \quad \Rightarrow \quad \left[\frac{x^2}{16} + cx\right]_0^2 = 1$$

$$\Rightarrow \quad \tfrac{1}{4} + 2c = 1$$

$$\Rightarrow \quad c = \tfrac{3}{8}$$

$$\text{Thus,} \quad f(x) = \tfrac{1}{8}(x+3)$$

b $E(X) = \int_0^2 x \tfrac{1}{8}(x+3)\,dx \quad = \tfrac{1}{8}\int_0^2 (x^2 + 3x)\,dx$

$$= \tfrac{1}{8}\left[\frac{x^3}{3} + \frac{3x^2}{2}\right]_0^2$$

$$= \tfrac{1}{8}(\tfrac{8}{3} + 6) - 0$$

$$= \tfrac{13}{12}$$

c $E(X^2) = \int_0^2 x^2 \tfrac{1}{8}(x+3)\,dx = \tfrac{1}{8}\int_0^2 (x^3 + 3x^2)\,dx$

$$= \tfrac{1}{8}\left[\frac{x^4}{4} + \frac{3x^3}{3}\right]_0^2$$

$$= \tfrac{1}{8}(12 - 0)$$

$$= \tfrac{3}{2}$$

Thus $\sigma^2 = E\left[(X-\mu)^2\right] = E(X^2) - \mu^2$

$$\Rightarrow \quad \sigma^2 = \tfrac{3}{2} - \left(\tfrac{13}{12}\right)^2 \approx 0.32639$$

$$\Rightarrow \quad \sigma \approx 0.571$$

241 $f(x) = x^2 e^x$ has $f'(x) = 2xe^x + x^2 e^x = e^x(2x + x^2)$

$$\text{and} \quad f''(x) = e^x(2x + x^2) + e^x(2 + 2x)$$

$$= e^x(x^2 + 4x + 2)$$

and is concave down when $f''(x) < 0$

i.e., $x^2 + 4x + 2 < 0$

$x^2 + 4x + 2$ has critical values

$$\frac{-4 \pm \sqrt{16 - 4(1)(2)}}{2} = \frac{-4 \pm 2\sqrt{2}}{2} = -2 \pm \sqrt{2}$$

and has sign diagram:

$$+ \quad\quad - \quad\quad +$$
$$-2-\sqrt{2} \quad\quad -2+\sqrt{2}$$

$\therefore$ $f(x)$ is concave down for $x \in \,]-2-\sqrt{2}, -2+\sqrt{2}[$

242 $\quad f(x) = \log_3\left(\frac{x^2+1}{3x+1}\right) = \dfrac{\ln\left(\frac{x^2+1}{3x+1}\right)}{\ln 3}$

$$\therefore \quad f(x) = \frac{1}{\ln 3}\left[\ln(x^2+1) - \ln(3x+1)\right]$$

$$\Rightarrow \quad f'(x) = \frac{1}{\ln 3}\left[\frac{2x}{x^2+1} - \frac{3}{3x+1}\right]$$

and if $f'(x) = 0$ then $\dfrac{2x}{x^2+1} = \dfrac{3}{3x+1}$

$$\Rightarrow \quad 6x^2 + 2x = 3x^2 + 3$$

$$\Rightarrow \quad 3x^2 + 2x - 3 = 0$$

$$\Rightarrow \quad x = \frac{-2 \pm \sqrt{4 - 4(3)(-3)}}{6}$$

$$\Rightarrow \quad x = \frac{-2 \pm \sqrt{40}}{6} = \frac{-1 \pm \sqrt{10}}{3}$$

But for $f(x)$ to exist $\dfrac{x^2+1}{3x+1}$ must be > 0.

As $x^2 + 1 > 0$ for all x then $3x + 1 > 0$ i.e., $x > -\tfrac{1}{3}$

Consequently, $x = \dfrac{-1 + \sqrt{10}}{3}$

i.e., only one stationary point exists and it is at $x = \dfrac{\sqrt{10} - 1}{3}$.

243 $\int \sin^3 x\, dx$

$$= \int \sin^2 x \sin x\, dx$$

$$= \int (1 - \cos^2 x)\sin x\, dx$$

$$= \int \sin x - \int \cos^2 x \sin x\, dx$$

$$= -\cos x - \int u^2\left(-\frac{du}{dx}\right) dx \quad\quad \begin{cases} u = \cos x \\ \dfrac{du}{dx} = -\sin x \end{cases}$$

$$= -\cos x + \int u^2\, du$$

$$= -\cos x + \frac{u^3}{3} + c$$

$$= -\cos x + \tfrac{1}{3}\cos^3 x + c$$

244 $y = ax^2$ meets $y = x$ where $ax^2 = x$

$$\Rightarrow \quad x(ax - 1) = 0 \quad \text{and so} \quad x = 0 \text{ or } \frac{1}{a}$$

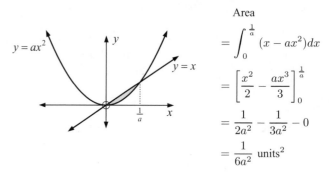

Area

$$= \int_0^{\frac{1}{a}} (x - ax^2)\, dx$$

$$= \left[\frac{x^2}{2} - \frac{ax^3}{3}\right]_0^{\frac{1}{a}}$$

$$= \frac{1}{2a^2} - \frac{1}{3a^2} - 0$$

$$= \frac{1}{6a^2} \text{ units}^2$$

245 Let $\quad u' = e^x \quad\quad v = x^2$
$$u = e^x \quad\quad v' = 2x$$

$$\therefore \quad \int x^2 e^x\, dx = e^x x^2 - \int 2xe^x\, dx$$

Let $\quad u' = e^x \quad\quad v = 2x$
$$u = e^x \quad\quad v' = 2$$

$$\therefore \quad \int x^2 e^x\, dx = e^x x^2 - \left[2xe^x - \int 2e^x\, dx\right]$$

$$= e^x x^2 - 2xe^x + 2e^x + c$$

246 a $\quad v = \dfrac{2t}{4+t^2} \text{ ms}^{-1}$

$$s = \int v\, dt = \int \frac{2t}{4+t^2}\, dt$$

$$\Rightarrow \quad s = \ln|4 + t^2| + c$$

and as $4 + t^2 > 0$ for all t,

$$s = \ln(4 + t^2) + c$$

But $s(0) = -3 \Rightarrow \ln 4 + c = -3$

$$\Rightarrow \quad c = -3 - \ln 4$$

So, $s = \ln(4 + t^2) - 3 - \ln 4$

i.e., $s = \ln\left(\dfrac{t^2+4}{4}\right) - 3$

b $\quad a = \dfrac{dv}{dt} = \dfrac{2(4+t^2) - 2t(2t)}{(4+t^2)^2} \Rightarrow a = \dfrac{8 - 2t^2}{(4+t^2)^2} \text{ ms}^{-2}$

247

$$\frac{dy}{dx} = 2xy^2 + y^2 = (2x+1)y^2$$

$$\therefore \quad \frac{1}{y^2}\frac{dy}{dx} = 2x+1$$

$$\Rightarrow \quad \int y^{-2}\frac{dy}{dx}\,dx = \int 2x+1\,dx$$

$$\Rightarrow \quad \frac{y^{-1}}{-1} = \frac{2x^2}{2} + x + c \quad \text{or} \quad \frac{1}{y} = -x^2 - x - c$$

But when $x = 0$, $y = 0.5$

Thus $2 = -c$, $c = -2$

$$\Rightarrow \quad \frac{1}{y} = -x^2 - x + 2 \quad \text{and so,} \quad y = \frac{1}{2 - x - x^2}$$

248 a Let X be the number of correct answers. $X \sim B(30, \frac{1}{5})$

i $P(X = 20) = \binom{30}{20}\left(\frac{1}{5}\right)^{20}\left(\frac{4}{5}\right)^{10} = 3.4 \times 10^{-8} \approx 0$

ii $P(X \geqslant 15) = 1 - P(X \leqslant 14)$
$= 1 - \text{binomcdf}\,(14, 30, \frac{1}{5})$
$\approx 1 - 0.99976$
≈ 0.00024

iii $P(X \leqslant 25) = \text{binomcdf}\,(25, 30, \frac{1}{5}) = 0.9999 \approx 1$

b Now $X \sim B(30, 0.85)$

i $P(X = 20) = \binom{30}{20}(0.85)^{20}(0.15)^{10} \approx 0.00672$

ii $P(X \geqslant 15) = 1 - P(X \leqslant 14)$
$= 1 - \text{binomcdf}\,(14, 30, 0.85)$
$= 1 - 1.14 \times 10^{-6}$
≈ 1

249 a i The two lines meet if $\begin{bmatrix} 3 + 4t \\ 4 + t \\ 1 \end{bmatrix} = \begin{bmatrix} -1 + 12\lambda \\ 7 + 6\lambda \\ 5 + 3\lambda \end{bmatrix}$

i.e., $3 + 4t = -1 + 12\lambda$ ...... (1)
$4 + t = 7 + 6\lambda$ ......(2)
$1 = 5 + 3\lambda$ ...... (3)

From (3) $\lambda = -\frac{4}{3}$

From (2) $4 + t = 7 + 6\left(-\frac{4}{3}\right) = 7 - 8$

i.e., $t = -5$

These values check in equation (1).

The point $(-17, -1, 1)$ lies on both lines.

ii A normal to both lines is

$$\mathbf{n} = \begin{bmatrix} 4 \\ 1 \\ 0 \end{bmatrix} \times \begin{bmatrix} 12 \\ 6 \\ 3 \end{bmatrix} = \begin{vmatrix} \mathbf{i} & \mathbf{j} & \mathbf{k} \\ 4 & 1 & 0 \\ 12 & 6 & 3 \end{vmatrix}$$

$$= \mathbf{i}\,(3 - 0) - \mathbf{j}\,(12 - 0) + \mathbf{k}\,(24 - 12)$$
$$= 3\mathbf{i} - 12\mathbf{j} + 12\mathbf{k}$$
$$= 3(\mathbf{i} - 4\mathbf{j} + 4\mathbf{k})$$

Since $(-17, -1, 1)$ lies on this plane, an equation is

$$\begin{bmatrix} 1 \\ -4 \\ 4 \end{bmatrix} \bullet \begin{bmatrix} x \\ y \\ z \end{bmatrix} = \begin{bmatrix} 1 \\ -4 \\ 4 \end{bmatrix} \bullet \begin{bmatrix} -17 \\ -1 \\ 1 \end{bmatrix}$$

i.e., $x - 4y + z = -9$

$$\text{or} \qquad \mathbf{r} = \begin{bmatrix} -17 \\ -1 \\ 1 \end{bmatrix} + s\begin{bmatrix} 4 \\ 1 \\ 0 \end{bmatrix} + t\begin{bmatrix} 12 \\ 6 \\ 3 \end{bmatrix}$$

b

i Position vector to top of the tower is $\mathbf{t} = \begin{bmatrix} -270 \\ -110 \\ 20 \end{bmatrix}$

A vector in descent direction is $\mathbf{d} = \begin{bmatrix} -\cos 24^o \\ 0 \\ -\sin 24^o \end{bmatrix}$

ii The distance is $\dfrac{|\mathbf{t} \times \mathbf{d}|}{|\mathbf{d}|} = |\mathbf{t} \times \mathbf{d}|$ {since $|\mathbf{d}| = 1$}

and $\mathbf{t} \times \mathbf{d} = \begin{bmatrix} 44.74 \\ -128.09 \\ -10.05 \end{bmatrix}$ and $|\mathbf{t} \times \mathbf{d}| \approx 136.1$ {using technology}

$\therefore$ closest distance the plane comes is 136.1 m.

250 a i $\begin{bmatrix} r\cos\theta & -r\sin\theta \\ r\sin\theta & r\cos\theta \end{bmatrix}^2 = \mathbf{M}^2$

$$= \begin{bmatrix} r\cos\theta & -r\sin\theta \\ r\sin\theta & r\cos\theta \end{bmatrix}\begin{bmatrix} r\cos\theta & -r\sin\theta \\ r\sin\theta & r\cos\theta \end{bmatrix}$$

$$= \begin{bmatrix} r^2\cos^2\theta - r^2\sin^2\theta & -r^2\sin\theta\cos\theta - r^2\sin\theta\cos\theta \\ r^2\sin\theta\cos\theta + r^2\sin\theta\cos\theta & -r^2\sin^2\theta + r^2\cos^2\theta \end{bmatrix}$$

$$= \begin{bmatrix} r^2\cos 2\theta & -r^2\sin 2\theta \\ r^2\sin 2\theta & r^2\cos 2\theta \end{bmatrix}$$

ii $\mathbf{M}^3 = \mathbf{M}^2\mathbf{M}$

$$= \begin{bmatrix} r^2\cos 2\theta & -r^2\sin 2\theta \\ r^2\sin 2\theta & r^2\cos 2\theta \end{bmatrix}\begin{bmatrix} r\cos\theta & -r\sin\theta \\ r\sin\theta & r\cos\theta \end{bmatrix}$$

$$= \begin{bmatrix} r^3[\cos 2\theta\cos\theta - \sin 2\theta\sin\theta] & -r^3[\sin\theta\cos 2\theta + \sin 2\theta\cos\theta] \\ r^3[\sin 2\theta\cos\theta + \cos 2\theta\sin\theta] & r^3[-\sin 2\theta\sin\theta + \cos 2\theta\cos\theta] \end{bmatrix}$$

$$= \begin{bmatrix} r^3\cos 3\theta & -r^3\sin 3\theta \\ r^3\sin 3\theta & r^3\cos 3\theta \end{bmatrix}$$

iii From **i** and **ii** we conjecture the proposition $P(n)$:

$$\begin{bmatrix} r\cos\theta & -r\sin\theta \\ r\sin\theta & r\cos\theta \end{bmatrix}^n = \begin{bmatrix} r^n\cos n\theta & -r^n\sin n\theta \\ r^n\sin n\theta & r^n\cos n\theta \end{bmatrix}$$

for all $n \in \mathbb{Z}^+$

iv Proof (By the Principle of Math Induction)

(1) If $n = 1$

$$\begin{bmatrix} r\cos\theta & -r\sin\theta \\ r\sin\theta & r\cos\theta \end{bmatrix}^1 = \begin{bmatrix} r\cos\theta & -r\sin\theta \\ r\sin\theta & r\cos\theta \end{bmatrix}$$

which is true. Thus $P(1)$ is true.

(2) If $P(k)$ is true then

$$\begin{bmatrix} r\cos\theta & -r\sin\theta \\ r\sin\theta & r\cos\theta \end{bmatrix}^k = \begin{bmatrix} r^k\cos k\theta & -r^k\sin k\theta \\ r^k\sin k\theta & r^k\cos k\theta \end{bmatrix}$$

So, $\begin{bmatrix} r\cos\theta & -r\sin\theta \\ r\sin\theta & r\cos\theta \end{bmatrix}^{k+1}$

$$= \begin{bmatrix} r\cos\theta & -r\sin\theta \\ r\sin\theta & r\cos\theta \end{bmatrix}^k\begin{bmatrix} r\cos\theta & -r\sin\theta \\ r\sin\theta & r\cos\theta \end{bmatrix}$$

$$= \begin{bmatrix} r^k\cos k\theta & -r^k\sin k\theta \\ r^k\sin k\theta & r^k\cos k\theta \end{bmatrix}\begin{bmatrix} r\cos\theta & -r\sin\theta \\ r\sin\theta & r\cos\theta \end{bmatrix}$$

$$= \begin{bmatrix} r^{k+1}[\cos k\theta\cos\theta - \sin k\theta\sin\theta] & -r^{k+1}[\cos k\theta\sin\theta + \sin k\theta\cos\theta] \\ r^{k+1}[\sin k\theta\cos\theta + \cos k\theta\sin\theta] & r^{k+1}[-\sin k\theta\sin\theta + \cos k\theta\cos\theta] \end{bmatrix}$$

$$= \begin{bmatrix} r^{k+1}\cos(k+1)\theta & -r^{k+1}\sin(k+1)\theta \\ r^{k+1}\sin(k+1)\theta & r^{k+1}\cos(k+1)\theta \end{bmatrix}$$

Thus $P(k+1)$ is true whenever $P(k)$ is true and as $P(1)$ is true $\Rightarrow P(n)$ is true. {P of MI}

b i $z^6 = 1 + i$ $\therefore$ $z^6 = \sqrt{2}\, \text{cis}\, \frac{\pi}{4}$

$\Rightarrow$ $z^6 = 2^{\frac{1}{2}}\, \text{cis}\left(\frac{\pi}{4} + k2\pi\right)$, $k \in Z$

$\Rightarrow$ $z = (2^{\frac{1}{2}})^{\frac{1}{6}}\, \text{cis}\left(\frac{\frac{\pi}{4} + k2\pi}{6}\right) = 2^{\frac{1}{12}}\, \text{cis}\left(\frac{\pi + k8\pi}{24}\right)$

$\Rightarrow$ $z = 2^{\frac{1}{12}} \cos\left(\frac{\pi}{24}\right),\ 2^{\frac{1}{12}}\, \text{cis}\left(\frac{9\pi}{24}\right),$
$\qquad 2^{\frac{1}{12}}\, \text{cis}\left(\frac{17\pi}{24}\right),\ 2^{\frac{1}{12}}\, \text{cis}\left(\frac{25\pi}{24}\right),$
$\qquad 2^{\frac{1}{12}}\, \text{cis}\left(\frac{33\pi}{24}\right),\ 2^{\frac{1}{12}}\, \text{cis}\left(\frac{41\pi}{24}\right)$

ii

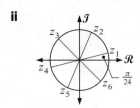

(all sector angles are 60° or $\frac{\pi}{3}$, radius of circle is $2^{\frac{1}{12}}$ or $\sqrt[12]{2}$)

251 $f(x) = \dfrac{2x^2 - 17x + 8}{x^2 - 5x + 4}$

a i $f(0) = \dfrac{8}{4} = 2$ $\quad \therefore$ y-intercept is 2

$\qquad f(x) = 0 \quad \Rightarrow \quad 2x^2 - 17x + 8 = 0$
$\qquad\qquad\qquad\quad \Rightarrow \quad (2x - 1)(x - 8) = 0$
$\qquad\qquad\qquad\qquad\qquad \Rightarrow \quad x = \tfrac{1}{2}$ or 8

$\qquad \therefore$ x-intercepts are $\tfrac{1}{2}$ and 8

ii VAs occur when $\qquad x^2 - 5x + 4 = 0$
$\qquad\qquad\qquad\qquad \Rightarrow \quad (x - 1)(x - 4) = 0$
$\qquad\qquad\qquad\quad$ i.e., are $x = 1$, $x = 4$

iii $y = \dfrac{2 - \frac{17}{x} + \frac{8}{x^2}}{1 - \frac{5}{x} + \frac{4}{x^2}} \to 2$ as $x \to \pm\infty$ $\therefore$ HA is $y = 2$

iv $f(x) = 2$ when $2x^2 - 17x + 8 = 2(x^2 - 5x + 4)$
$\qquad\qquad\qquad \Rightarrow \quad -17x + 8 = -10x + 8$
$\qquad\qquad\qquad\qquad \Rightarrow \quad 7x = 0$
$\qquad\qquad\qquad\qquad\quad \Rightarrow \quad x = 0$, i.e., at $(0, 2)$

b i $f'(x)$

$= \dfrac{(4x - 17)(x^2 - 5x + 4) - (2x^2 - 17x + 8)(2x - 5)}{(x - 1)^2(x - 4)^2}$

$= \dfrac{4x^3 - 37x^2 + 101x - 68 - 4x^3 + 44x^2 - 101x + 40}{(x - 1)^2(x - 4)^2}$

$= \dfrac{7x^2 - 28}{(x - 1)^2(x - 4)^2}$

$= \dfrac{7(x + 2)(x - 2)}{(x - 1)^2(x - 4)^2}$

ii $f'(x) = 0$ when $x = \pm 2$

SD of $f'(x)$:

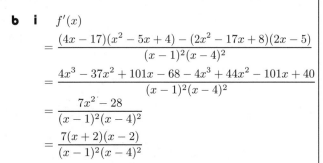

$\therefore$ local max. at $(-2, f(-2))$ i.e., at $\left(-2, \frac{25}{9}\right)$
$\qquad$ local min. at $(2, 9)$

c i

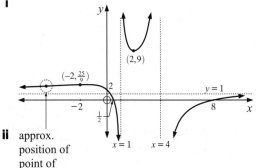

ii approx. position of point of inflection

252 $\qquad S_3 = u_1\left(\dfrac{r^3 - 1}{r - 1}\right)$ and $S_\infty = \dfrac{u_1}{r - 1}$

So, $\dfrac{u_1(r^3 - 1)}{r - 1} = \tfrac{1}{2}u_1\left(\dfrac{1}{r - 1}\right)$

$\Rightarrow$ $r^3 - 1 = \tfrac{1}{2}$

$\Rightarrow$ $r^3 = \tfrac{3}{2}$

$\Rightarrow$ $r = \sqrt[3]{\tfrac{3}{2}}$ (≈ 1.1447)

253 $\ln(x^2 + 9) - 2 = \ln|x + 5|$

We graph $y = \ln(x^2 + 9) - 2$ and
$\qquad\qquad y = \ln|x + 5|$ on the same set of axes.

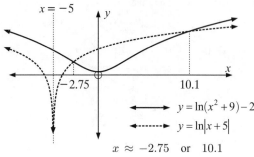

$x \approx -2.75$ or 10.1

254 $2 - i$ is a solution

$\Rightarrow$ $2 + i$ is also a solution {theorem on real polynomials}

These have sum $= 4$ and product $= 5$ and so come from the factor $z^2 - 4z + 5$

Thus $z^3 - 6z^2 + 13z - 10 = (z^2 - 4z + 5)(z - 2)$

$\therefore$ other solutions are $2 + i$ and 2

255 a Domain $x \leqslant 5$; Range $y \geqslant 0$.

b Domain set of all real numbers $\mathbb{R}$; Range $0 \leqslant y \leqslant 0.5$

256 Find a such that $\qquad e^{-\frac{1}{2}a^2} = e^{\frac{1}{2}a^2} - 1$

i.e., $e^{\frac{1}{2}a^2} - 1 - e^{-\frac{1}{2}a^2} = 0$

$\Rightarrow$ $e^{a^2} - e^{\frac{1}{2}a^2} - 1 = 0$ {multiply by $e^{\frac{1}{2}a^2}$}

$\Rightarrow$ $y^2 - y - 1 = 0$ {letting $y = e^{\frac{1}{2}a^2}$}

$\Rightarrow$ $y = \dfrac{1 \pm \sqrt{1 + 4}}{2}$

$\Rightarrow$ $e^{\frac{1}{2}a^2} = \dfrac{1 \pm \sqrt{5}}{2}$

$\Rightarrow$ $e^{\frac{1}{2}a^2} = \dfrac{1 + \sqrt{5}}{2}$ {as $e^x > 0$}

$\Rightarrow$ $\tfrac{1}{2}a^2 = \ln\left(\dfrac{1 + \sqrt{5}}{2}\right)$

$\Rightarrow$ $a = \pm\sqrt{2\ln\left(\dfrac{1 + \sqrt{5}}{2}\right)}$

$\Rightarrow$ $a \approx \pm 0.981$

257 $y = \ln\left|4x - x^3\right|$

a

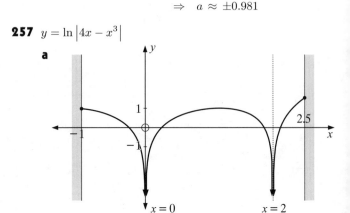

b The zeros of $f(x)$ occur if $\;|\,4x - x^3\,| = 1$

$\quad 4x - x^3 = 1, \quad \text{if} \quad x \doteq -1.861, \; -0.254 \text{ or } 2.115$

$\quad 4x - x^3 = -1 \quad \text{if} \quad x \doteq -2.115 \text{ or } 1.861$

i..e, for $\;-0.5 \leqslant x \leqslant 2.5\;$ zeros occur at

$x = -0.254, \; 0.254, \; 1.861, \; 2.115$

c f will not be defined at $\qquad |\,4x - x^3\,| = 0$

$\qquad\qquad\qquad \Rightarrow \quad (4 - x^2)x = 0$

$\qquad\qquad\qquad \Rightarrow \quad (2 - x)(2 + x)x = 0$

$\qquad\qquad\qquad\qquad \text{i.e., at} \quad x = 2, \, 0, \, -2$

But -2 is not in the given domain, so f is not defined at $x = 0$ or 2, i.e., $x \neq 0$ or 2. So, h and k are 0 and 2.

258 $f(x) = x^2 + (2 - k)x + k^2. \quad f(x) > 0$ for all x if $\Delta < 0$

$\qquad \Delta = (2 - k)^2 - 4k^2$

$\qquad\quad = 4 - 4k + k^2 - 4k^2$

$\qquad\quad = -(3k^2 + 4k - 4)$

$\qquad\quad = -(3k - 2)(k + 2)$

So, Δ has sign diag:

i.e., $\Delta < 0$ if $\;k < -2\;$ or $\;k > \frac{2}{3}$.

259 The yield grows like compound interest at 3% per annum.

If $Y(n) = $ yield at end of n years.

$Y(n) = 200 \left(1 + \frac{3}{100}\right)^n$

To double we need n so that $\qquad 400 = 200 \left(1 + \frac{3}{100}\right)^n$

$\qquad\qquad\qquad \text{i.e.,} \quad 2 = \left(1 + \frac{3}{100}\right)^n$

$\qquad\qquad \Rightarrow \quad n \ln\left(1 + \frac{3}{100}\right) = \ln(2)$

$\qquad\qquad\qquad \Rightarrow \quad n = \dfrac{\ln 2}{\ln(1.03)} \approx 23.45$

i.e., It takes 24 years for the yield to double.

The total yield at the end of the 8th year will be 1636 tonnes (to the nearest tonne).

260

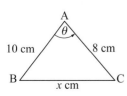

$\qquad\qquad \text{Area} = \frac{1}{2}r^2\theta$

$\qquad\qquad \Rightarrow \quad \frac{1}{2}r^2\theta = 15$

$\qquad\qquad \Rightarrow \quad r^2\theta = 30 \quad \text{...... (1)}$

$\qquad\quad \text{Perimeter} = 16 \;\Rightarrow\; 2r + r\theta = 16 \quad \text{...... (2)}$

$\Rightarrow \quad 2r + r\left(\dfrac{30}{r^2}\right) = 16$

$\qquad \Rightarrow \quad 2r + \dfrac{30}{r} = 16$

$\qquad \Rightarrow \quad 2r^2 + 30 = 16r$

$\Rightarrow \quad r^2 - 8r + 15 = 0$

$\Rightarrow \quad (r - 3)(r - 5) = 0 \;$ and so $\; r = 3$ or 5

When $\; r = 3, \;\; \theta = \dfrac{30}{3^2} = \dfrac{30}{9} = \dfrac{10}{3}$.

When $\; r = 5, \;\; \theta = \dfrac{30}{5^2} = \dfrac{30}{25} = \dfrac{6}{5}$.

So, $r = 3, \;\; \theta = 3\frac{1}{3}^c \;$ or $\; r = 5, \;\; \theta = 1.2^c$.

261

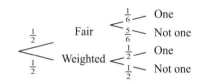

$\text{Area} = \frac{1}{2} \times 10 \times 8 \times \sin\theta = 23$

$\qquad \Rightarrow \quad 40\sin\theta = 23 \;$ and so $\; \sin\theta = \frac{23}{40}$

$\quad \text{But} \quad \cos^2\theta + \sin^2\theta = 1$

$\qquad \Rightarrow \quad \cos^2\theta = 1 - \frac{23}{40} = \frac{17}{40}$

$\qquad \Rightarrow \quad \cos\theta = \pm\frac{\sqrt{17}}{\sqrt{40}}$

Now $\quad x^2 = 8^2 + 10^2 - 2 \times 8 \times 10 \times \cos\theta$

$\quad \Rightarrow \quad x^2 = 164 - 160\left(\pm\dfrac{\sqrt{17}}{\sqrt{40}}\right)$

$\quad \Rightarrow \quad x \approx 7.73 \;$ or $\; 16.38$

i.e., $\;$ BC ≈ 7.73 cm or 16.38 cm

262

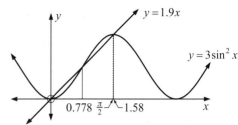

So, $\;x \approx 0, \;\; 0.778 \;$ or $\; 1.58$

263 Length of $\;2\mathbf{i} - 3\mathbf{j} + \mathbf{k}\;$ is $\;\sqrt{2^2 + 3^2 + 1^2} = \sqrt{14}$

A vector in the same direction as $\;2\mathbf{i} - 3\mathbf{j} + \mathbf{k}\;$ of length 5 is $\;\frac{5}{\sqrt{14}}(2\mathbf{i} - 3\mathbf{j} + \mathbf{k}) = \frac{10}{\sqrt{14}}\mathbf{i} - \frac{15}{\sqrt{14}}\mathbf{j} + \frac{5}{\sqrt{14}}\mathbf{k}$

264 $\mathbf{MM}^{-1} = \frac{1}{2}\begin{bmatrix} 1 & -1 & 2 \\ 1 & 1 & -2 \\ 1 & 2 & a \end{bmatrix}\begin{bmatrix} b & -5 & 4 \\ -1 & 1 & 0 \\ 1 & -3 & 2 \end{bmatrix}$

$\qquad\quad = \frac{1}{2}\begin{bmatrix} b - 1 & 0 & 0 \\ b - 3 & 2 & 0 \\ b - 2 + a & -3 - 3a & 4 + 2a \end{bmatrix}$

$\qquad\quad = \begin{bmatrix} 1 & 0 & 0 \\ 0 & 1 & 0 \\ 0 & 0 & 1 \end{bmatrix} \;\Rightarrow\; \begin{matrix} \frac{1}{2}(b - 1) = 1 & \text{i.e., } b = 3 \\ \frac{1}{2}(4 + 2a) = 1 & \text{i.e., } a = -1 \end{matrix}$

These value check in all other entries, i.e., $a = -1, \; b = 3$.

265 Consider this tree diagram:

$\frac{1}{2} \diagup \text{Fair} <^{\frac{1}{6}\diagup \text{One}}_{\frac{5}{6}\diagdown \text{Not one}}$

$\frac{1}{2} \diagdown \text{Weighted} <^{\frac{1}{2}\diagup \text{One}}_{\frac{1}{2}\diagdown \text{Not one}}$

a P(One) $= $ P(Fair $\cap$ One or Weighted $\cap$ One)

$\qquad\qquad = \frac{1}{2} \times \frac{1}{6} + \frac{1}{2} \times \frac{1}{2}$

$\qquad\qquad = \frac{1}{3}$

b P(Weighted | One) $= \dfrac{\text{P(Weighted } \cap \text{ One)}}{\text{P(One)}}$

$\qquad\qquad\qquad\qquad = \dfrac{\frac{1}{2} \times \frac{1}{2}}{\frac{1}{3}}$

$\qquad\qquad\qquad\qquad = \frac{3}{4}$

266 $\qquad (1 + x)^{2n} = \displaystyle\sum_{k=0}^{2n} \binom{2n}{k} x^k \quad$ and

$\qquad \left(1 + 15x^2\right)^n = \displaystyle\sum_{l=0}^{n} \binom{n}{l} (15x^2)^l$

If the coefficients of x^2 are equal then $\;k = 2\;$ and $\;l = 1$

and so, $\qquad \binom{2n}{2} = \binom{n}{1}(15)^1$

i.e., $\quad \dfrac{(2n)(2n - 1)}{2!} = n \times 15$

$\qquad\quad \text{i.e., } \; 2n - 1 = 15 \quad \{\text{as } n \neq 0\}$

$\qquad\qquad\quad \Rightarrow \quad n = 8$

267 Let X be the net weight of a jar, then $\;X \sim N(475, 7.5^2)$

$\text{P}(X < 460) = \text{normalcdf}\,(-\text{E}99, \, 460, \, 475, \, 7.5)$

$\qquad\qquad\qquad \approx 0.0228$

So, about 2.28% of the jars have weight less than 460 g.

268 $3x^2 - 2y^2 = 10$, $\therefore$ $6x - 4y\dfrac{dy}{dx} = 0$

Now when $x = 2$, $3(4) - 2y^2 = 10$
$$\Rightarrow \quad 2y^2 = 2$$
$$\Rightarrow \quad y^2 = 1$$
$$\Rightarrow \quad y = \pm 1$$
But $y < 0$ $\therefore$ $y = -1$

and at $(2, -1)$, $6(2) - 4(-1)\dfrac{dy}{dx} = 0$
$$\Rightarrow \quad 4\dfrac{dy}{dx} = -12 \quad \Rightarrow \quad \dfrac{dy}{dx} = -3$$

$\therefore$ the tangent has equation $y - (-1) = -3(x - 2)$
i.e., $y + 1 = -3x + 6$
i.e., $y = -3x + 5$

269 $f(x) = x^3 + 3x^2 + bx + 4$

a $f'(x) = 3x^2 + 6x + b$
and $f''(x) = 6x + 6 = 6(x + 1)$
So $f''(x) = 0$ when $x = -1$
and $f(-1) = -1 + 3 - b + 4 = -b + 6$
$\therefore$ $(-1, 6 - b)$ is a point of inflection.

b   A stationary point occurs when $f'(x) = 0$
i.e., $f'(-1) = 0$ in this case. $\therefore$ $3 - 6 + b = 0$
$$\therefore \quad b = 3$$

c   No stationary points exist when $3x^2 + 6x + b$ has no real
roots. i.e., $\Delta < 0$
$$\Rightarrow \quad 36 - 4(3)(b) < 0$$
$$\Rightarrow \quad 36 - 12b < 0$$
$$\Rightarrow \quad 12b > 36$$
$$\Rightarrow \quad b > 3$$

270 a $\displaystyle\int \dfrac{1 + x}{4 + x^2}\, dx$
$$= \int \dfrac{1}{4 + x^2}\, dx + \int \dfrac{x}{4 + x^2}\, dx$$
$$= \tfrac{1}{2}\arctan\left(\dfrac{x}{2}\right) + \tfrac{1}{2}\int \dfrac{2x}{4 + x^2}\, dx$$
$$= \tfrac{1}{2}\arctan\left(\dfrac{x}{2}\right) + \tfrac{1}{2}\ln\left|4 + x^2\right| + c$$
$$= \tfrac{1}{2}\arctan\left(\dfrac{x}{2}\right) + \tfrac{1}{2}\ln\left(4 + x^2\right) + c$$
$\{$as $4 + x^2 > 0$ for all $x\}$

b $u' = x^2$ $v = \ln x$ $\therefore$ $\int x^2 \ln x\, dx$

$u = \dfrac{x^3}{3}$ $v' = \dfrac{1}{x}$ $= \dfrac{x^3 \ln x}{3} - \int \dfrac{x^2}{3}\, dx$
$$= \dfrac{x^3 \ln x}{3} - \dfrac{1}{3}\dfrac{x^3}{3} + c$$
$$= \dfrac{x^3 \ln x}{3} - \dfrac{x^3}{9} + c$$

271

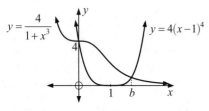

$y = \dfrac{4}{1 + x^3}$ $y = 4(x - 1)^4$

From a gcalc, $b \approx 1.653$

Area $\approx \displaystyle\int_0^{1.653} \dfrac{4}{1 + x^3} - 4(x - 1)^4\, dx \approx 3.27$ units^2

272
$$\dfrac{dy}{dx} = 3x^2 y + 3x^2 = 3x^2(y + 1)$$
$$\Rightarrow \quad \dfrac{1}{y + 1}\dfrac{dy}{dx} = 3x^2$$

$$\Rightarrow \quad \int \dfrac{1}{y + 1}\, dy = \int 3x^2\, dx$$
$$\Rightarrow \quad \ln|y + 1| = x^3 + c$$
$$\Rightarrow \quad |y + 1| = e^{x^3 + c}$$
$$\Rightarrow \quad y + 1 = \pm e^c e^{x^3}$$
$$\Rightarrow \quad y + 1 = Ae^{x^3}$$
$$\Rightarrow \quad y = Ae^{x^3} - 1$$
But $y(0) = 3$ $\therefore$ $3 = A - 1$ and so $A = 4$
Thus $y = 4e^{x^3} - 1$

273 $s = t\sin\left(\tfrac{t}{2}\right) + 2\cos\left(\tfrac{t}{2}\right)$ metres

a $v = \dfrac{ds}{dt} = 1\sin\left(\tfrac{t}{2}\right) + t\left(\tfrac{1}{2}\right)\cos\left(\tfrac{t}{2}\right) - 2\left(\tfrac{1}{2}\right)\sin\left(\tfrac{t}{2}\right)$
$\therefore$ $v = \sin\left(\tfrac{t}{2}\right) + \tfrac{t}{2}\cos\left(\tfrac{t}{2}\right) - \sin\left(\tfrac{t}{2}\right)$
i.e., $v = \tfrac{t}{2}\cos\left(\tfrac{t}{2}\right)$

b   It is 'at rest' when $v = 0$
$$\Rightarrow \quad \tfrac{t}{2}\cos\left(\tfrac{t}{2}\right) = 0$$
$$\Rightarrow \quad t = 0 \ \text{or} \ \cos\left(\tfrac{t}{2}\right) = 0$$
$$\Rightarrow \quad t = 0 \ \text{or} \ \tfrac{t}{2} = \tfrac{\pi}{2} + k\pi$$
$$\Rightarrow \quad t = 0 \ \text{or} \ \pi + k2\pi \ \text{sec}$$
At $t = 0$, $v = 0$ $\Rightarrow$ initial velocity is 0 ms^{-1}.
When $t = \pi + k2\pi$ the period's direction of motion is reversing.

c $a = \dfrac{dv}{dt} = \tfrac{1}{2}\cos\left(\tfrac{t}{2}\right) + \tfrac{t}{2}\left(-\tfrac{1}{2}\sin\left(\tfrac{t}{2}\right)\right)$
$\therefore$ $a = \tfrac{1}{2}\cos\left(\tfrac{t}{2}\right) - \tfrac{t}{4}\sin\left(\tfrac{t}{2}\right)$
and $a\left(\tfrac{\pi}{3}\right) = \tfrac{1}{2}\cos\left(\tfrac{\pi}{6}\right) - \tfrac{\pi}{12}\left(\tfrac{1}{2}\right)$
$$= \tfrac{1}{2}\left(\dfrac{\sqrt{3}}{2}\right) - \tfrac{\pi}{24}$$
$$= \dfrac{\sqrt{3}}{4} - \tfrac{\pi}{24} \ \text{ms}^{-2}$$

274 a   Mean score $\mu = \dfrac{109}{25} = 4.36$

b   Unbiased estimate of variance is calculated from
$$\sum (x_i - \overline{x})^2 = \sum x_i^2 - n\,\overline{x}^2$$
Hence $\dfrac{1}{n - 1}\sum (x_i - \overline{x})^2 = \dfrac{1}{n - 1}\left(\sum x_i^2 - n\overline{x}^2\right)$
$$= \tfrac{1}{24}(579 - 25 \times 4.36^2)$$
$$\doteqdot 4.323$$

275 a $P(n)$ is: $2^{4n+3} + 3^{3n+1}$ is divisible by 11 for all $n \in Z^+$
Proof: (By the Principle of Mathematical Induction)

(1)   If $n = 1$, $2^7 + 3^4 = 128 + 81 = 209 = 19 \times 11$
So, $2^7 + 3^4$ is divisible by 11

(2)   If $P(k)$ is true then $2^{4k+3} + 3^{3k+1} = 11A$, $A \in \mathbb{Z}^+$
Now $2^{4(k+1)+3} + 3^{3(k+1)+1}$
$$= 2^{4k+4+3} + 3^{3k+3+1}$$
$$= 2^4 2^{4k+3} + 3^3 3^{3k+1}$$
$$= 16\left(11A - 16 \times 3^{3k+1} + 27 \times 3^{3k+1}\right)$$
$$= 16 \times 11A + 11 \times 3^{3k+1}$$
$$= 11(16A + 3^{3k+1}) \quad \text{where} \quad 16A + 3^{3k+1} \in \mathbb{Z}$$
Thus $P(k + 1)$ is true when $P(k)$ is true and as $P(1)$ is
true, $P(n)$ is true. $\{$Principle of Math. Induction$\}$

b   As a, b, c are arithmetic, $b - a = c - b$
$$\Rightarrow \quad 2b = a + c$$
$$\Rightarrow \quad 2b = 33 - b \quad \{a + b + c = 33\}$$
$$\Rightarrow \quad 3b = 33$$
$$\Rightarrow \quad b = 11 \quad \text{and} \quad a + c = 22$$

Now as a, $b+1$, $c+29$ are geometric,

$$\frac{b+1}{a} = \frac{c+29}{b+1} \quad \Rightarrow \quad \frac{12}{a} = \frac{22-a+29}{12}$$

$$\Rightarrow \quad 144 = a(51-a)$$
$$\Rightarrow \quad a^2 - 51a + 144 = 0$$
$$\Rightarrow \quad (a-48)(a-3) = 0$$
$$\Rightarrow \quad a = 48 \quad \text{or} \quad 3$$

If $a = 48$, $c = -26$, $b = 11$

If $a = 3$, $c = 19$, $b = 11$

c $\ln x + (\ln x)^2 + (\ln x)^3 + \ldots\ldots$

  i converges when $-1 < r < 1$

      i.e., $-1 < \ln x < 1$

        $\Rightarrow \quad e^{-1} < x < e$

      $\therefore$ converges from $x \in\,]\frac{1}{e}, e[$.

  ii $\qquad S_\infty = \dfrac{a}{1-r} = \dfrac{\ln x}{1 - \ln x}$

    and $S_\infty = 2$ when $\dfrac{\ln x}{1 - \ln x} = 2$

$$\Rightarrow \quad \ln x = 2 - 2\ln x$$
$$\Rightarrow \quad 3\ln x = 2$$
$$\Rightarrow \quad \ln x = \tfrac{2}{3}$$
$$\Rightarrow \quad x = e^{\frac{2}{3}}$$

276 a **i** $\cos x + \sin x \cos x + \sin^2 x \cos x + \ldots\ldots$ is geometric with $u_1 = \cos x$, $r = \sin x$

    Now as $0 < x < \frac{\pi}{2}$, $0 < \sin x < 1$,

    $\Rightarrow$ the series converges and $S_\infty = \dfrac{u_1}{1-r} = \dfrac{\cos x}{1 - \sin x}$

  ii If $S_\infty = \sqrt{3}$, $\dfrac{\cos x}{1 - \sin x} = \sqrt{3}$

$$\Rightarrow \quad \frac{\cos^2 x}{1 - 2\sin x + \sin^2 x} = 3$$
$$\Rightarrow \quad \cos^2 x = 3 - 6\sin x + 3\sin^2 x$$
$$\Rightarrow \quad 3\sin^2 x - 6\sin x + 3 = 1 - \sin^2 x$$
$$\Rightarrow \quad 4\sin^2 x - 6\sin x + 2 = 0$$
$$\Rightarrow \quad 2\sin^2 x - 3\sin x + 1 = 0$$
$$\Rightarrow \quad (2\sin x - 1)(\sin x - 1) = 0$$
$$\Rightarrow \quad \sin x = \tfrac{1}{2} \text{ or } 1$$

    But $0 < \sin x < 1$, $0 < x < \frac{\pi}{2}$.

    So $\sin x = \tfrac{1}{2}$ and so, $x = \frac{\pi}{6}$

b LHS $= \dfrac{\cos x}{1 - \sin x} = \left(\dfrac{\cos x}{1 - \sin x}\right)\left(\dfrac{1 + \sin x}{1 + \sin x}\right)$

$$= \frac{\cos x + \sin x \cos x}{1 - \sin^2 x}$$
$$= \frac{\cos x + \sin x \cos x}{\cos^2 x}$$
$$= \frac{1}{\cos x} + \frac{\sin x}{\cos x}$$
$$= \sec x + \tan x \quad \text{which is the RHS}$$

c $\displaystyle\int \frac{\cos x}{1 - \sin x}\, dx$

$\displaystyle = -\int \frac{-\cos x}{1 - \sin x}\, dx$ $\qquad \begin{bmatrix} u = 1 - \sin x \\ \dfrac{du}{dx} = -\cos x \end{bmatrix}$

$= -\ln|1 - \sin x| + c$ where $\sin x < 1 \Rightarrow 1 - \sin x > 0$

$= -\ln(1 - \sin x) + c$

d From **b**

$\displaystyle\int \sec x + \tan x\, dx = \int \frac{\cos x}{1 - \sin x}\, dx$

$\Rightarrow \displaystyle\int \sec x\, dx = \int \frac{\cos x}{1 - \sin x}\, dx - \int \tan x\, dx$

$\Rightarrow \displaystyle\int \sec x\, dx = -\ln(1 - \sin x) - \int \frac{\sin x}{\cos x}\, dx$

$\Rightarrow \displaystyle\int \sec x\, dx = -\ln(1 - \sin x) + \int \frac{-\sin x}{\cos x}\, dx$

$\qquad = \ln|\cos x| - \ln(1 - \sin x) + c$

$\qquad = \ln\left(\dfrac{\cos x}{1 - \sin x}\right) + c$

$\qquad\qquad \{\text{as } |\cos x| = \cos x \text{ for } 0 < x < \tfrac{\pi}{2}\}$

$\qquad = \ln(\sec x + \tan x) + c \quad \{\text{from } \mathbf{b}\}$

e Area $= \displaystyle\int_{\frac{\pi}{4}}^{\frac{\pi}{3}} \sec x\, dx$

$\qquad = [\ln(\sec x + \tan x)]_{\frac{\pi}{4}}^{\frac{\pi}{3}}$

$\qquad = \ln(2 + \sqrt{3}) - \ln(\sqrt{2} + 1)$

$\qquad = \ln\left(\dfrac{2 + \sqrt{3}}{1 + \sqrt{2}}\right)$

277 a Let θ be the angle between the lines, then

$$\begin{bmatrix} 1 \\ 2 \\ -1 \end{bmatrix} \bullet \begin{bmatrix} 2 \\ -1 \\ 1 \end{bmatrix} = \sqrt{1+4+1}\sqrt{4+1+1}\cos\theta$$

$$\Rightarrow \quad 2 - 2 - 1 = \sqrt{6}\sqrt{6}\cos\theta$$
$$\Rightarrow \quad \cos\theta = -\tfrac{1}{6} \quad \text{and so} \quad \theta \approx 99.6^o$$

and the acute angle between the lines is 80.4^o.

b A vector perpendicular to both lines is

$$\begin{bmatrix} 1 \\ 2 \\ -1 \end{bmatrix} \times \begin{bmatrix} 2 \\ -1 \\ 1 \end{bmatrix} = \begin{vmatrix} \mathbf{i} & \mathbf{j} & \mathbf{k} \\ 1 & 2 & -1 \\ 2 & -1 & 1 \end{vmatrix}$$

$$= \mathbf{i}(2-1) - \mathbf{j}(1--2) + \mathbf{k}(-1-4)$$
$$= \mathbf{i} - 3\mathbf{j} - 5\mathbf{k}$$

c Since $(2, -3, 1)$ is a point on the line, an equation is

$$\begin{bmatrix} 1 \\ -3 \\ -5 \end{bmatrix} \bullet \begin{bmatrix} x \\ y \\ z \end{bmatrix} = \begin{bmatrix} 1 \\ -3 \\ -5 \end{bmatrix} \bullet \begin{bmatrix} 2 \\ -3 \\ 1 \end{bmatrix}$$

i.e., $x - 3y - 5z = 6$

d

$\overrightarrow{AB} = \begin{bmatrix} 1 \\ 0 \\ -1 \end{bmatrix} + \mu\begin{bmatrix} 2 \\ -1 \\ 1 \end{bmatrix} - \left(\begin{bmatrix} 2 \\ -3 \\ 1 \end{bmatrix} + \lambda\begin{bmatrix} 1 \\ 2 \\ -1 \end{bmatrix}\right) = \begin{bmatrix} -1 - \lambda + 2\mu \\ 3 - 2\lambda - \mu \\ -2 + \lambda + \mu \end{bmatrix}$

e $\overrightarrow{AB}$ is parallel to $\mathbf{n}$ if $\begin{bmatrix} -1 - \lambda + 2\mu \\ 3 - 2\lambda - \mu \\ -2 + \lambda + \mu \end{bmatrix} = k\begin{bmatrix} 1 \\ -3 \\ -5 \end{bmatrix}$

This gives the three equations $\quad -\lambda + 2\mu - k = 1$
$$-2\lambda - \mu + 3k = -3$$
$$\lambda + \mu + 5k = 2$$

This has unique solution

$\lambda = 1 \quad \mu = 1 \quad k = 0 \qquad \text{and} \quad \overrightarrow{AB} = \begin{bmatrix} 0 \\ 0 \\ 0 \end{bmatrix}$

The distance between the lines L and M is zero.

Also, as $\lambda = 1$, $\begin{bmatrix} x \\ y \\ z \end{bmatrix} = \begin{bmatrix} 2 \\ -3 \\ 1 \end{bmatrix} + \begin{bmatrix} 1 \\ 2 \\ -1 \end{bmatrix} = \begin{bmatrix} 3 \\ -1 \\ 0 \end{bmatrix}$

So, the lines intersect at the point $(3, -1, 0)$

278
$$(a + 2i)(b - i) = 17 + 7i$$
$\Rightarrow \quad ab + 2 = 17 \quad \text{and} \quad 2b - a = 7$
$\quad \Rightarrow \quad ab = 15 \quad \text{and} \quad 2b - a = 7$
$\quad\quad\quad \Rightarrow \quad (2b - 7)b = 15$
$\quad\quad\quad \Rightarrow \quad 2b^2 - 7b - 15 = 0$
$\quad\quad\quad \Rightarrow \quad (2b + 3)(b - 5) = 0$
$\quad\quad\quad\quad\quad \Rightarrow \quad b = -\frac{3}{2} \quad \text{or} \quad 5$

when $b = -\frac{3}{2}$, $a = -10$ and when $b = 5$, $a = 3$
So, $a = 3$, $b = 5$ or $a = -10$, $b = -\frac{3}{2}$.

279 $\quad \log_{64}(x + 5) + \log_2 \sqrt[6]{3x - 1} = 1$

$\Rightarrow \quad \dfrac{\log(x + 5)}{\log 2^6} + \dfrac{\log(3x - 1)^{\frac{1}{6}}}{\log 2} = 1$

$\Rightarrow \quad \dfrac{\log(x + 5)}{6 \log 2} + \dfrac{\frac{1}{6}\log(3x - 1)}{\log 2} = 1$

$\Rightarrow \quad \log(x + 5) + \log(3x - 1) = 6 \log 2$
$\quad \Rightarrow \quad \log(x + 5)(3x - 1) = \log 2^6$
$\quad \Rightarrow \quad \log(3x^2 + 14x - 5) = \log 64$
$\quad \Rightarrow \quad 3x^2 + 14x - 5 = 64$
$\quad \Rightarrow \quad 3x^2 + 14x - 69 = 0$
$\quad \Rightarrow \quad (3x + 23)(x - 3) = 0$
$\quad\quad\quad \Rightarrow \quad x = -\frac{23}{3} \text{ or } 3$

But $x + 5 > 0$ and $3x - 1 > 0 \Rightarrow x > \frac{1}{3}$
Thus $x = 3$.

280 a In 2000, $u_1 = 4000$, $r = 1.06$. In 2010, $n = 11$.

$u_{11} = u_1 r^{10}$
$\quad = 4000 \times 1.06^{10}$
$\quad \approx 7160$ i.e., about 7160 people

b Total number of people
$= u_1 + u_2 + u_3 + \ldots\ldots + u_{10} + u_{11}$
$= S_{11}$
$= \dfrac{4000 \times (1.06^{11} - 1)}{1.06 - 1} : 59886.57$
≈ 59886.57

$\therefore$ total charge is $= 59\,886.57 \times \$5 \approx \$299\,000$

281 a $x^2 - 1 \geqslant 0$ i.e., $x^2 \geqslant 1$; i.e., $x \leqslant -1$ or $x \geqslant 1$

b $1 - x^2 > 0$ i.e., $x^2 < 1$; i.e., $-1 < x < 1$

c $x \neq 0$

d $x \neq -2$ and $\dfrac{2x - 3}{x + 2} \geqslant 0$

But $\dfrac{2x - 3}{x + 2}$ has sign diag:
$\quad\quad\quad\quad \dfrac{+ \quad | \quad - \quad | \quad +}{\quad -2 \quad\quad \frac{3}{2}}$

$G(x)$ takes on real values if $x < -2$ or $x \geqslant \frac{3}{2}$.

282 Vertical asymptote is $x = -1$
Horizontal asymptote is $y = 3$

a

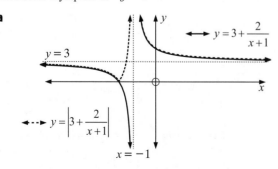

Note that the graphs of $y = 3 + \dfrac{2}{x + 1}$ and $y = \left|3 + \dfrac{2}{x + 1}\right|$ coincide for all $y \geqslant 0$.

b

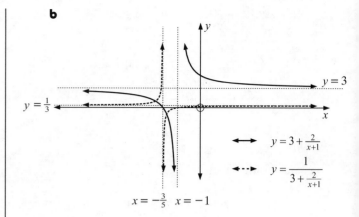

Note: $\dfrac{1}{f(x)}$ is not defined at $x = -1$.

283 $g(x) = 2x^2 - 3x + \sin x$
$\therefore$ f is a reflection of g in x-axis
$f(x) = -g(x) = -2x^2 + 3x - \sin x$
h is the reflection of g in the y-axis.
$\therefore \quad h(x) = g(-x)$
$\quad\quad\quad = 2(-x)^2 - 3(-x) + \sin(-x)$
$\quad\quad\quad = 2x^2 + 3x - \sin x$

284 a $W_t = W_0 e^{-\frac{t}{5000}}$ If $W_t = \frac{1}{2}W_0$
then $\frac{1}{2}W_0 = W_0 e^{-\frac{t}{5000}}$
$\Rightarrow \quad \frac{1}{2} = e^{-\frac{t}{5000}}$
$\Rightarrow \quad \ln(\frac{1}{2}) = -\frac{t}{5000}$
$\quad\quad \Rightarrow \quad t = -5000 \ln(\frac{1}{2}) \approx 3465 \text{ year}$

b To fall to 0.1% of its original value
$0.001 W_0 = W_0 e^{-\frac{t}{5000}}$
$\Rightarrow \quad 0.001 = e^{-\frac{t}{5000}}$
$\Rightarrow \quad \ln(0.001) = -\frac{t}{5000}$
$\quad\quad \Rightarrow \quad t = -5000 \times \ln(0.001) \approx 34\,500 \text{ years}$

c After 1000 years $W_t = W_0 e^{-\frac{1000}{5000}} = W_0 e^{-0.2}$
Weight loss is $W_0 - W_0 e^{-0.2} = W_0(1 - e^{-0.2})$
the percent weight loss is $\dfrac{W_0(1 - e^{-0.2})}{W_0} \times 100\% \approx 18.1$

285 $\quad \sin A = \frac{3}{4} \quad\quad\quad\quad \cos B = \frac{2}{3}$

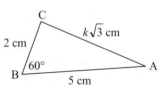

$\cos A = \frac{\sqrt{7}}{4} \quad\quad\quad\quad \sin B = \frac{\sqrt{5}}{3}$

$\sin(A - B) = \sin A \cos B - \cos A \sin B$
$\quad\quad\quad = \left(\frac{3}{4}\right)\left(\frac{2}{3}\right) - \left(\frac{\sqrt{7}}{4}\right)\left(\frac{\sqrt{5}}{3}\right)$
$\quad\quad\quad = \frac{6 - \sqrt{35}}{12}$

286

$(k\sqrt{3})^2 = 2^2 + 5^2 - 2 \times 2 \times 5 \times \cos 60° \quad \{\text{Cosine Rule}\}$
$\Rightarrow \quad 3k^2 = 4 + 25 - 10$
$\Rightarrow \quad 3k^2 = 19$
$\Rightarrow \quad k^2 = \frac{19}{3}$
$\Rightarrow \quad k = \sqrt{\frac{19}{3}} \quad \{\text{as } k > 0\}$

287 $\tan\alpha = \frac{3}{\sqrt{5}}, \quad \pi < \alpha < \frac{3\pi}{2}$

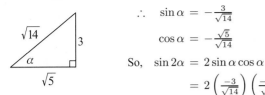

$$\therefore \quad \sin\alpha = -\frac{3}{\sqrt{14}}$$

$$\cos\alpha = -\frac{\sqrt{5}}{\sqrt{14}}$$

So, $\sin 2\alpha = 2\sin\alpha\cos\alpha$

$$= 2\left(\frac{-3}{\sqrt{14}}\right)\left(\frac{-\sqrt{5}}{\sqrt{14}}\right)$$

$$= \frac{3\sqrt{5}}{7}$$

288 A normal to first plane is

$$\mathbf{n}_1 = \begin{bmatrix} 2 \\ -1 \\ 1 \end{bmatrix} \times \begin{bmatrix} 1 \\ -1 \\ 2 \end{bmatrix} = \begin{vmatrix} \mathbf{i} & \mathbf{j} & \mathbf{k} \\ 2 & -1 & 1 \\ 1 & -1 & 2 \end{vmatrix}$$

$$= \mathbf{i}(-2+1) - \mathbf{j}(4-1) + \mathbf{k}(-2+1)$$

$$= -1\mathbf{i} - 3\mathbf{j} - 1\mathbf{k}$$

A normal to the second plane is

$$\mathbf{n}_2 = \begin{bmatrix} 1 \\ 1 \\ 1 \end{bmatrix} \times \begin{bmatrix} 2 \\ 0 \\ -1 \end{bmatrix} = \begin{vmatrix} \mathbf{i} & \mathbf{j} & \mathbf{k} \\ 1 & 1 & 1 \\ 2 & 0 & -1 \end{vmatrix}$$

$$= \mathbf{i}(-1-0) - \mathbf{j}(-1-2) + \mathbf{k}(0-2) = -1\mathbf{i} + 3\mathbf{j} - 2\mathbf{k}$$

But $\mathbf{n}_1 \bullet \mathbf{n}_2 = (-1\mathbf{i} - 3\mathbf{j} - \mathbf{k}) \bullet (-1\mathbf{i} + 3\mathbf{j} - 2\mathbf{k})$

$$= 1 - 9 + 2$$

$$= -6$$

and $\mathbf{n}_1 \bullet \mathbf{n}_2 = \sqrt{1+9+1}\sqrt{9+1+4}\cos\theta$

$$\Rightarrow \quad \cos\theta = \frac{-6}{\sqrt{11}\sqrt{14}}$$

and $\theta = 118.9^o$

$\therefore$ the acute angle is $180^o - 118.9^o = 61.1^o$

289 If $\mathbf{AX} = \mathbf{BA} + \mathbf{A}$ then $\mathbf{X} = \mathbf{A}^{-1}(\mathbf{BA} + \mathbf{A})$

$$\mathbf{BA} + \mathbf{A} = \begin{bmatrix} 2 & -1 & 1 \\ 0 & 2 & 3 \\ -3 & 1 & 2 \end{bmatrix}\begin{bmatrix} 3 & 2 & 1 \\ 0 & -2 & 0 \\ 2 & 1 & -2 \end{bmatrix} + \begin{bmatrix} 3 & 2 & 1 \\ 0 & -2 & 0 \\ 2 & 1 & -2 \end{bmatrix}$$

$$= \begin{bmatrix} 11 & 9 & 1 \\ 6 & -3 & -6 \\ -3 & -5 & -9 \end{bmatrix}$$

Using technology, $\mathbf{A}^{-1} = \begin{bmatrix} \frac{1}{4} & \frac{5}{16} & \frac{1}{8} \\ 0 & -\frac{1}{2} & 0 \\ \frac{1}{4} & \frac{1}{16} & -\frac{3}{8} \end{bmatrix}$ Hence,

$$\mathbf{X} = \begin{bmatrix} \frac{1}{4} & \frac{5}{16} & \frac{1}{8} \\ 0 & -\frac{1}{2} & 0 \\ \frac{1}{4} & \frac{1}{16} & -\frac{3}{8} \end{bmatrix}\begin{bmatrix} 11 & 9 & 1 \\ 6 & -3 & -6 \\ -3 & -5 & -9 \end{bmatrix} = \begin{bmatrix} \frac{17}{4} & \frac{11}{16} & -\frac{11}{4} \\ -3 & \frac{3}{2} & 3 \\ \frac{17}{4} & \frac{63}{16} & \frac{13}{4} \end{bmatrix}$$

290 The situation can be represented by a tree diagram.

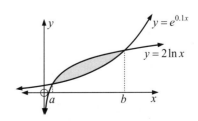

Probability a component is faulty is

$$0.4 \times 0.05 + 0.25 \times 0.03 + 0.35 \times 0.04$$

$$= 0.0415$$

291 Let X be the lengths of the fish, then $X \sim N(m, 0.12^2)$

$$P(X \geqslant 13) = 0.20$$

$$\Rightarrow P\left(\frac{X-m}{0.12} \geqslant \frac{13-m}{0.12}\right) = 0.20$$

$$\Rightarrow P\left(Z \geqslant \frac{13-m}{0.12}\right) = 0.2$$

$$\Rightarrow P\left(Z \leqslant \frac{13-m}{0.12}\right) = 0.8$$

$$\Rightarrow \frac{13-m}{0.12} = \text{invNorm}(0.8)$$

$$\Rightarrow m = 13 - 0.12 \times \text{invNorm}(0.8)$$

$$\Rightarrow m \approx 12.9$$

The mean length of fish is about 12.9 cm.

292 If $Y \sim \text{Po}(m)$, then $\text{E}(Y) = \text{Var}(Y) = m$

Hence, $m^2 = 2m + 3$

$$\Rightarrow m^2 - 2m - 3 = 0$$

$$\Rightarrow (m-3)(m+1) = 0$$

$$\Rightarrow m = 3 \text{ or } -1$$

But, $m > 0$, $\therefore m = 3$

$$P(Y \geqslant 3) = 1 - P(Y \leqslant 2)$$

$$= 1 - \text{poissoncdf}(3, 2)$$

$$\approx 0.577$$

293 $y = xe^{x^{-2}}$

$$\therefore \quad \frac{dy}{dx} = 1e^{x^{-2}} + xe^{x^{-2}}(-2x^{-3})$$

$$= e^{x^{-2}}(1 - 2x^{-2})$$

$$= 0 \Leftrightarrow x^{-2} = \frac{1}{2} \Leftrightarrow x^2 = 2 \Leftrightarrow x = \pm\sqrt{2}$$

When $x = \sqrt{2}$, $y = \sqrt{2}e^{\frac{1}{2}}$

When $x = -\sqrt{2}$, $y = -\sqrt{2}e^{\frac{1}{2}}$

$\therefore$ the stationary points are $(\sqrt{2}, \sqrt{2e})$ and $(-\sqrt{2}, -\sqrt{2e})$

294 $$6x^2 + 4xy + 2y^2 = 3 \quad ......\ (1)$$

$$\therefore \quad 12x + 4y + 4x\frac{dy}{dx} + 4y\frac{dy}{dx} = 0$$

$$\Rightarrow (4x + 4y)\frac{dy}{dx} = -(12x + 4y)$$

$$\Rightarrow \frac{dy}{dx} = \frac{-3x - y}{x + y}$$

which is $0 \Leftrightarrow y = -3x$

Sub. into (1): $6x^2 + 4x(-3x) + 2(-3x)^2 = 3$

$$\Rightarrow 6x^2 - 12x^2 + 18x^2 = 3$$

$$\Rightarrow 12x^2 = 3$$

$$\Rightarrow x^2 = \frac{1}{4}$$

$$\Rightarrow x = \pm\frac{1}{2}$$

When $x = \frac{1}{2}$, $y = -\frac{3}{2}$. When $x = -\frac{1}{2}$, $y = \frac{3}{2}$.

$\therefore$ points are $(\frac{1}{2}, -\frac{3}{2})$ and $(-\frac{1}{2}, \frac{3}{2})$.

295 $$\int \frac{1 - 2x}{\sqrt{1 - x^2}}\, dx$$

$$= \int \frac{1}{\sqrt{1 - x^2}}\, dx + \int \frac{-2x}{\sqrt{1 - x^2}}\, dx$$

$$= \arcsin x + \int \frac{1}{\sqrt{u}}\frac{du}{dx}\, dx \quad \text{where} \quad u = 1 - x^2$$

$$= \arcsin x + \int u^{-\frac{1}{2}}\, du$$

$$= \arcsin x + \frac{u^{\frac{1}{2}}}{\frac{1}{2}} + c$$

$$= \arcsin x + 2\sqrt{1 - x^2} + c$$

296

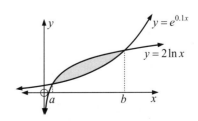

From a gcalc, $a \approx 1.821......$, $b \approx 17.43......$
and area ≈ 21.1 units^2.

297 $\quad u' = x \qquad\qquad v = \arctan x$

$\qquad\quad u = \dfrac{x^2}{2} \qquad v' = \dfrac{1}{1+x^2}$

$\quad \therefore \displaystyle\int x \arctan x \, dx$

$\qquad = \dfrac{x^2}{2} \arctan x - \displaystyle\int \dfrac{x^2}{2}\left(\dfrac{1}{1+x^2}\right) dx$

$\qquad = \dfrac{x^2}{2} \arctan x - \tfrac{1}{2}\displaystyle\int \dfrac{x^2}{1+x^2} dx$

$\qquad = \dfrac{x^2}{2} \arctan x - \tfrac{1}{2}\displaystyle\int \dfrac{1+x^2-1}{1+x^2} dx$

$\qquad = \dfrac{x^2}{2} \arctan x - \tfrac{1}{2}\displaystyle\int 1 - \dfrac{1}{1+x^2} dx$

$\qquad = \dfrac{x^2}{2} \arctan x - \tfrac{1}{2}\{x - \arctan x\} + c$

$\qquad = \dfrac{x^2}{2} \arctan x - \tfrac{1}{2}x + \tfrac{1}{2}\arctan x + c$

298 $\quad s = 4e^{0.2t} - e^{0.3t} + 10$ m

  a $\quad s(0) = 4 - 1 + 10 = 13$ m right of O.

  b $\qquad v(t) = \dfrac{ds}{dt} = 0.8e^{0.2t} - 0.3e^{0.3t}$ ms^{-1}

  $\qquad \therefore \quad v(0) = 0.8 - 0.3 = 0.5$ ms^{-1}

  c It is at rest when $\quad v(t) = 0$

  $\qquad \Rightarrow \quad 0.8e^{0.2t} - 0.3e^{0.3t} = 0$

  $\qquad\qquad \Rightarrow \quad 0.8e^{0.2t} = 0.3e^{0.3t}$

  $\qquad\qquad \Rightarrow \quad \dfrac{e^{0.3t}}{e^{0.2t}} = \dfrac{8}{3}$

  $\qquad\qquad \Rightarrow \quad e^{0.1t} = \tfrac{8}{3}$

  $\qquad\qquad \Rightarrow \quad 0.1t = \ln\left(\tfrac{8}{3}\right)$

  $\qquad\qquad \Rightarrow \quad t = 10\ln\left(\tfrac{8}{3}\right)$ sec

299 $\qquad\qquad e^y \dfrac{dy}{dx} = 2xe^y + 2x$

  $\qquad \Rightarrow \quad e^y \dfrac{dy}{dx} = 2x(e^y + 1)$

  $\qquad \Rightarrow \quad \dfrac{e^y}{e^y+1}\dfrac{dy}{dx} = 2x$

  $\qquad \Rightarrow \displaystyle\int \dfrac{e^y}{e^y+1}\dfrac{dy}{dx}\, dx = \int 2x\, dx$

  $\qquad \Rightarrow \displaystyle\int \dfrac{e^y}{e^y+1}\, dy = \int 2x\, dx$

  $\qquad \Rightarrow \quad \ln|e^y + 1| = x^2 + c$

  $\qquad \Rightarrow \quad e^y + 1 = \pm e^c e^{x^2}$

  $\qquad \Rightarrow \quad e^y + 1 = Ae^{x^2}$

  $\qquad$ But when $\quad x = 0, \quad y = 0 \quad \therefore \quad 2 = A$

  $\qquad$ So $\quad e^y + 1 = 2e^{x^2}$

  $\qquad\qquad \Rightarrow \quad e^y = 2e^{x^2} - 1$

  $\qquad\qquad \Rightarrow \quad y = \ln\left(2e^{x^2} - 1\right)$

300 The following tree diagram shows what is happening.

  R: alarm rings $\qquad$ S: alarm does not ring

  T: arrives for training $\qquad$ N: does not arrive for training

$\qquad \dfrac{9}{10} \diagup$ R $\begin{cases} \frac{5}{6} - \text{T} \\ \frac{1}{6} - \text{N} \end{cases}$

$\qquad \dfrac{1}{10} \diagdown$ S $\begin{cases} \frac{2}{15} - \text{T} \\ \frac{13}{15} - \text{N} \end{cases}$

  a P(arrives) $= \dfrac{9}{10} \times \dfrac{5}{6} + \dfrac{1}{10} \times \dfrac{2}{15} = \dfrac{229}{300}$

  b P(S $|$ N) $= \dfrac{\text{P(S} \cap \text{N)}}{\text{P(N)}} = \dfrac{\frac{1}{10} \times \frac{13}{15}}{\frac{9}{10} \times \frac{1}{6} + \frac{1}{10} \times \frac{13}{15}} = \dfrac{26}{71}$

---

301 $\quad f(x) = x - 3 + \dfrac{6}{x+4}$

  a $\quad$ **i** VA is $x = -4$ $\qquad$ **ii** OA is $y = x - 3$

  $\qquad$ **iii** cuts x-axis when $y = 0$

  $\qquad\qquad\qquad \Rightarrow \quad 0 = x - 3 + \dfrac{6}{x+4}$

  $\qquad\qquad\qquad \Rightarrow \quad \dfrac{-6}{x+4} = x - 3$

  $\qquad\qquad\qquad\qquad \Rightarrow \quad -6 = x^2 + x - 12$

  $\qquad\qquad\qquad \Rightarrow \quad x^2 + x - 6 = 0$

  $\qquad\qquad\qquad \Rightarrow \quad (x-2)(x+3) = 0$ and so, $x = 2$ or -3

  $\qquad$ Cuts y-axis when $x = 0 \Rightarrow \quad y = -3 + \tfrac{3}{2} = -1\tfrac{1}{2}$

  b

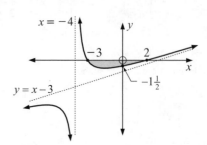

  c $\quad f(x) = k$ is a horizontal line, so we look for all possible horizontal lines which do not cut the graph.

  $\qquad$ Min. turning point is $(-1.55, -2.10)$

  $\qquad$ Max. turning point is $(-6.45, -11.9)$ {from a gcalc}

  $\qquad \therefore \quad f(x) = k$ has no real solutions for $x \in\,]-11.9, -2.10[$

  d $\qquad\qquad f(x) = x - 3 + 6(x+4)^{-1}$

  $\qquad \Rightarrow \quad f'(x) = 1 - 6(x+4)^{-2}(1)$

  $\qquad$ Now $\quad f'(x) = \tfrac{1}{3}$ {slope of tangent}

  $\qquad \therefore \quad 1 - \dfrac{6}{(x+4)^2} = \tfrac{1}{3} \quad \Rightarrow \quad \dfrac{6}{(x+4)^2} = \tfrac{2}{3}$

  $\qquad\qquad\qquad\qquad\qquad \Rightarrow \quad (x+4)^2 = 9$

  $\qquad\qquad\qquad\qquad\qquad\qquad \Rightarrow \quad x + 4 = \pm 3$

  $\qquad\qquad\qquad\qquad\qquad\qquad\qquad \Rightarrow \quad x = -1$ or -7

  $\qquad$ when $\quad x = -1, \quad y = -4 + \tfrac{6}{3} = -2$

  $\qquad$ when $\quad x = -7, \quad y = -10 + \tfrac{6}{-3} = -12$

  $\qquad \therefore$ at $(-1, -2)$ and at $(-7, -12)$

  e Area $= \displaystyle\int_{-3}^{2} 0 - \left(x - 3 + \dfrac{6}{x+4}\right) dx$

  $\qquad\qquad = \displaystyle\int_{-3}^{2} -x + 3 - \dfrac{6}{x+4}\, dx$

  $\qquad\qquad = \left[\dfrac{-x^2}{2} + 3x - 6\ln|x+4|\right]_{-3}^{2}$

  $\qquad\qquad = -2 + 6 - 6\ln 6 + \tfrac{9}{2} + 9 + 6\ln 1$

  $\qquad\qquad = 17\tfrac{1}{2} - 6\ln 6$ units^2

302 **a** $\quad \sin 77° \cos 17° - \cos 77° \sin 17° = \sin(77° - 17°) = \sin 60$

  $\qquad\qquad\qquad\qquad\qquad\qquad\qquad\qquad\qquad\qquad = \dfrac{\sqrt{3}}{2}$

  b **i** $P(n)$ is $\quad \cos\theta + \cos 3\theta + \ldots\ldots + \cos(2n-1)\theta$

  $\qquad\qquad\qquad = \dfrac{\sin 2n\theta}{2\sin\theta}$ for all $n \in \mathbb{Z}^+, \quad \sin\theta \neq 0$

  $\qquad$ **Proof** (By the Principle of Mathematical Induction)

  $\qquad$ (1) If $n = 1$, LHS $= \cos\theta$ and

  $\qquad\qquad\qquad$ RHS $= \dfrac{\sin 2\theta}{2\sin\theta} = \dfrac{2\sin\theta\cos\theta}{2\sin\theta} = \cos\theta$

  $\qquad\qquad$ i.e., LHS $=$ RHS $\Rightarrow \quad P(1)$ is true.

  $\qquad$ (2) If $P(k)$ is true,

  $\qquad\qquad S_k$ is $\cos\theta + \cos 3\theta + \ldots\ldots + \cos(2k-1)\theta = \dfrac{\sin(2k\theta)}{2\sin\theta}$

Thus S_{k+1} is

$$\cos\theta + \cos 3\theta + \ldots\ldots + \cos(2k-1)\theta + \cos(2k+1)\theta$$

$$= \frac{\sin 2k\theta}{2\sin\theta} + \cos(2k+1)\theta$$

$$= \frac{\sin(2k\theta) + 2\sin\theta\cos(2k+1)\theta}{2\sin\theta}$$

But $2\sin A\cos B = \sin(A+B) + \sin(A-B)$

$\Rightarrow 2\sin\theta\cos(2k+1)\theta$

$$= \sin(\theta + (2k+1)\theta) + \sin(\theta - (2k+1)\theta)$$

$$= \sin((2k+2)\theta) + \sin(-2k\theta)$$

$$= \sin 2(k+1)\theta - \sin(2k\theta)$$

$\therefore \quad S_{k+1}$ is $\dfrac{\sin(2k\theta) + \sin 2(k+1)\theta - \sin(2k\theta)}{2\sin\theta}$

$$= \frac{\sin 2(k+1)\theta}{2\sin\theta}$$

Thus $P(k+1)$ is true whenever $P(k)$ is true and $P(1)$ is true. $\Rightarrow P(n)$ is true {P of MI}

ii $(\cos\theta + i\sin\theta)^3$

$= \cos^3\theta + 3\cos^2\theta(i\sin\theta) + 3\cos\theta(i\sin\theta)^2 + (i\sin\theta)^3$

$= \cos^3\theta + i3\cos^2\theta\sin\theta - 3\cos\theta\sin^2\theta - i\sin^3\theta$

$= \left[\cos^3\theta - 3\cos\theta\sin^2\theta\right] + i\left[3\cos^2\theta\sin\theta - \sin^3\theta\right]$

iii $\cos 3\theta + i\sin 3\theta$

$= \operatorname{cis} 3\theta$

$= [\operatorname{cis}\theta]^3$ {De Moivre}

$= (\cos\theta + i\sin\theta)^3$

$= \left[\cos^3\theta - 3\cos\theta\sin^2\theta\right] + i\left[3\cos^2\theta\sin\theta - \sin^3\theta\right]$

Equating real parts

$$\cos 3\theta = \cos^3\theta - 3\cos\theta\sin^2\theta$$

$$= \cos^3\theta - 3\cos\theta(1 - \cos^2\theta)$$

i.e., $\cos 3\theta = 4\cos^3\theta - 3\cos\theta$

iv From **i** with $n = 2$

$$\cos\theta + \cos 3\theta = \frac{\sin 4\theta}{2\sin\theta}$$

$\therefore \quad \sin 4\theta = 2\sin\theta(\cos\theta + \cos 3\theta)$

$$= 2\sin\theta(4\cos^3\theta - 2\cos\theta)$$

$$= 8\sin\theta\cos^3\theta - 4\sin\theta\cos\theta$$

c $\displaystyle\int_{\frac{\pi}{6}}^{\frac{\pi}{2}} \frac{\sin 6\theta}{2\sin\theta}\, d\theta = \int_{\frac{\pi}{6}}^{\frac{\pi}{2}} (\cos\theta + \cos 3\theta + \cos 5\theta)\, d\theta$

$$= \left[\sin\theta + \tfrac{1}{3}\sin 3\theta + \tfrac{1}{5}\sin 5\theta\right]_{\frac{\pi}{6}}^{\frac{\pi}{2}}$$

$$= \left(1 - \tfrac{1}{3} + \tfrac{1}{5}\right) - \left(\tfrac{1}{2} + \tfrac{1}{3} + \tfrac{1}{10}\right)$$

$$= -\tfrac{1}{15}$$

303 a

$$L_1: \quad \overrightarrow{r} = \begin{bmatrix} 1 \\ 3 \\ 1 \end{bmatrix} + \lambda\begin{bmatrix} 2 \\ 3 \\ 2 \end{bmatrix} = \begin{bmatrix} 1 + 2\lambda \\ 3 + 3\lambda \\ 1 + 2\lambda \end{bmatrix}$$

$$L_2: \quad \overrightarrow{r} = \begin{bmatrix} 3 \\ \frac{3}{2} \\ -1 \end{bmatrix} + \mu\begin{bmatrix} -4 \\ \frac{3}{2} \\ 2 \end{bmatrix} = \begin{bmatrix} 3 - 4\mu \\ \frac{3}{2} + \frac{3}{2}\mu \\ -1 + 2\mu \end{bmatrix}$$

b If the lines intersect, then for some λ and μ

$1 + 2\lambda = 3 - 4\mu$ ...... (1)

$3 + 3\lambda = \frac{3}{2} + \frac{3}{2}\mu$ ...... (2)

$1 + 2\lambda = -1 + 2\mu$ ...... (3)

Using (1) and (3) we have $2\lambda + 4\mu = 2$ ...... (1)

$\qquad\qquad\qquad\qquad\qquad 2\lambda - 2\mu = -2$ ...... (3)

From (1) $-$ (3) $\quad 6\mu = 4$ or $\mu = \frac{2}{3}$

From (1) $\quad \lambda = 1 - 2\mu = 1 - 2(\frac{2}{3}) = -\frac{1}{3}$

But, for (2), $\quad 3 + 3\lambda = 3 + 3(-\frac{1}{3}) = 2$

and $\quad \frac{3}{2} + \frac{3}{2}\mu = \frac{3}{2} + \frac{3}{2}(\frac{2}{3}) = \frac{5}{2}$

So, equation(2) is not satisfied.

Hence, the lines do not intersect.

Since $\begin{bmatrix} 2 \\ 3 \\ 2 \end{bmatrix}$ and $\begin{bmatrix} -4 \\ \frac{3}{2} \\ 2 \end{bmatrix}$ are not parallel, the lines are not parallel.

c A normal to the plane is $\begin{bmatrix} -4 \\ \frac{3}{2} \\ 2 \end{bmatrix}$

Since the point $(1, 3, 1)$ lies on a line L_1, the plane

$$\begin{bmatrix} -4 \\ \frac{3}{2} \\ 2 \end{bmatrix} \bullet \begin{bmatrix} x \\ y \\ z \end{bmatrix} = \begin{bmatrix} -4 \\ \frac{3}{2} \\ 2 \end{bmatrix} \bullet \begin{bmatrix} 1 \\ 3 \\ 1 \end{bmatrix}$$

i.e., $-4x + \frac{3}{2}y + 2z = \frac{5}{2}$ which is $8x - 3y - 4z = 5$

is perpendicular to L_2 and intersects L_1

d A vector perpendicular to both lines is

$$\begin{bmatrix} 2 \\ 3 \\ 2 \end{bmatrix} \times \begin{bmatrix} -4 \\ \frac{3}{2} \\ 2 \end{bmatrix} = \begin{vmatrix} \mathbf{i} & \mathbf{j} & \mathbf{k} \\ 2 & 3 & 2 \\ -4 & \frac{3}{2} & 2 \end{vmatrix}$$

$$= \mathbf{i}\,(6 - 3) - \mathbf{j}\,(4 + 8) + \mathbf{k}\,(3 + 12)$$

$$= 3\mathbf{i} - 12\mathbf{j} + 15\mathbf{k}$$

$$= 3(\mathbf{i} - 4\mathbf{j} + 5\mathbf{k})$$

e Let X be a typical point on line L_1 and Y on line L_2

then $\overrightarrow{XY} = \left(\begin{bmatrix} 3 \\ \frac{3}{2} \\ -1 \end{bmatrix} + \mu\begin{bmatrix} -4 \\ \frac{3}{2} \\ 2 \end{bmatrix}\right) - \left(\begin{bmatrix} 1 \\ 3 \\ 1 \end{bmatrix} + \lambda\begin{bmatrix} 2 \\ 3 \\ 2 \end{bmatrix}\right)$

$$= \begin{bmatrix} 2 - 4\mu - 2\lambda \\ -\frac{3}{2} + \frac{3}{2}\mu - 3\lambda \\ -2 + 2\mu - 2\lambda \end{bmatrix}$$

From **d** this is perpendicular to both planes if there is a k so that

$$\begin{bmatrix} 2 - 4\mu - 2\lambda \\ -\frac{3}{2} + \frac{3}{2}\mu - 3\lambda \\ -2 + 2\mu - 2\lambda \end{bmatrix} = k\begin{bmatrix} 1 \\ -4 \\ 5 \end{bmatrix}$$

This gives the 3 equations $\quad 4\mu + 2\lambda + k = 2$

$$\tfrac{3}{2}\mu - 3\lambda + 4k = \tfrac{3}{2}$$

$$2\mu - 2\lambda - 5k = 2$$

Using technology, this has solution $\quad k = -\frac{1}{21}$

So, the distance between the lines is $\left| -\frac{1}{21}\begin{bmatrix} 1 \\ -4 \\ 5 \end{bmatrix} \right| = \frac{\sqrt{42}}{21}$ units

SOLUTIONS TO EXAMINATION PRACTICE SET 8

304 $u_1 = 500, \quad d = 50, \quad$ arithmetic

a $\quad u_{30}$

$= u_1 + 29d$

$= 500 + 29 \times 50$

$= 500 \times 1458$

$= 1950$ m

b $\quad u_1 + u_2 + u_3 + \ldots\ldots u_{30}$

$= S_{30}$

$= \frac{30}{2}(2u_1 + (n-1)d)$

$= 15(1000 + 29 \times 50)$

$= 36\,750$ metres

305

$$\frac{6}{7^x} - 2 \times 7^x = 1$$

$\Rightarrow \quad 6 - 2 \times (7^x)^2 = 7^x$

$\Rightarrow \quad 2(7^x)^2 + 7^x - 6 = 0$

$\qquad\qquad$ Let $\quad 7^x = m$

Thus $\quad 2m^2 + m - 6 = 0$

$\Rightarrow \quad (2m - 3)(m + 2) = 0$

$\qquad\qquad \Rightarrow \quad m = \frac{3}{2}$ or -2

Thus $\quad 7^x = \frac{3}{2}$ as $\quad 7^x > 0$ for all x

Hence $\quad x = \dfrac{\log\frac{3}{2}}{\log 7}$ (or $\log_7 \frac{3}{2}$)

306

$$(p+qi)^2 = -3 + 6i\sqrt{6}$$
$$\Rightarrow \quad p^2 - q^2 + 2pqi = -3 + 6\sqrt{6}i$$
$$\Rightarrow \quad p^2 - q^2 = -3 \quad \text{and} \quad pq = 3\sqrt{6}$$
$$\Rightarrow \quad p^2 - \frac{54}{p^2} + 3 = 0$$
$$\Rightarrow \quad p^4 + 3p^2 - 54 = 0$$
$$\Rightarrow \quad (p^2 + 9)(p^2 - 6) = 0 \quad \text{and so} \quad p^2 = -9 \text{ or } 6$$

But p is real $\therefore \quad p = \pm\sqrt{6}$

when $p = \sqrt{6}, \quad q = 3; \quad p = -\sqrt{6}, \quad q = -3$

So $p = \sqrt{6}, \quad q = 3 \quad$ or $\quad p = -\sqrt{6}, \quad q = -3$.

307 From the binomial theorem $\left(x + \dfrac{1}{x}\right)^9$ has general term

$$T_{r+1} = \binom{9}{r} x^r \left(x^{-1}\right)^{9-r} = \binom{9}{r} x^{2r-9}$$

a $2r - 9 = -1$ if $2r = 8$ or $r = 4$

$\therefore$ coefficient of $\dfrac{1}{x}$ is $\binom{9}{4} = 126$

b $2r - 9 = -2$ if $2r - 9 = -2$ or $2r = 7$ i.e., $r = \frac{7}{2}$

But k is an integer, $\therefore$ coefficient of $\dfrac{1}{x^2}$ is 0.

308 a Domain of f are all real numbers x such that $9 - x^2 > 0$
i.e., $x^2 < 9$ i.e., $-3 < x < 3$.

b Range of f are all real numbers y such that $y \geqslant \frac{1}{3}$.

309 a

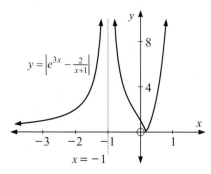

$$y = \left|e^{3x} - \frac{2}{x+1}\right|$$

b The graph of $y = \left|e^{3x} - \dfrac{2}{x+1}\right|$ intersects $y = 1$

if $x = 0$ or $x \approx 0.309$

310 If α and β are the roots of $x^2 - kx + 4 = 0$

then $(x - \alpha)(x - \beta) = x^2 - (\alpha + \beta)x + \alpha\beta$

i.e., $\alpha + \beta = k$ and $\alpha\beta = 4$

a $\alpha^2 + \beta^2 = (\alpha + \beta)^2 - 2\alpha\beta = k^2 - 2(4) = k^2 - 8$

b All quadratic equation with roots $\dfrac{1}{\alpha}$ and $\dfrac{1}{\beta}$ have form

$$a\left(x - \frac{1}{\alpha}\right)\left(x - \frac{1}{\beta}\right) = 0, \quad a \neq 0$$

i.e., $a\left[x^2 - \left(\dfrac{1}{\alpha} + \dfrac{1}{\beta}\right)x + \dfrac{1}{\alpha\beta}\right] = 0$

But $\dfrac{1}{\alpha} + \dfrac{1}{\beta} = \dfrac{\beta + \alpha}{\alpha\beta} = \dfrac{k}{4}$ and $\dfrac{1}{\alpha\beta} = \dfrac{1}{4}$

Equation could be $a\left[x^2 - \frac{k}{4}x + \frac{1}{4}\right] = 0, \quad a \neq 0$.

311

$$\log\left(x^2 y^3\right) = a$$
i.e., $\log(x^2) + \log(y^3) = a$
i.e., $2\log x + 3\log y = a \quad \ldots\ldots (1)$
$$\log\frac{x}{y} = b$$
i.e., $\log x - \log y = b \quad \ldots\ldots (2)$

$(1) + 3\times (2)$ gives $5\log x = a + 3b$ i.e., $\log x = \dfrac{a + 3b}{5}$

$(1) - 2\times (2)$ gives $5\log y = a - 2b$ i.e., $\log y = \dfrac{a - 2b}{5}$

312

$$\sin x = \cos\left(x + \frac{\pi}{3}\right)$$
$$\Rightarrow \quad \sin x = \cos x \cos\frac{\pi}{3} - \sin x \sin\frac{\pi}{3}$$
$$\Rightarrow \quad \sin x = \cos x \left(\frac{1}{2}\right) - \sin x \left(\frac{\sqrt{3}}{2}\right)$$
$$\Rightarrow \quad \sin x \left(1 + \frac{\sqrt{3}}{2}\right) = \frac{1}{2}\cos x$$
$$\Rightarrow \quad \frac{\sin x}{\cos x} = \frac{\frac{1}{2}}{1 + \frac{\sqrt{3}}{2}} = \frac{1}{2 + \sqrt{3}}$$
$$\Rightarrow \quad \tan x = \left(\frac{1}{2 + \sqrt{3}}\right)\left(\frac{2 - \sqrt{3}}{2 - \sqrt{3}}\right)$$
$$\Rightarrow \quad \tan x = \frac{2 - \sqrt{3}}{1} = 2 - \sqrt{3}$$

313

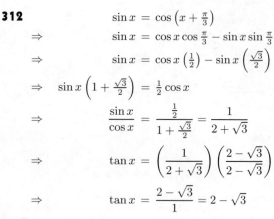

a $\cos B = \dfrac{3^2 + 5^2 - 7^2}{2 \times 3 \times 5} = \dfrac{-15}{30} = -\dfrac{1}{2}$

b and so $\sin B = \dfrac{\sqrt{3}}{2}$

and area $= \frac{1}{2} \times 3 \times 5 \times \sin B$
$$= \frac{15}{2} \times \frac{\sqrt{3}}{2}$$
$$= \frac{15}{4}\sqrt{3} \text{ cm}^2$$

314 $\sin\gamma = \dfrac{\sqrt{3}}{7} \quad \therefore \quad \cos 2\gamma = 1 - 2\sin^2\gamma$
$$= 1 - 2\left(\frac{3}{49}\right)$$
$$= 1 - \frac{6}{49}$$
$$= \frac{43}{49}$$

315

B (6, 1, 1) ——→ C

A (2, −1, 3) ——— D (7, 5, 6)

$$\overrightarrow{AB} = \begin{bmatrix} 4 \\ 2 \\ -2 \end{bmatrix}$$

$$\overrightarrow{AD} = \begin{bmatrix} 5 \\ 6 \\ 3 \end{bmatrix}$$

Area of parallelogram is

$$|\overrightarrow{AB} \times \overrightarrow{AD}| = \left\|\begin{matrix} \mathbf{i} & \mathbf{j} & \mathbf{k} \\ 4 & 2 & -2 \\ 5 & 6 & 3 \end{matrix}\right\|$$
$$= |\mathbf{i}(6 + 12) - \mathbf{j}(12 + 10) + \mathbf{k}(24 - 10)|$$
$$= |18\mathbf{i} - 22\mathbf{k} + 14\mathbf{k}|$$
$$= \sqrt{18^2 + 22^2 + 14^2}$$
$$\doteqdot 31.7 \text{ units}^2$$

316 a $\overrightarrow{AB} = \begin{bmatrix} -2 \\ -1 \\ 6 \end{bmatrix}, \quad \overrightarrow{AC} = \begin{bmatrix} 5 \\ 2 \\ 2 \end{bmatrix}$

and $\overrightarrow{AB} \bullet \overrightarrow{AC} = \begin{bmatrix} -2 \\ -1 \\ 6 \end{bmatrix}\begin{bmatrix} 5 \\ 2 \\ 2 \end{bmatrix} = -10 - 2 + 12 = 0$

So $\overrightarrow{AB}$ is perpendicular to $\overrightarrow{AC}$.

b $\overrightarrow{BA} = \begin{bmatrix} 2 \\ 1 \\ -6 \end{bmatrix}, \quad \overrightarrow{BC} = \begin{bmatrix} 7 \\ 3 \\ -4 \end{bmatrix}$. Let θ be the angle ABC,

then

$$\begin{bmatrix} 2 \\ 1 \\ -6 \end{bmatrix} \bullet \begin{bmatrix} 7 \\ 3 \\ -4 \end{bmatrix} = \sqrt{4 + 1 + 36}\sqrt{49 + 9 + 16}\cos\theta$$
$$\Rightarrow \quad 14 + 3 + 24 = \sqrt{41}\sqrt{74}\cos\theta$$

$$\Rightarrow \quad \cos\theta = \frac{41}{\sqrt{41}\sqrt{74}}$$

$$\Rightarrow \quad \theta = \arccos\left(\frac{41}{\sqrt{41}\sqrt{74}}\right) \approx 41.9^o$$

or

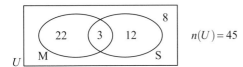

B(2, 1, 5)

$\begin{bmatrix} -2 \\ -1 \\ 6 \end{bmatrix}$

$\begin{bmatrix} 5 \\ 2 \\ 2 \end{bmatrix}$

A(4, 2, −1)   C(9, 4, 1)

From **a** $\angle BAC = 90^o$

so $\tan\angle ABC = \dfrac{\sqrt{5^2 + 2^2 + 2^2}}{\sqrt{(-2)^2 + (-1)^2 + 6^2}} = \sqrt{\dfrac{33}{41}}$

$\tan\angle ABC \approx 0.8971$ and so $\angle ABC \approx 41.9^o$

317 Let M = students with American passport
S = students with Australian passport

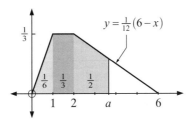

22   3   12   8

$n(U) = 45$

U M   S

Total number of students is $45 = 8 + 25 + 15 - n(M \cap S)$
i.e., $n(M \cap S) = 3$

So there are 3 students who hold both American and Australian passports.

a Probability a student holds both Australian and American passport is $\frac{3}{45}$ (or $\frac{1}{15}$).

b Probability a student has neither passport is $\frac{8}{45}$.

c Probability a student has only 1 passport is $\frac{34}{45}$.

318 a Let X be the number of mistakes the typist makes in 1500 words. Since the typist makes an average of $m = 6$ errors per 1500 words we assume that $X \sim Po(6)$.

Hence, $P(X \leqslant 5) = \text{poissoncdf}(6, 5) \approx 0.446$

b $P(X \leqslant 5 \mid X \geqslant 1) = \dfrac{P(X \leqslant 5 \cap X \geqslant 1)}{P(X \geqslant 1)}$

$= \dfrac{P(1 \leqslant X \leqslant 5)}{P(X \geqslant 1)}$

$= \dfrac{P(X \leqslant 5) - P(X = 0)}{1 - P(X = 0)}$

$= \dfrac{0.445680 - 0.002479}{1 - 0.002479}$

≈ 0.444

319 a Since f is a density function the area between graph and x-axis is 1.

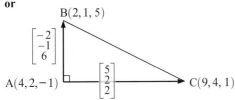

$\frac{1}{3}$

$y = \frac{1}{12}(6 - x)$

$\frac{1}{6}$ $\frac{1}{3}$ $\frac{1}{2}$

1   2 a 6

Since area from 0 to 2 is $\frac{1}{6} + \frac{1}{3} = \frac{1}{2}$ we have to find a
so that area between graph and x-axis for $2 \leqslant x \leqslant a$ is $\frac{1}{2}$.

i.e., $\displaystyle\int_2^a \frac{1}{12}(6 - x)\,dx = \frac{1}{2}$

$\Rightarrow \displaystyle\int_2^a (6 - x)\,dx = 6$

$\Rightarrow \left[6x - \dfrac{x^2}{2}\right]_2^a = 6$

$\Rightarrow \left(6a - \dfrac{a^2}{2}\right) - (12 - 2) = 6$

$\Rightarrow \quad -\dfrac{a^2}{2} + 6a - 16 = 0$

$\Rightarrow \quad a^2 - 12a + 32 = 0$

$\Rightarrow \quad (a - 4)(a - 8) = 0$

$\Rightarrow \quad a = 4 \text{ or } 8$

But if $a = 8$, the graph lies below the x-axis, hence $a = 4$ is the only solution.

b The median value of X is the point m for which
$P(X \leqslant m) = P(X \geqslant m) = \frac{1}{2}$
From the above discusssion $m = 2$.

320 a $f(x) = \dfrac{x^3 + 5x^2 - 2x}{x^2 + 3x - 10}$ has

VAs when $x^2 + 3x - 10 = 0$
$(x + 5)(x - 2) = 0$
$x = -5 \text{ or } 2$

$\therefore$ VAs are $x = -5$ and $x = 2$

$$\begin{array}{r} x + 2 \\ x^2 + 3x - 10 \overline{\smash{\big)}\, x^3 + 5x^2 - 2x } \\ \underline{x^3 + 3x^2 - 10x } \\ 2x^2 + 8x + 0 \\ \underline{2x^2 + 6x - 20} \\ 2x + 20 \end{array}$$

$\therefore \quad f(x) = x + 2 + \dfrac{2x + 20}{x^2 + 3x - 10}$

as $|x| \to \infty$, $f(x) \to x + 2$
and so $y = x + 2$ is an oblique asymptote.

b The graph crosses its oblique asymptote when $2x + 20 = 0$
i.e., $x = -10$ i.e., at $(-10, -8)$.

321
$$x^3 y^2 - xy + y = 4$$

when $x = 1$, $y^2 - y + y = 4 \Rightarrow y^2 = 4$
$\Rightarrow y = \pm 2$

But $y > 0$, $\therefore y = 2$
So, point of contact is $(1, 2)$.

Now $3x^2 y^2 + x^3\left(2y\dfrac{dy}{dx}\right) - \left[1y + x\dfrac{dy}{dx}\right] + \dfrac{dy}{dx} = 0$

Thus $12 + 4\dfrac{dy}{dx} - \left[2 + \dfrac{dy}{dx}\right] + \dfrac{dy}{dx} = 0$

$\Rightarrow 10 + 4\dfrac{dy}{dx} = 0$

$\Rightarrow \dfrac{dy}{dx} = -\dfrac{5}{2}$

$\therefore$ the tangent has equation $y - 2 = -\dfrac{5}{2}(x - 1)$

i.e., $2y - 4 = -5x + 5$

i.e., $5x + 2y = 9$

322 $\displaystyle\int x\sqrt{x - 3}\,dx$ $\qquad u = x - 3$

$= \displaystyle\int (u + 3)\sqrt{u}\,du$ $\qquad \dfrac{du}{dx} = 1$

$= \displaystyle\int \left(u^{\frac{3}{2}} + 3u^{\frac{1}{2}}\right)du$

$= \dfrac{u^{\frac{5}{2}}}{\frac{5}{2}} + \dfrac{3u^{\frac{3}{2}}}{\frac{3}{2}} + c$

$= \dfrac{2}{5}(x - 3)^{\frac{5}{2}} + 2(x - 3)^{\frac{3}{2}} + c$

323 a $f(x) = \sin 2x + \sin 4x, \quad 0 \leqslant x \leqslant \pi$
$= \sin 2x + 2\sin 2x \cos 2x$
$= \sin 2x(1 + 2\cos 2x)$

which is $0 \Leftrightarrow \sin 2x = 0$ or $\cos 2x = -\dfrac{1}{2}$

$\Leftrightarrow \quad 2x = k\pi$

or $\quad 2x = \frac{2\pi}{3}$

or $\quad 2x = \frac{4\pi}{3}$

$\Leftrightarrow \quad x = 0, \frac{\pi}{2}, \pi, \frac{\pi}{3}, \frac{2\pi}{3}$

Using a gcalc the graph is

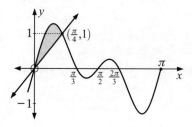

b We notice that

when $x = 0$, $y = \frac{4}{\pi}(0) = 0$ and $f(0) = 0 + 0 = 0$ and

when $x = \frac{\pi}{4}$, $y = \frac{4}{\pi}\left(\frac{\pi}{4}\right) = 1$ and

$f\left(\frac{\pi}{4}\right) = \sin\left(\frac{\pi}{2}\right) + \sin(\pi) = 1 + 0 = 1$

$\therefore \quad y = \frac{4}{\pi}x$ meets $y = f(x)$ at the origin and at $\left(\frac{\pi}{4}, 1\right)$.

c $\therefore$ shaded area

$= \int_0^{\frac{\pi}{4}} \left(f(x) - \frac{4}{\pi}x\right) dx$

$= \int_0^{\frac{\pi}{4}} \left(\sin 2x + \sin 4x - \frac{4}{\pi}x\right) dx$

$= \left[-\frac{1}{2}\cos 2x - \frac{1}{4}\cos 4x - \frac{4}{\pi}\frac{x^2}{2}\right]_0^{\frac{\pi}{4}}$

$= -\frac{1}{2}(0) - \frac{1}{4}(-1) - \frac{2}{\pi}\left(\frac{\pi^2}{16}\right) + \frac{1}{2}(1) + \frac{1}{4}(1) + 0$

$= \frac{1}{4} - \frac{\pi}{8} + \frac{1}{2} + \frac{1}{4}$

$= \left(1 - \frac{\pi}{8}\right)$ units^2

324 $\int \arcsin x \, dx$

$= \int 1 \arcsin x \, dx$ $\quad \begin{bmatrix} u' = 1 & v = \arcsin x \\ u = x & v' = \dfrac{1}{\sqrt{1-x^2}} \end{bmatrix}$

$= x \arcsin x - \int \dfrac{x}{\sqrt{1-x^2}} \, dx$ $\quad \begin{bmatrix} w = 1 - x^2 \\ \dfrac{dw}{dx} = -2x \end{bmatrix}$

$= x \arcsin x - \int w^{-\frac{1}{2}} \left(\dfrac{1}{-2}\dfrac{dw}{dx}\right) dx$

$= x \arcsin x + \frac{1}{2} \int w^{-\frac{1}{2}} \, dw$

$= x \arcsin x + \frac{1}{2}\dfrac{w^{\frac{1}{2}}}{\frac{1}{2}} + c$

$= x \arcsin x + \sqrt{1 - x^2} + c$

325 $v = 2s$, $\therefore \quad \dfrac{ds}{dt} = 2s$

$\Rightarrow \quad \dfrac{1}{s}\dfrac{ds}{dt} = 2$

$\Rightarrow \quad \int \dfrac{1}{s}\dfrac{ds}{dt} \, dt = \int 2 \, dt$

$\Rightarrow \quad \int \dfrac{1}{s} \, ds = \int 2 \, dt$

$\Rightarrow \quad \ln|s| = 2t + c$

$\Rightarrow \quad |s| = e^{2t+c} = e^c e^{2t}$

$\Rightarrow \quad s = \pm e^c e^{2t}$

$\Rightarrow \quad s = Ae^{2t}$, A a constant.

But when $t = 0$, $s = 3$ $\quad \therefore \quad A = 3$

Thus $s = 3e^{2t}$ metres.

326 $\quad (x^2 + 1)\dfrac{dy}{dx} = 2xy$

$\Rightarrow \quad \dfrac{1}{y}\dfrac{dy}{dx} = \dfrac{2x}{x^2 + 1}$

$\Rightarrow \quad \int \dfrac{1}{y}\dfrac{dy}{dx} \, dx = \int \dfrac{2x}{x^2 + 1} \, dx$

$\Rightarrow \quad \ln|y| = \ln|x^2 + 1| + c$

$\Rightarrow \quad \ln|y| = \ln(x^2 + 1) + c$

$\Rightarrow \qquad \{$as $x^2 + 1 > 0$ for all $x\}$

But when $x = 2$, $y = 10$

$\Rightarrow \quad \ln 10 = \ln 5 + c$ and so $c = \ln 2$

Thus $\ln|y| = \ln(x^2 + 1) + \ln 2$

$\Rightarrow \quad \ln|y| = \ln 2(x^2 + 1)$

$\qquad |y| = 2(x^2 + 1)$

$\Rightarrow \quad y = \pm 2(x^2 + 1)$

$\Rightarrow \quad y = 2(x^2 + 1)$ $\{$as when $x = 2$, $y = 10\}$

327 a l_1 meets the plane $2x + y - z = 2$

if $2(3\lambda - 4) + 1(\lambda + 2) - (2\lambda - 1) = 2$

i.e., $5\lambda - 5 = 2$

i.e., $\lambda = \frac{7}{5}$

and $x = \frac{1}{5}$, $y = \frac{17}{5}$, $z = \frac{9}{5}$

So, they meet at $\left(\frac{1}{5}, \frac{17}{5}, \frac{9}{5}\right)$.

b The lines meet if

$(3\lambda - 4) = \dfrac{(\lambda + 2) - 5}{2} = \dfrac{-(2\lambda - 1) - 1}{2}$

From the first equation $\quad 2(3\lambda - 4) = \lambda - 3$

i.e., $6\lambda - 8 = \lambda - 3$

i.e., $\lambda = 1$

Substituting $\lambda = 1$ in the equation for l_2 we have

$(3 - 4) = \dfrac{(1 + 2) - 5}{2} = \dfrac{-(2 - 1) - 1}{2}$

i.e., $-1 = -1 = -1$

As this checks the point $x = -1$, $y = 3$, $z = 1$ lies on both lines.

c Line l_1 has direction $\begin{bmatrix} 3 \\ 1 \\ 2 \end{bmatrix}$, line l_2 has direction $\begin{bmatrix} 1 \\ 2 \\ -2 \end{bmatrix}$

As $(-1, 3, 1)$ is a point on both lines, and equation of the plane that contains both l_1 and l_2 is

$\begin{bmatrix} x \\ y \\ z \end{bmatrix} = \begin{bmatrix} -1 \\ 3 \\ 1 \end{bmatrix} + s\begin{bmatrix} 3 \\ 1 \\ 2 \end{bmatrix} + t\begin{bmatrix} 1 \\ 2 \\ -2 \end{bmatrix}$

or $\begin{bmatrix} 3 \\ 1 \\ 2 \end{bmatrix} \times \begin{bmatrix} 1 \\ 2 \\ -2 \end{bmatrix} = \begin{vmatrix} \mathbf{i} & \mathbf{j} & \mathbf{k} \\ 3 & 1 & 2 \\ 1 & 2 & -2 \end{vmatrix} = \begin{bmatrix} -6 \\ 8 \\ 5 \end{bmatrix}$

An equation is $\begin{bmatrix} -6 \\ 8 \\ 5 \end{bmatrix} \bullet \begin{bmatrix} x \\ y \\ z \end{bmatrix} = \begin{bmatrix} -6 \\ 8 \\ 5 \end{bmatrix} \bullet \begin{bmatrix} -1 \\ 3 \\ 1 \end{bmatrix}$

i.e., $-6x + 8y + 5z = 35$

328 $f(x) = e^{\sin^2 x}$, $0 \leqslant x \leqslant \pi$

a i $f'(x) = e^{\sin^2 x} \times 2\sin x \cos x = \sin 2x \, e^{\sin^2 x}$

ii $f'(x) = 0 \quad \Leftrightarrow \quad \sin 2x = 0$

$\Leftrightarrow \quad 2x = 0 + k\pi$

$\Leftrightarrow \quad x = k\frac{\pi}{2}$

$\Leftrightarrow \quad x = 0, \frac{\pi}{2}, \pi$

Sign diagram of $f'(x)$:

∴ local min. at $(0, 1)$ and $(\pi, 1)$

local max. at $(\frac{\pi}{2}, e)$

iii $f''(x) = 2\cos 2x e^{\sin^2 x} + \sin 2x \sin 2x e^{\sin^2 x}$

$= e^{\sin^2 x}[2\cos 2x + \sin^2 2x]$

b **i** At $x = \frac{3\pi}{4}$, $\sin x = \frac{1}{\sqrt{2}}$, $\sin 2x = -1$

∴ $f'(x) = -1e^{\frac{1}{2}} = -\sqrt{e}$

∴ tangent at $\left(\frac{3\pi}{4}, \sqrt{e}\right)$ has equation

$y - \sqrt{e} = -\sqrt{e}\left(x - \frac{3\pi}{4}\right)$

i.e., $y = -\sqrt{e}x + \sqrt{e} + \frac{3\pi\sqrt{e}}{4}$

ii The tangent cuts the x-axis when $y = 0$

$\Rightarrow 0 = -\sqrt{e}x + \sqrt{e} + \frac{3\pi\sqrt{e}}{4}$

$\Rightarrow 0 = -x + 1 + \frac{3\pi}{4}$

$\Rightarrow x = 1 + \frac{3\pi}{4}$

c

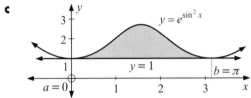

Area $= \int_0^\pi \left(e^{\sin^2 x} - 1\right)\, dx \approx 2.37$ units^2 {gcalc}

329 a i

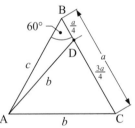

As $BD : DC = 1 : 3$, $BD = \frac{a}{4}$, $DC = \frac{3a}{4}$

By the Cosine Rule

In $\triangle ABC$, $b^2 = c^2 + a^2 - 2ac\cos 60°$

$\Rightarrow b^2 = c^2 + a^2 - ac$ ...... (1)

In $\triangle ABD$, $b^2 = c^2 + \left(\frac{a}{4}\right)^2 - 2c\left(\frac{a}{4}\right)\cos 60°$

$\Rightarrow b^2 = c^2 + \frac{a^2}{16} - \frac{ac}{4}$ ...... (2)

ii From (1) and (2)

$c^2 + a^2 - ac = c^2 + \frac{a^2}{16} - \frac{ac}{4}$

$\Rightarrow 16a^2 - 16ac = a^2 - 4ac$

$\Rightarrow 15a^2 - 12ac = 0$

$\Rightarrow 3a(5a - 4c) = 0$

$\Rightarrow 5a = 4c$

$\Rightarrow a = \frac{4}{5}c$

b

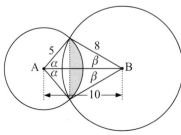

By the Cosine Rule $\cos\alpha = \frac{5^2 + 10^2 - 8^2}{2 \times 5 \times 10} = \frac{61}{100}$

$\cos\beta = \frac{10^2 + 8^2 - 5^2}{2 \times 10 \times 8} = \frac{139}{160}$

Thus, in radians, $\alpha \approx 0.9147$ and $\beta \approx 0.5181$

So, $2\alpha \approx 1.829$ and $2\beta \approx 1.036$

Using area of segment $= \frac{1}{2}r^2(\theta - \sin\theta)$

Total area

$= \frac{1}{2} \times 5^2 \times (2\alpha - \sin 2\alpha) + \frac{1}{2} \times 8^2 \times (2\beta - \sin 2\beta)$

$= \frac{25}{2}(1.829 - \sin 1.829) + 32(1.036 - \sin 1.036)$

≈ 16.4 cm^2

SOLUTIONS TO EXAMINATION PRACTICE SET 9

330 a Let $z = x + iy$, $x, y \in \mathbb{R}$

∴ $(x + iy)^2 = 2(x - iy)$

$\Rightarrow x^2 - y^2 + 2xyi = 2x - 2yi$

$\Rightarrow x^2 - y^2 = 2x$ and $2xy = -2y$

Thus, $2y(x + 1) = 0$

$\Rightarrow y = 0$ or $x = -1$.

As z is non real, $y \neq 0$ and so $x = -1$

Hence, $1 - y^2 = -2$

$\Rightarrow y^2 = 3$

$\Rightarrow y = \pm\sqrt{3}$

Thus, $z = -1 + i\sqrt{3}$ or $-1 - i\sqrt{3}$

b $|z| < 2|z - 1 - i|$

$\Rightarrow \sqrt{x^2 + 4} < 2|x + 2i - 1 - i|$

$\Rightarrow \sqrt{x^2 + 4} < 2\sqrt{(x - 1)^2 + 1}$

$\Rightarrow x^2 + 4 < 4\left[x^2 - 2x + 2\right]$

$\Rightarrow x^2 + 4 < 4x^2 - 8x + 8$

$\Rightarrow 3x^2 - 8x + 4 > 0$

$\Rightarrow (3x - 2)(x - 2) > 0$

$\Rightarrow x \in \,]-\infty, \frac{2}{3}[\, \cup \,]2, \infty[$.

331 $\log_6(x + 3) = 1 - \log_6(x - 2)$

$\Rightarrow \log_6(x + 3) + \log_6(x - 2) = 1$

$\Rightarrow \log_6(x + 3)(x - 2) = 1$

$\Rightarrow (x + 3)(x - 2) = 6^1$

$\Rightarrow x^2 + x - 6 = 6$

$\Rightarrow x^2 + x - 12 = 0$

$\Rightarrow (x + 4)(x - 3) = 0$

$\Rightarrow x = -4$ or 3

But $x + 3 > 0$ and $x - 2 > 0$

$\Rightarrow x > 2$

Hence, $x = 3$.

332 Growth is geometric with $u_1 = 1250$ and $r = 1.03$

We need to find n such that $u_n > 2000$.

i.e., $u_1 r^{n-1} > 2000$

$\Rightarrow 1250(1.03)^{n-1} > 2000$

$\Rightarrow (1.03)^{n-1} > 1.6$

$\Rightarrow \log(1.03)^{n-1} > \log(1.6)$

$\Rightarrow n - 1 > \frac{\log(1.6)}{\log(1.03)}$

$\Rightarrow n > \frac{\log(1.6)}{\log(1.03)} + 1$

$\Rightarrow n > 16.9......$

i.e., $n = 17, 18, 19, ...$

i.e., 17 years

u_1 corresponds to year 2005

u_{17} corresponds to year 2021 i.e., in year 2021.

333 Domain of f is all real numbers x such that $x^2 - 1 \geqslant 0$

i.e., $x^2 \geqslant 1$ i.e., $x \leqslant -1$ or $x \geqslant 1$.

Range of f is all real numbers $y \geqslant e^0 + 0$ i.e., $y \geqslant 1$

Graph of $y = e^{x^2-1} + \sqrt{x^2-1}$ for $-2 \leqslant x \leqslant 0$.

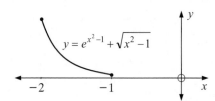

334 a f is defined providing $x > 0$, $x + 3 > 0$ and $x^2 - 9 > 0$

i.e., $x > 0$, $x > -3$ and $x < -3$ or $x > 3$.

The three conditions are satisfied if $x > 3$.

Domain of f is $x \in \mathbb{R}$, with $x > 3$

b $\ln x + \ln(x + 3) - \ln(x^2 - 9) = \ln\left(\dfrac{x(x+3)}{x^2-9}\right)$

$$= \ln\left(\dfrac{x(x+3)}{(x-3)(x+3)}\right)$$

$$= \ln\left(\dfrac{x}{x-3}\right)$$

c f is $y = \ln\left(\dfrac{x}{x-3}\right)$ and so f^{-1} is $x = \ln\left(\dfrac{y}{y-3}\right)$

i.e., $\dfrac{y}{y-3} = e^x \quad \Rightarrow \quad y = (y-3)e^x$

$\Rightarrow \quad y = ye^x - 3e^x$

$\Rightarrow \quad y(1 - e^x) = -3e^x$

i.e., $y = \dfrac{3e^x}{e^x - 1}$ and so $f^{-1}(x) = \dfrac{3e^x}{e^x - 1}$

335 If $1 + ai$ is a zero of $x^2 + ax + 5$, then so is $1 - ai$.

These have sum 2 and product $1 + a^2$ and so come from the quadratic equation $x^2 - 2x + (1 + a^2) = 0$

Comparing coefficients, $a = -2$ and $1 + a^2 = 5$

So $a = -2$ (as $a \neq 2$).

336 Since -2 and 3 are x-intercepts the polynomial has factors $(x + 2)$ and $(x - 3)$.

Since the polynomial touches the x-axis at 1, then $(x - 1)^2$ is a factor.

Hence, $P(x) = a(x + 2)(x - 3)(x - 1)^2$

But $P(0) = a(2)(-3)(1) = -12$ and so $a = 2$

Hence $f(x)$ $2(x + 2)(x - 3)(x - 1)^2$

$2(x^2 - x - 6)(x^2 - 2x + 1)$

$2x^4 - 6x^3 - 6x^2 + 22x - 12$

337

$\therefore \quad \tan A = \frac{4}{3}$ and $\tan B = \frac{8}{15}$

$\tan(A + B) = \dfrac{\tan A + \tan B}{1 - \tan A \tan B}$

$$= \left[\dfrac{\frac{4}{3} + \frac{8}{15}}{1 - \left(\frac{4}{3}\right)\left(\frac{8}{15}\right)}\right] \dfrac{45}{45}$$

$$= \dfrac{60 + 24}{45 - 32}$$

$$= \dfrac{84}{13}$$

338 $\sqrt{2}\sin x = \tan x, \quad 0 \leqslant x \leqslant 2\pi$

$\Rightarrow \quad \sqrt{2}\sin x = \dfrac{\sin x}{\cos x}$

$\Rightarrow \quad \sqrt{2}\sin x \cos x = \sin x$

$\Rightarrow \quad \sqrt{2}\sin x \cos x - \sin x = 0$

$\Rightarrow \quad \sin x(\sqrt{2}\cos x - 1) = 0$

$\Rightarrow \quad \sin x = 0 \quad \text{or} \quad \cos x = \dfrac{1}{\sqrt{2}}$

$\Rightarrow \quad x = 0, \frac{\pi}{4}, \pi, \frac{7\pi}{4}, 2\pi$

339 $\sin A = -\frac{2}{3}, \quad 0 < A < \frac{3\pi}{2}$ A is in quadrant 3.

$\tan A = \dfrac{2}{\sqrt{5}}$

Now $\tan 2A = \dfrac{2\tan A}{1 - \tan^2 A} = \dfrac{\frac{4}{\sqrt{5}}}{1 - \frac{4}{5}}$

$\therefore \quad \tan 2A = \dfrac{\frac{4}{\sqrt{5}}}{\frac{1}{5}} = \dfrac{4}{\sqrt{5}} \times 5 = 4\sqrt{5}$

340 $\begin{bmatrix} 16 & -8 \\ 2x & 16 \end{bmatrix} = \begin{bmatrix} x & y \\ x & 0 \end{bmatrix}\begin{bmatrix} 2 & x \\ 3 & -3 \end{bmatrix} = \begin{bmatrix} 2x + 3y & x^2 - 3y \\ 2x & x^2 \end{bmatrix}$

This gives the three equations $\quad 2x + 3y = 16$ ...... (1)

$x^2 - 3y = -8$ ...... (2)

$x^2 = 16$ ...... (3)

From (3) $\quad x = \pm 4$

From (2) $\quad 16 - 3y = -8$ i.e., $y = 8$

From (1) $\quad 2x + 24 = 16 \quad \Rightarrow \quad x = -4$

Solution is $\quad x = -4$ and $y = 8$.

341 a $\mathbf{A} \times \mathbf{B} = \begin{vmatrix} \mathbf{i} & \mathbf{j} & \mathbf{k} \\ 1 & 1 & -3 \\ 0 & 1 & 2 \end{vmatrix} = \mathbf{i}(2 + 3) - \mathbf{j}(2 - 0) + \mathbf{k}(1 - 0)$

$= \begin{bmatrix} 5 \\ -2 \\ 1 \end{bmatrix}$

b $\mathbf{A} \times \mathbf{B}$ is perpendicular to both $\mathbf{A}$ and $\mathbf{B}$

$|\mathbf{A} \times \mathbf{B}| = \sqrt{5^2 + (-2)^2 + 1^2} = \sqrt{30}$

A vector perpendicular to $\mathbf{A}$ and $\mathbf{B}$ of length 5 units is

$\dfrac{5}{\sqrt{30}}\begin{bmatrix} 5 \\ -2 \\ 1 \end{bmatrix} = \begin{bmatrix} \frac{25}{\sqrt{30}} \\ \frac{-10}{\sqrt{30}} \\ \frac{5}{\sqrt{30}} \end{bmatrix}$

342 A double is $(1, 1), (2, 2), (3, 3), (4, 4), (5, 5), (6, 6)$.

$\therefore \quad P(\text{double}) = \frac{6}{36} = \frac{1}{6}$.

$P(\text{no double in } n \text{ throws}) = \binom{n}{0}\left(\frac{1}{6}\right)^0\left(\frac{5}{6}\right)^n = \left(\frac{5}{6}\right)^n$.

$\Rightarrow \quad P(\text{double in } n \text{ throws}) = 1 - \left(\frac{5}{6}\right)^n$.

So, we need to find n such that $\quad 1 - \left(\frac{5}{6}\right)^n \geqslant 0.7$

$\Rightarrow \quad \left(\frac{5}{6}\right)^n \leqslant 0.3$

$\Rightarrow \quad \log\left(\frac{5}{6}\right)^n \leqslant \log(0.3)$

$\Rightarrow \quad n\log\left(\frac{5}{6}\right) \leqslant \log(0.3)$

$\Rightarrow \quad n \geqslant \dfrac{\log(0.3)}{\log\left(\frac{5}{6}\right)}$

$\Rightarrow \quad n \geqslant 6.6.....$

and since n is an integer, $\quad n \geqslant 7$.

343 Each of the nine tickets can be allocated in 2 ways; either to one student, or the other.

There are 2^9 ways of allocating 9 tickets if there are no restrictions.

There are 2 ways in which one student has no tickets allocated.

Total number of ways of allocating 9 tickets so that each student has a least 1 ticket is $2^9 - 2 = 510$ ways.

344

$$P(|Z|) \leqslant a \qquad \text{Thus,} \quad 1 - 2P(Z \leqslant -a) = 0.72$$
$$= P(-a \leqslant Z \leqslant a) \qquad \Rightarrow \quad 2P(Z \leqslant -a) = 0.28$$
$$= 1 - 2P(Z \leqslant -a) \qquad \Rightarrow \quad P(Z \leqslant -a) = 0.14$$

But $Z \sim N(0, 1^2) \Rightarrow -a = \text{invNorm}(0.14)$
$$\Rightarrow -a = -1.0803$$
$$\Rightarrow a \approx 1.08$$

345 $f(x) = \dfrac{ax+b}{x^2 - 5x + 7}$ Now $f(3) = 5 \Rightarrow \dfrac{3a+b}{9 - 15 + 7} = 5$

$$\text{i.e.,} \quad 3a + b = 5 \quad \text{...... (1)}$$

Also $f'(x) = \dfrac{a(x^2 - 5x + 7) - (ax+b)(2x-5)}{(x^2 - 5x + 7)^2}$

$$= \dfrac{ax^2 - 5ax + 7a - 2ax^2 - 2bx + 5ax + 5b}{(x^2 - 5x + 7)^2}$$

$$= \dfrac{-ax^2 - 2bx + 7a + 5b}{(x^2 - 5x + 7)^2}$$

and $f'(3) = 0 \Rightarrow -9a - 6b + 7a + 5b = 0$
$$\Rightarrow -2a - b = 0$$
$$\Rightarrow b = -2a \quad \text{...... (2)}$$

Substituting (2) into (1)

$$3a - 2a = 5 \quad \therefore \quad a = 5 \quad \text{and so} \quad b = -10$$

346

$$x^2 + x \ln y - y = 3$$

$$\therefore \quad 2x + 1 \ln y + x\left(\frac{1}{y}\right)\frac{dy}{dx} - \frac{dy}{dx} = 0$$

$$\Rightarrow \quad 2x + \ln y + \frac{x}{y}\frac{dy}{dx} - \frac{dy}{dx} = 0$$

So, at (2, 1), $\quad 4 + 0 + 2\dfrac{dy}{dx} - \dfrac{dy}{dx} = 0$

$$\Rightarrow \quad \frac{dy}{dx} = -4$$

So, the equation is $\quad y - 1 = -4(x - 2)$

$$\text{i.e.,} \quad y = -4x + 9$$

347 $\int \sin^3 x \cos^3 x \, dx$

$$= \int \sin^3 x (1 - \sin^2 x) \cos x \, dx$$

$$= \int (\sin^3 x - \sin^5 x) \cos x \, dx \qquad u = \sin x$$

$$= \int (u^3 - u^5)\frac{du}{dx} dx \qquad \frac{du}{dx} = \cos x$$

$$= \frac{u^4}{4} - \frac{u^6}{6} + c$$

$$= \frac{1}{4}\sin^4 x - \frac{1}{6}\sin^6 x + c$$

348 $y = x\sqrt{4 - x^2}$

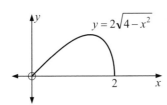

$$\text{Area} = \int_0^2 x\sqrt{4 - x^2} \, dx$$

$$= \int_0^2 \sqrt{u}\left(-\frac{1}{2}\frac{du}{dx}\right) dx \qquad u = 4 - x^2$$

$$\frac{du}{dx} = -2x$$

$$= \int_4^0 -\frac{1}{2}u^{\frac{1}{2}} \, du \qquad u(0) = 4$$

$$u(2) = 0$$

$$= \frac{1}{2}\int_0^4 u^{\frac{1}{2}} \, du$$

$$= \frac{1}{2}\left[\frac{u^{\frac{3}{2}}}{\frac{3}{2}}\right]_0^4$$

$$= \frac{1}{3}\left[u^{\frac{3}{2}}\right]_0^4$$

$$= \frac{1}{2}\left[\frac{2}{3}4^{\frac{3}{2}} - \frac{2}{3}(0)\right]$$

$$= \frac{8}{3} \text{ units}^2$$

349 $\int e^x \sin x \, dx \qquad \left[\text{Let} \begin{array}{ll} u' = \sin x & v = e^x \\ u = -\cos x & v' = e^x \end{array}\right]$

$$= -e^x \cos x - \int -e^x \cos x \, dx$$

$$= -e^x \cos x + \int e^x \cos x \, dx \quad \left[\text{Let} \begin{array}{ll} u' = \cos x & v = e^x \\ u = \sin x & v' = e^x \end{array}\right]$$

$$= -e^x \cos x + e^x \sin x - \int e^x \sin x \, dx + c'$$

$$\therefore \quad 2\int e^x \sin x \, dx = e^x(\sin x - \cos x) + c'$$

$$\therefore \quad \int e^x \sin x \, dx = \frac{1}{2}e^x(\sin x - \cos x) + c$$

350 $a = -4s, \quad \therefore \quad \dfrac{dv}{dt} = -4s$

$$\Rightarrow \quad \frac{dv}{ds}\frac{ds}{dt} = -4s \quad \{\text{chain rule}\}$$

$$\Rightarrow \quad \frac{dv}{ds}v = -4s$$

$$\Rightarrow \quad \int v\frac{dv}{ds} \, ds = \int -4s \, ds$$

$$\Rightarrow \quad \int v \, dv = -\int 4s \, ds$$

$$\Rightarrow \quad \frac{v^2}{2} = -\frac{4s^2}{2} + c$$

$$\Rightarrow \quad v^2 = 2c - 4s^2$$

But when $s = 5$, $v = 0$ $\therefore$ $2c - 100 = 0$
$$\Rightarrow \quad 2c = 100$$

So, $v^2 = 100 - 4s^2$

and when $s = 3$

$$\therefore \quad v^2 = 100 - 36 = 64 \quad \Rightarrow \quad v = \pm 8$$

As it is moving towards 0

s is decreasing, so $\dfrac{ds}{dt} < 0$ i.e., $v < 0$

$\therefore$ the velocity is -8 ms^{-1}.

351 $(x^2 + 1)y\dfrac{dy}{dx} = 2$

$$\Rightarrow \quad y\frac{dy}{dx} = \frac{2}{x^2 + 1}$$

$$\Rightarrow \quad \int y\frac{dy}{dx}dx = \int \frac{2}{x^2 + 1} dx$$

$$\Rightarrow \quad \int y \, dy = 2\int \frac{1}{x^2 + 1} dx$$

$$\Rightarrow \quad \frac{y^2}{2} = 2\arctan x + c$$

But when $x = 0$, $y = -\sqrt{2\pi}$

$$\therefore \quad \pi = 2\arctan 0 + c \quad \text{and so} \quad c = \pi$$

Thus $\dfrac{y^2}{2} = 2\arctan x + \pi$

$$\Rightarrow \quad y^2 = 4\arctan x + 2\pi$$

$$\Rightarrow \quad y = \pm\sqrt{4\arctan x + 2\pi}$$

But at $x = 0$, $y = -\sqrt{2\pi} < 0$

So, $y = -\sqrt{4\arctan x + 2\pi}$

352 a

$$\overrightarrow{AB} = \begin{bmatrix} 2 \\ 1 \\ 5 \end{bmatrix} - \begin{bmatrix} 4 \\ 2 \\ -1 \end{bmatrix} = \begin{bmatrix} -2 \\ -1 \\ 6 \end{bmatrix}$$

$$\overrightarrow{AC} = \begin{bmatrix} 9 \\ 4 \\ 1 \end{bmatrix} - \begin{bmatrix} 4 \\ 2 \\ -1 \end{bmatrix} = \begin{bmatrix} 5 \\ 2 \\ 2 \end{bmatrix}$$

and $\overrightarrow{AB} \bullet \overrightarrow{AC} = -10 + (-2) + 12 = 0$

So $\overrightarrow{AB}$ is perpendicular to $\overrightarrow{AC}$.

b A vector **n** normal to the plane is given by $\quad \mathbf{n} = \overrightarrow{AB} \times \overrightarrow{AC}$

$$\mathbf{n} = \begin{vmatrix} \mathbf{i} & \mathbf{j} & \mathbf{k} \\ -2 & -1 & 6 \\ 5 & 2 & 2 \end{vmatrix}$$

$$= \mathbf{i}\,(-2 - 12) - \mathbf{j}\,(-4 - 30) + \mathbf{k}\,(-4 + 5)$$

$$= -14\mathbf{i} + 34\mathbf{j} + \mathbf{k}$$

Equation of plane is:

$$\begin{bmatrix} -14 \\ 34 \\ 1 \end{bmatrix} \bullet \begin{bmatrix} x \\ y \\ z \end{bmatrix} = \begin{bmatrix} -14 \\ 34 \\ 1 \end{bmatrix} \bullet \begin{bmatrix} 4 \\ 2 \\ -1 \end{bmatrix}$$

$$-14x + 34y + z = -56 + 68 - 1$$

i.e., $\quad -14x + 34y + z = 11$

Distance of $(8, 1, 0)$ to the plane is

$$\frac{|-14 \times 8 + 34 \times 1 + 1 \times 0 - 11|}{\sqrt{14^2 + 34^2 + 1^2}} \doteq 2.42 \text{ units}$$

c $\overrightarrow{AB} = \begin{bmatrix} 2 - 4 \\ 1 - 2 \\ 5 - -1 \end{bmatrix} = \begin{bmatrix} -2 \\ -1 \\ 6 \end{bmatrix}$

An equation of a line through A and B is

$$\begin{bmatrix} x \\ y \\ z \end{bmatrix} = \begin{bmatrix} 4 \\ 2 \\ -1 \end{bmatrix} + \lambda \begin{bmatrix} -2 \\ -1 \\ 6 \end{bmatrix}$$

d

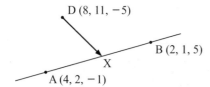

D $(8, 11, -5)$

B $(2, 1, 5)$

X

A $(4, 2, -1)$

Let X be a typical point on the line through A and B.

From **c** $\quad \overrightarrow{DX} = \begin{bmatrix} 4 \\ 2 \\ -1 \end{bmatrix} + \lambda \begin{bmatrix} -2 \\ -1 \\ 6 \end{bmatrix} - \begin{bmatrix} 8 \\ 11 \\ -5 \end{bmatrix}$

$$= \begin{bmatrix} -4 - 2\lambda \\ -9 - \lambda \\ 4 + 6\lambda \end{bmatrix}$$

$\overrightarrow{DX} \bullet \overrightarrow{AB} = \left(\begin{bmatrix} -4 - 2\lambda \\ -9 - \lambda \\ 4 + 6\lambda \end{bmatrix} \bullet \begin{bmatrix} -2 \\ -1 \\ 6 \end{bmatrix} \right)$

$$= 8 + 4\lambda + 9 + \lambda + 24 + 36\lambda$$

$$= 41 + 41\lambda$$

DX is perpendicular to AB if $\quad 41 + 41\lambda = 0$ i.e., $\lambda = -1$

So, $\overrightarrow{DX} = \begin{bmatrix} -2 \\ -8 \\ -2 \end{bmatrix}$ and $|\overrightarrow{DX}| = \sqrt{4 + 64 + 4}$

$$= \sqrt{72}$$

Distance of D to the line is $\sqrt{72}$ units.

353 a $\overrightarrow{OM} = \frac{1}{4}\begin{bmatrix} -4 \\ 12 \\ 8 \end{bmatrix} + \frac{3}{4}\begin{bmatrix} 4 \\ 8 \\ 0 \end{bmatrix} = \begin{bmatrix} -1 \\ 3 \\ 2 \end{bmatrix} + \begin{bmatrix} 3 \\ 6 \\ 0 \end{bmatrix} = \begin{bmatrix} 2 \\ 9 \\ 2 \end{bmatrix}$

and so M is $(2, 9, 2)$.

b M divides the segment $\overline{AB}$ in the ratio $3 : 1$.

c $\overrightarrow{AB} = \begin{bmatrix} 8 \\ -4 \\ -8 \end{bmatrix}$, $\quad |AB| = \sqrt{8^2 + 4^2 + 8^2} = 12$ units

i.e., the line segment $\overleftrightarrow{AB}$ is 12 units long.

The point 3 units from A in the direction of B has position

vector $\begin{bmatrix} -4 \\ 12 \\ 8 \end{bmatrix} + \frac{1}{4}\begin{bmatrix} 8 \\ -4 \\ -8 \end{bmatrix} = \begin{bmatrix} -2 \\ 11 \\ 6 \end{bmatrix}$

Thus the point is $(-2, 11, 6)$.

d

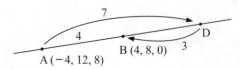

7

4

B $(4, 8, 0)$ 3   D

A $(-4, 12, 8)$

D has position vector $-\frac{3}{4}\begin{bmatrix} -4 \\ 12 \\ 8 \end{bmatrix} + \frac{7}{4}\begin{bmatrix} 4 \\ 8 \\ 0 \end{bmatrix} = \begin{bmatrix} 10 \\ 5 \\ -6 \end{bmatrix}$

Thus D is $(10, 5, -6)$.

e $\overrightarrow{BA} = -\overrightarrow{AB} = \begin{bmatrix} -8 \\ 4 \\ 8 \end{bmatrix}$ and $\overrightarrow{BO} = \begin{bmatrix} -4 \\ -8 \\ 0 \end{bmatrix}$

Let θ be the angle ABO, using the dot product

$$\overrightarrow{BA} \bullet \overrightarrow{BO} = |\,\overrightarrow{BA}\,||\,\overrightarrow{BO}\,| \cos\theta$$

$$\Rightarrow \quad \cos\theta = \frac{32 - 32 + 0}{\sqrt{64 + 16 + 64}\sqrt{16 + 64}} = 0$$

$$\Rightarrow \quad \theta = 90°$$

354 a $P(n)$ is:

$$\sum_{r=1}^{n} (r^2 + r) = \frac{n(n+1)(n+2)}{3} \quad \text{for all } n \in \mathbb{Z}^+$$

Proof: (By the Principle of Math Induction)

(1) If $n = 1$, LHS $= 1^2 + 1 = 2$, RHS $= \frac{(1)(2)(3)}{3} = 2$

$\qquad\qquad \therefore \quad P(1)$ is true.

(2) If $P(k)$ is true,

$$(1^2 + 1) + (2^2 + 2) + \cdots\cdots + (k^2 + k) = \frac{k(k+1)(k+2)}{3}$$

Now $(1^2 + 1) + (2^2 + 2) + \cdots\cdots + (k^2 + k) + \left((k+1)^2 + (k+1)\right)$

$$= \frac{k(k+1)(k+2)}{3} + (k+1)^2 + k + 1$$

$$= \frac{k(k+1)(k+2)}{3} + \frac{3(k+1)^2 + 3(k+1)}{3}$$

$$= \frac{(k+1)\,[k(k+2) + 3(k+1) + 3]}{3}$$

$$= \frac{(k+1)(k^2 + 2k + 3k + 6)}{3}$$

$$= \frac{(k+1)(k+2)(k+3)}{3}$$

$$= \frac{(k+1)([k+1]+1)([k+1]+2)}{3}$$

Thus $P(k+1)$ is true whenever $P(k)$ is true and $P(1)$ is true. $\Rightarrow \quad P(n)$ is true $\quad$ {P of MI}

b Rate/month $= \frac{5}{12}\% = \frac{0.05}{12}$ i.e., $R = \frac{0.05}{12}$

i After 3 months, her amount is

$$60(1 + R)^3 + 60(1 + R)^2 + 60(1 + R)$$

which is geometric with

$$u_1 = 60(1 + R) \quad \text{and} \quad r = 1 + R$$

So, $S_3 = 60(1 + R)\left[\dfrac{(1 + R)^3 - 1}{1 + R - 1}\right]$

$$= 60\left(1 + \frac{0.05}{12}\right)\left[\dfrac{\left(1 + \frac{0.05}{12}\right)^3 - 1}{\frac{0.05}{12}}\right]$$

$$= \$181.50$$

ii After k years i.e., $12k$ months

$$S_{12k} = 60\left(1 + \frac{0.05}{12}\right)\left[\dfrac{\left(1 + \frac{0.05}{12}\right)^{12k} - 1}{\frac{0.05}{12}}\right]$$

i.e., $S_{12k} = 14\,460\left([1.004\,166.....]^{12k} - 1\right)$

iii After 20 years, $k = 20$

$$S_{240} = 14\,460\left([1.004\,166\,6....]^{240} - 1\right)$$

$$\approx \$24\,765 \quad \text{(nearest \$)}$$

355 a

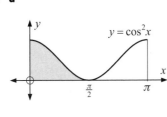

$y = \cos^2 x$

$$\text{Area} = \int_0^{\frac{\pi}{2}} \cos^2 x \, dx$$

$$= \int_0^{\frac{\pi}{2}} \tfrac{1}{2} + \tfrac{1}{2}\cos 2x \, dx$$

$$= \left[\frac{x}{2} + \tfrac{1}{4}\sin 2x \right]_0^{\frac{\pi}{2}}$$

$$= \tfrac{\pi}{4} + \tfrac{1}{4}\sin\pi - (0+0)$$

$$= \tfrac{\pi}{4} \text{ units}^2$$

b

$$\int \cos^n x \, dx$$

$$= \int \cos^{n-1} x \cos x \, dx$$

$$\begin{cases} u = \cos^{n-1} x & v' = \cos x \\ u' = (n-1)\cos^{n-2} x(-\sin x) & v = \sin x \end{cases}$$

$$= \cos^{n-1} x \sin x + \int (n-1)\cos^{n-2} x \sin^2 x \, dx$$

$$= \cos^{n-1} x \sin x + (n-1)\int \cos^{n-2} x \,(1 - \cos^2 x)\, dx$$

$$= \cos^{n-1} x \sin x + (n-1)\int \cos^{n-2} x \, dx - (n-1)\int \cos^n x \, dx$$

Thus $(1 + n - 1)\int \cos^n x \, dx$

$$= \cos^{n-1} x \sin x + (n-1)\int \cos^{n-2} x \, dx$$

$$\Rightarrow \ n\int \cos^n x \, dx = \cos^{n-1} x \sin x + (n-1)\int \cos^{n-2} x \, dx$$

$$\Rightarrow \ \int \cos^n x \, dx = \tfrac{1}{n}\sin x \cos^{n-1} x + \frac{n-1}{n}\int \cos^{n-2} x \, dx$$

c

$$\text{Volume} = \pi \int_0^{\frac{\pi}{2}} y^2 \, dx = \pi \int_0^{\frac{\pi}{2}} \cos^4 x \, dx$$

where $\int \cos^4 x \, dx = \tfrac{1}{4}\sin x \cos^3 x + \tfrac{3}{4}\int \cos^2 x \, dx$

$$\therefore \int_0^{\frac{\pi}{2}} \cos^4 x \, dx = \left[\tfrac{1}{4}\sin x \cos^3 x\right]_0^{\frac{\pi}{2}} + \tfrac{3}{4}\int_0^{\frac{\pi}{2}} \cos^2 x \, dx$$

$$= \tfrac{\pi}{8}(0) - (0) + \tfrac{3}{4}\times\tfrac{\pi}{4}$$

$$= \tfrac{3\pi}{16}$$

$$\therefore \ \text{Volume} = \pi \times \tfrac{3\pi}{16} = \tfrac{3\pi^2}{16} \text{ units}^3$$

SOLUTIONS TO EXAMINATION PRACTICE SET 10

356 a $x^2 + bx + c = 0$ is a real polynomial

$\therefore \ 3 - 2i$ and $3 + 2i$ are zeros.

have sum $= 6$ and product $= 9 + 4 = 13$.

$\therefore$ come from $x^2 - 6x + 13 = 0$

Thus $b = -6$ and $c = 13$

b $\log_2 x + \log_2(x-1) = 2 - \log_2(\tfrac{1}{3})$

$\Rightarrow \ \log_2 x(x-1) = \log_2 2^2 - \log_2\left(\tfrac{1}{3}\right)$

$\Rightarrow \ \log_2 x(x-1) = \log_2(4 \div \tfrac{1}{3})$

$\Rightarrow \ x^2 - x = 12$

$\Rightarrow \ x^2 - x - 12 = 0$

$\Rightarrow \ (x-4)(x+3) = 0$ and so $x = 4$ or -3

But $x > 0$ and $x - 1 > 0$

$\Rightarrow \ x > 1$ and so $x = 4$.

357 a We have a geometric series where

$u_1 - u_2 = 9$ and $S_\infty = 81 \ \Rightarrow \ \dfrac{u_1}{1-r} = 81$

Thus $u_1 - u_1 r = 9$ and $u_1 = 81(1-r)$

$\therefore \ u_1(1-r) = 9$ and $u_1 = 81(1-r)$

$\Rightarrow \ \dfrac{9}{1-r} = 81(1-r)$

$\Rightarrow \ (1-r)^2 = \tfrac{1}{9}$

$\Rightarrow \ 1 - r = \pm\tfrac{1}{3}$ and so $r = \tfrac{4}{3}$ or $\tfrac{2}{3}$

But $-1 < r < 1$, so $r = \tfrac{2}{3}$.

b $u_1 = 81(1-r) = 81\times\tfrac{1}{3} = 27$ i.e., the first term is 27.

358 a $g(x) = f(f(x))$

$$= f\left(\frac{x}{x-2}\right)$$

$$= \frac{\dfrac{x}{x-2}}{\dfrac{x}{x-2} - 2}$$

$$= \frac{x}{x - 2(x-2)}$$

$$= \frac{x}{-x+4}$$

b $g(g(2))$

$$= g\left(\frac{2}{-2+4}\right)$$

$$= g(1)$$

$$= \frac{1}{-1+4}$$

$$= \tfrac{1}{3}$$

359 a From a gcalc, the graph of $y = \dfrac{x^2 - 2x + 4}{x^2 + 2x + 4}$ is:

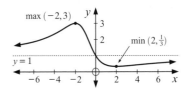

max $(-2,3)$, min $(2,\tfrac{1}{3})$, $y = 1$

Note:

$$f'(x) = \frac{(2x-2)(x^2+2x+4) - (x^2-2x+4)(2x+2)}{(x^2+2x+4)^2}$$

$$= \frac{4(x-2)(x+2)}{(x^2+2x+4)^2} \quad \text{\{on simplification\}}$$

can be used to find the local max./min.

Sign diag. of $f'(x)$ is:

This shows a local max. at $x = -2$ and a local min. at $x = 2$.

As $f(-2) = 3$ and $f(2) = \tfrac{1}{3}$ the range of f is all $y \in \mathbb{R}$ such that $\tfrac{1}{3} \leqslant y \leqslant 3$.

b Now $f \circ f = f(f(x)) = f(y)$, $\tfrac{1}{3} \leqslant y \leqslant 3$ {from **a**}

Consider:

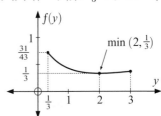

$f(y)$, $\tfrac{31}{43}$, min $(2,\tfrac{1}{3})$

This graph is identical to that of $f(x)$ against x on the domain $\tfrac{1}{3} \leqslant x \leqslant 3$.

So, the range of $f \circ f$ is $\left[\tfrac{1}{3}, \tfrac{31}{43}\right]$.

360 a $f(x) = \dfrac{2}{\sqrt{5-x^2}}$ takes real values if $5 - x^2 > 0$

i.e., if $-\sqrt{5} < x < \sqrt{5}$.

b $\sqrt{5-x^2}$ has maximum value of $\sqrt{5}$ when $x = 0$

Range of $f(x) = \dfrac{2}{\sqrt{5-x^2}}$ is $y \in \mathbb{R}$, $y \geqslant \tfrac{2}{\sqrt{5}}$.

361

$$\frac{5}{x+2} \geqslant \frac{2}{x+3}$$

$$\Leftrightarrow \ \frac{5}{x+2} - \frac{2}{x+3} \geqslant 0$$

$$\Leftrightarrow \ \frac{5x+15}{(x+2)(x+3)} - \frac{2(x+2)}{(x+2)(x+3)} \geqslant 0$$

$$\Leftrightarrow \ \frac{5x+15-2x-4}{(x+2)(x+3)} \geqslant 0$$

$$\Leftrightarrow \ \frac{3x+11}{(x+2)(x+3)} \geqslant 0$$

Sign diagram:

$$- \quad + \quad - \quad +$$
$$-\tfrac{11}{3} \quad -3 \quad -2$$

Inequality is satisfied if $-\tfrac{11}{3} \leqslant x \leqslant -3$ or $x > -2$.

362 $\tan 75^\circ = \tan(45^\circ + 30^\circ)$

$$= \frac{\tan 45^\circ + \tan 30^\circ}{1 - \tan 45^\circ \tan 30^\circ}$$

$$= \frac{1 + \frac{1}{\sqrt{3}}}{1 - \frac{1}{\sqrt{3}}}$$

$$= \left(\frac{1 + \frac{1}{\sqrt{3}}}{1 - \frac{1}{\sqrt{3}}} \right) \frac{\sqrt{3}}{\sqrt{3}}$$

$$= \frac{\sqrt{3} + 1}{\sqrt{3} - 1}$$

$$= \left(\frac{\sqrt{3} + 1}{\sqrt{3} - 1} \right) \left(\frac{\sqrt{3} + 1}{\sqrt{3} + 1} \right)$$

$$= \frac{4 + 2\sqrt{3}}{2}$$

$$= 2 + \sqrt{3}$$

363

$$2\cos\theta + 2\sec\theta = 5, \quad 0 \leqslant \theta \leqslant \pi$$

$$\Rightarrow 2\cos\theta + \frac{2}{\cos\theta} - 5 = 0$$

$$\Rightarrow 2\cos^2\theta - 5\cos\theta + 2 = 0$$

$$\Rightarrow (2\cos\theta - 1)(\cos\theta - 2) = 0$$

$$\Rightarrow \cos\theta = \tfrac{1}{2} \text{ or } 2$$

$$\Rightarrow \cos\theta = \tfrac{1}{2} \quad \{\text{as } -1 \leqslant \cos\theta \leqslant 1\}$$

$$\Rightarrow \theta = \tfrac{\pi}{3}$$

364

$$y = a\sin bx + c \text{ has}$$

$$y(0) = c, \qquad \text{period} = \frac{2\pi}{b}$$

$$\text{amplitude} = a$$

$$y = -2a\sin\left(\frac{b}{2}\right)x \text{ has}$$

$$y(0) = 0, \qquad \text{period} = \frac{2\pi}{\frac{b}{2}} = \frac{4\pi}{b}$$

$$\text{amplitude} = 2a$$

365
$$\begin{vmatrix} 4 & x \\ x & x \end{vmatrix} = 4x - x^2$$

$$\begin{vmatrix} 2 & 0 & -1 \\ 4 & 5 & 0 \\ 0 & 1 & 2 \end{vmatrix} = 2\begin{vmatrix} 5 & 0 \\ 1 & 2 \end{vmatrix} + 0\begin{vmatrix} 0 & 4 \\ 2 & 0 \end{vmatrix} + (-1)\begin{vmatrix} 4 & 5 \\ 0 & 1 \end{vmatrix}$$

$$= 20 + 0 - 4$$

$$= 16$$

So, $4x - x^2 = 16$

$$\Rightarrow x^2 - 4x + 16 = 0$$

$$\Rightarrow x = 2 \pm 2\sqrt{3}i \quad \text{(i.e., no real solutions).}$$

366

$$\mathbf{t} = 2\mathbf{i} + 2\mathbf{j} - \mathbf{k}$$
$$\mathbf{t} - \mathbf{r}$$
$$\mathbf{r} = 2\mathbf{i} - \mathbf{j} + 2\mathbf{k}$$
$$\mathbf{s} - \mathbf{r}$$
$$\mathbf{s} = 3\mathbf{i} - \mathbf{j} + 2\mathbf{k}$$

$$\mathbf{t} - \mathbf{r} = 0\mathbf{i} + 3\mathbf{j} - 3\mathbf{k}$$
$$\mathbf{s} - \mathbf{r} = \mathbf{i} + 0\mathbf{j} + 0\mathbf{k}$$

Area of the triangle is $\frac{1}{2}|(\mathbf{t} - \mathbf{r}) \times (\mathbf{s} - \mathbf{r})|$

$$(\mathbf{t} - \mathbf{r}) \times (\mathbf{s} - \mathbf{r}) = \begin{vmatrix} \mathbf{i} & \mathbf{j} & \mathbf{k} \\ 0 & 3 & -3 \\ 1 & 0 & 0 \end{vmatrix} \begin{array}{l} = \mathbf{i}(0) - \mathbf{j}(3) + \mathbf{k}(-3) \\ = 0\mathbf{i} - 3\mathbf{j} - 3\mathbf{k} \end{array}$$

Area of the triangle is $\frac{1}{2}\sqrt{0^2 + (-3)^2 + (-3)^2} = \frac{1}{2}\sqrt{18}$ units^2

367

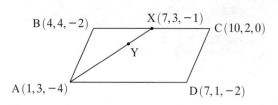

B$(4, 4, -2)$ X$(7, 3, -1)$ C$(10, 2, 0)$ Y A$(1, 3, -4)$ D$(7, 1, -2)$

a $\overrightarrow{BC} = \begin{bmatrix} 10 - 4 \\ 2 - 4 \\ 0 - (-2) \end{bmatrix} = \begin{bmatrix} 6 \\ -2 \\ 2 \end{bmatrix}$

Since $\overrightarrow{BC} = \overrightarrow{AD}$, position vector of D is

$$\begin{bmatrix} 1 \\ 3 \\ -4 \end{bmatrix} + \begin{bmatrix} 6 \\ -2 \\ 2 \end{bmatrix} = \begin{bmatrix} 7 \\ 1 \\ -2 \end{bmatrix} \quad \begin{array}{l} \text{and coordinates of D} \\ \text{are } (7, 1, -2) \end{array}$$

The position vector of the midpoint of BC is $\begin{bmatrix} \frac{4+10}{2} \\ \frac{4+2}{2} \\ \frac{-2+0}{2} \end{bmatrix} = \begin{bmatrix} 7 \\ 3 \\ -1 \end{bmatrix}$ So, the coordinates of X are $(7, 3, -1)$

Ratio AY : YX $= 2 : 1$, so position vector of Y is

$$\frac{1}{3}\begin{bmatrix} 1 \\ 3 \\ -4 \end{bmatrix} + \frac{2}{3}\begin{bmatrix} 7 \\ 3 \\ -1 \end{bmatrix} = \begin{bmatrix} 5 \\ 3 \\ -2 \end{bmatrix}$$

Coordinates of Y are $(5, 3, -2)$.

b $\overrightarrow{BY} = \begin{bmatrix} 5 - 4 \\ 3 - 4 \\ -2 - -2 \end{bmatrix} = \begin{bmatrix} 1 \\ -1 \\ 0 \end{bmatrix}$, $\overrightarrow{BD} = \begin{bmatrix} 7 - 4 \\ 1 - 4 \\ -2 - -2 \end{bmatrix} = \begin{bmatrix} 3 \\ -3 \\ 0 \end{bmatrix}$

Since $\overrightarrow{BY} = \frac{1}{3}\overrightarrow{BD}$, $\overrightarrow{BY}$ and $\overrightarrow{BD}$ are parallel and B, Y and D are collinear.

368 Graph of $f(x)$ is shown.

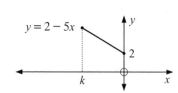

$y = 2 - 5x$ y 2 k x

a Since f is a probability density function

$$\int_{-\infty}^{\infty} f(x)\,dx = 1 \quad \Rightarrow \quad \int_{k}^{0} (2 - 5x)\,dx = 1$$

$$\Rightarrow \left[2x - \frac{5x^2}{2} \right]_{k}^{0} = 1$$

$$\Rightarrow 0 - \left(2k - \frac{5k^2}{2} \right) = 1$$

$$\Rightarrow \frac{5}{2}k^2 - 2k = 1$$

$$\Rightarrow 5k^2 - 4k - 2 = 0$$

$$\Rightarrow k = \frac{4 \pm \sqrt{16 - 4(5)(-2)}}{10} = \frac{4 \pm \sqrt{56}}{10}$$

But $k < 0$ so $k = \frac{4 - \sqrt{56}}{10} \approx -0.34833 \approx -0.348$

b The mean $\mu = \int_{k}^{0} x(2 - 5x)\,dx$

$$= \int_{k}^{0} (2x - 5x^2)\,dx$$

$$\therefore \quad \mu = \left[\frac{2x^2}{2} - \frac{5x^3}{3}\right]_k^0$$
$$= \frac{5}{3}k^3 - k^2$$
$$\approx \frac{5}{3}(-0.34833)^3 - (-0.34833)^2$$
$$\approx -0.192$$

369

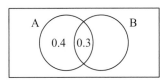

Since $\text{P}(A) = \text{P}(A \cap B) + \text{P}(A \cap B')$ {disjoint sets}
$$= 0.7$$
and $\text{P}(A \cap B) = \text{P}(A).\text{P}(B)$ {A and B are independent}
$$\Rightarrow \quad \text{P}(B) = \frac{0.3}{0.7} = \frac{3}{7}$$
$$\Rightarrow \quad \text{P}(A \cup B) = \text{P}(A) + \text{P}(B) - \text{P}(A \cap B) = \frac{7}{10} + \frac{3}{7} - \frac{3}{10}$$
$$= \frac{29}{35}$$

370 a Since $\text{P}(X \geqslant 1) = 0.01$,
$$\text{P}(X = 0) = 1 - 0.01 = 0.99$$
But $\text{P}(X = 0) = \dfrac{m^0 e^{-m}}{0!} = e^{-m}$

where m is the expected number of errors/page.
$$\text{i.e., } \quad e^{-m} = 0.99$$
$$\text{and } \quad m = -\ln(0.99) \approx 0.0101$$

b $\text{P}(X = 1) = \dfrac{m^1 e^{-m}}{1!} = 0.01 e^{-0.01} \approx 0.00990$
and so we expect about $750 \times 0.0099 \approx 7.4$ pages with
exactly 1 mistake   i.e.,   between 7 and 8 pages.

371 $y = Ae^{kt} \quad \therefore \quad \dfrac{dy}{dt} = Ake^{kt} \quad$ and $\quad \dfrac{d^2y}{at^2} = Ak^2 e^{kt}$
$$\text{But } \quad \frac{d^2y}{at^2} + 3\frac{dy}{dt} + 2y = 0$$
$$\Rightarrow \quad Ak^2 e^{kt} + 3Ake^{kt} + 2Ae^{kt} = 0$$
$$\Rightarrow \quad Ae^{kt}(k^2 + 3k + 2) = 0$$
$$\Rightarrow \quad k^2 + 3k + 2 = 0$$
as A is not necessarily 0 and $e^{kt} > 0$
$$\Rightarrow \quad (k+1)(k+2) = 0 \text{ and so } k = -1 \text{ or } -2$$

372 If $y^2 = 3 - xy$ then $\quad 2y\dfrac{dy}{dx} = 0 - \left[1y + x\dfrac{dy}{dx}\right]$
$$\Rightarrow \quad 2y\frac{dy}{dx} = -y - x\frac{dy}{dx}$$
$$\Rightarrow \quad (x + 2y)\frac{dy}{dx} = -y$$
$$\Rightarrow \quad \frac{dy}{dx} = \frac{-y}{x + 2y}$$

and if tangents have slope $-\frac{3}{4}$, then $\quad \dfrac{-y}{x+2y} = -\dfrac{3}{4}$
$$\Rightarrow \quad 4y = 3(x + 2y)$$
$$\Rightarrow \quad 4y = 3x + 6y$$
$$\Rightarrow \quad -2y = 3x$$
$$\Rightarrow \quad y = -\frac{3x}{2}$$

and substituting into $y^2 = 3 - xy$ gives
$$\frac{9x^2}{4} = 3 - x\left(\frac{-3x}{2}\right) \quad \Rightarrow \quad \frac{9x^2}{4} = 3 + \frac{3x^2}{2}$$
$$\Rightarrow \quad 9x^2 = 12 + 6x^2$$
$$\Rightarrow \quad 3x^2 = 12$$
$$\Rightarrow \quad x^2 = 4 \text{ and so } x = \pm 2$$

$\therefore \quad$ points are $(2, -3)$ and $(-2, 3)$.

373 $\int x^2 \sqrt{1 - x}\, dx \qquad\qquad u = 1 - x$
$$= \int (1 - u)^2 \sqrt{u}(-dx) \qquad\qquad \frac{du}{dx} = -1$$
$$= \int -(1 - 2u + u^2)u^{\frac{1}{2}}\, du$$
$$= \int -u^{\frac{1}{2}} + 2u^{\frac{3}{2}} - u^{\frac{5}{2}}\, du$$
$$= \frac{-u^{\frac{3}{2}}}{\frac{3}{2}} + \frac{2u^{\frac{5}{2}}}{\frac{5}{2}} - \frac{u^{\frac{7}{2}}}{\frac{7}{2}} + c$$
$$= -\frac{2}{3}(1 - x)^{\frac{3}{2}} + \frac{4}{5}(1 - x)^{\frac{5}{2}} - \frac{2}{7}(1 - x)^{\frac{7}{2}} + c$$

374 $y^2 + 2y - 3x = 0 \quad$ meets $\quad 2x - y - 1 = 0 \quad$ where
$$y^2 + 2y - 3\left[\frac{y+1}{2}\right] = 0 \Rightarrow 2y^2 + 4y - 3y - 3 = 0$$
$$\Rightarrow \quad 2y^2 + y - 3 = 0$$
$$\Rightarrow \quad (2y + 3)(y - 1) = 0$$
$$\Rightarrow \quad y = -\frac{3}{2} \text{ or } 1$$

When $y = -\frac{3}{2}, \quad x = \dfrac{-\frac{3}{2} + 1}{2} = -\frac{1}{4}$

When $y = 1, \quad x = \dfrac{1 + 1}{2} = 1$

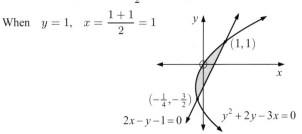

$$\text{Area} = \int_{-\frac{3}{2}}^{1} \left(\frac{y + 1}{2}\right) - \left(\frac{y^2 + 2y}{3}\right) dy$$
$$= \int_{-\frac{3}{2}}^{1} \tfrac{1}{2}y + \tfrac{1}{2} - \tfrac{1}{3}y^2 - \tfrac{2}{3}y \, dy$$
$$= \int_{-\frac{3}{2}}^{1} \tfrac{1}{2} - \tfrac{1}{3}y^2 - \tfrac{1}{6}y \, dy$$
$$= \left[\tfrac{1}{2}y - \frac{y^3}{9} - \tfrac{1}{12}y^2\right]_{-\frac{3}{2}}^{1}$$
$$= \left(\tfrac{1}{2} - \tfrac{1}{9} - \tfrac{1}{12}\right) - \left(-\tfrac{3}{4} + \tfrac{3}{8} - \tfrac{3}{16}\right)$$
$$= \frac{125}{144} \text{ units}^2$$

375 $\int \dfrac{x^2}{(1 - x)^3}\, dx \qquad\qquad u = 1 - x$
$$= -\int \frac{(1 - u)^2}{u^3}\frac{du}{dx}\, dx \qquad\qquad \frac{du}{dx} = -1$$
$$= -\int \frac{1 - 2u + u^2}{u^3}\, du$$
$$= -\int u^{-3} - 2u^{-2} + \frac{1}{u}\, du$$
$$= -\frac{u^{-2}}{-2} + \frac{2u^{-1}}{-1} - \ln|u| + c$$
$$= \frac{1}{2(1 - x)^2} - \frac{2}{1 - x} - \ln|1 - x| + c$$

376 $v = e^t \cos 2t$

a distance travelled in first 5 seconds $= \int_0^5 |v|\, dt$
$$= \int_0^5 |e^t \cos 2t|\, dt$$

b Using a gcalc, this distance ≈ 107.8 m.

377
$$y\frac{dy}{dx} = xy^2 + x = x(y^2 + 1)$$
$$\Rightarrow \quad \frac{y}{y^2 + 1}\frac{dy}{dx} = x$$
$$\Rightarrow \quad \int \frac{y}{y^2 + 1}\frac{dy}{dx}\, dx = \int x\, dx$$

$$\Rightarrow \int \frac{y}{y^2+1}\,dy = \int x\,dx$$

$$\Rightarrow \frac{1}{2}\int \frac{2y}{y^2+1}\,dy = \int x\,dx$$

$$\Rightarrow \frac{1}{2}\ln\left|y^2+1\right| = \frac{x^2}{2}+c$$

But $y^2+1 > 0$ for all y

$$\Rightarrow \frac{1}{2}\ln\left(y^2+1\right) = \frac{x^2}{2}+c$$

Now when $x = 0$, $y = 2$ and so $c = \frac{1}{2}\ln 5$

So, $\frac{1}{2}\ln\left(y^2+1\right) = \frac{x^2}{2}+\frac{1}{2}\ln 5$

i.e., $\ln\left(\dfrac{y^2+1}{5}\right) = x^2 \Rightarrow \dfrac{y^2+1}{5} = e^{x^2}$

$$\Rightarrow y^2+1 = 5e^{x^2}$$

$$\Rightarrow y = \pm\sqrt{5e^{x^2}-1}$$

Thus $y = \sqrt{5e^{x^2}-1}$

{when $x = 0$, $y = 2$ which is > 0}

378 a i $P(n)$ is: $\displaystyle\sum_{r=1}^{n} r^3 = \frac{n^2(n+1)^2}{4}$, $n \in \mathbb{Z}^+$

Proof: (By the Principle of Math Induction)

(1) If $n = 1$, LHS $= 1^3 = 1$, RHS $= \dfrac{1^2 \times 2^2}{4} = 1$
$\therefore$ $P(1)$ is true.

(2) If $P(k)$ is true
$$1^3 + 2^3 + 3^3 + \ldots\ldots + k^3 = \frac{k^2(k+1)^2}{4}$$

$\therefore$ $1^3 + 2^3 + 3^3 + \ldots\ldots + k^3 + (k+1)^3$

$$= \frac{k^2(k+1)^2}{4} + (k+1)^3$$

$$= \frac{k^2(k+1)^2 + 4(k+1)^3}{4}$$

$$= \frac{(k+1)^2\left[k^2 + 4(k+1)\right]}{4}$$

$$= \frac{(k+1)^2(k+2)^2}{4}$$

$$= \frac{(k+1)^2([k+1]+1)^2}{4}$$

Thus $P(k+1)$ is true whenever $P(k)$ is true and $P(1)$ is true $\Rightarrow P(n)$ is true {P of MI}

ii $1^3 + 2^3 + \ldots\ldots + 100^3 = \dfrac{100^2(101)^2}{4} = 25\,502\,500$

b $\displaystyle\sum_{r=1}^{n} r = 1 + 2 + 3 + \ldots\ldots + n$

which is arithmetic with $u_1 = 1$, $d = 1$

$\therefore$ $\displaystyle\sum_{r=1}^{n} r = \frac{n}{2}[2u_1 + (n-1)d] = \frac{n}{2}[2+n-1]$

$$= \frac{n(n+1)}{2}$$

So $\left(\displaystyle\sum_{r=1}^{n} r\right)^2 = \dfrac{n^2(n+1)^2}{4} = \displaystyle\sum_{r=1}^{n} r^3$ {from **a i**}

379 a $\overrightarrow{OM} = \frac{1}{2}(\mathbf{a} + \mathbf{b})$

b $\overrightarrow{OM} \bullet \overrightarrow{AB} = \frac{1}{2}(\mathbf{a} + \mathbf{b}) \bullet (\mathbf{b} - \mathbf{a})$

$$= \frac{1}{2}(\mathbf{a} \bullet \mathbf{b} - \mathbf{a} \bullet \mathbf{a} + \mathbf{b} \bullet \mathbf{b} - \mathbf{b} \bullet \mathbf{a})$$

$$= \frac{1}{2}(-|\mathbf{a}|^2 + |\mathbf{b}|^2)$$

Since $\triangle OAB$ is equilateral $|\mathbf{a}|^2 = |\mathbf{b}|^2$ and $\overrightarrow{OM} \bullet \overrightarrow{AB} = 0$
$\therefore$ $\overrightarrow{OM}$ is perpendicular to $\overrightarrow{AB}$.

c $|\mathbf{b} - \mathbf{a}|$ is the length of side AB. Since $\triangle OAB$ is equilateral, all sides are equal and $|\mathbf{b} - \mathbf{a}| = |\mathbf{a}|$

$$\mathbf{b} \bullet (\mathbf{b} - 2\mathbf{a}) = \mathbf{b} \bullet (\mathbf{b} - \mathbf{a}) - \mathbf{b} \bullet \mathbf{a}$$

$$= |\mathbf{b}||\mathbf{b} - \mathbf{a}|\cos 60^\circ - |\mathbf{b}||\mathbf{a}|\cos 60^\circ$$

$$= |\mathbf{a}|^2 \tfrac{1}{2} - |\mathbf{a}|^2 \tfrac{1}{2}$$

$$= 0$$

d

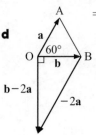

380 $f(x) = 2x \sin x$, $g(x) = x$, $0 \leqslant x \leqslant 2\pi$

a i They meet when $f(x) = g(x)$

$$\Rightarrow 2x \sin x = x$$

$$\Rightarrow x(2\sin x - 1) = 0$$

$$\Rightarrow x = 0 \quad \text{or} \quad \sin x = \frac{1}{2}$$

$$\Rightarrow x = 0, \ \frac{\pi}{6}, \ \frac{5\pi}{6}$$

i.e., at $(0, 0)$, $\left(\frac{\pi}{6}, \frac{\pi}{6}\right)$, $\left(\frac{5\pi}{6}, \frac{5\pi}{6}\right)$

ii $f'(x) = 2\sin x + 2x\cos x$ and so we have stationary points where $2\sin x + 2x\cos x = 0$

iii From a gcalc, the graph of $f'(x) = 2\sin x + 2x\cos x$ is:

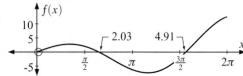

The stationary points are at A$(0, 0)$, B$(2.03, 3.64)$, C$(4.91, -9.63)$

iv

b i $\displaystyle\int 2x \sin x\,dx$ $\begin{cases} u = 2x & v' = \sin x \\ u' = 2 & v = -\cos x \end{cases}$

$$= -2x\cos x - \int -2\cos x\,dx$$

$$= -2x\cos x + 2\sin x + c$$

ii Total area

$$= \int_0^{\frac{\pi}{6}} g(x) - f(x)\,dx + \int_{\frac{\pi}{6}}^{\frac{5\pi}{6}} f(x) - g(x)\,dx$$

$$= \int_0^{\frac{\pi}{6}} x - 2x\sin x\,dx + \int_{\frac{\pi}{6}}^{\frac{5\pi}{6}} 2x\sin x - x\,dx$$

$$= \left[\frac{x^2}{2} + 2x\cos x - 2\sin x\right]_0^{\frac{\pi}{6}}$$

$$\quad + \left[-2x\cos x + 2\sin x - \frac{x^2}{2}\right]_{\frac{\pi}{6}}^{\frac{5\pi}{6}}$$

$$= \frac{\pi^2}{72} + \frac{\pi}{3}\left(\frac{\sqrt{3}}{2}\right) - 1 - 0 + \left(-\frac{5\pi}{3}\left(\frac{-\sqrt{3}}{2}\right) + 1 - \frac{25\pi^2}{72}\right)$$

$$\quad - \left(-2\left(\frac{\pi}{6}\right)\left(\frac{\sqrt{3}}{2}\right) + 1 - \frac{\pi^2}{72}\right)$$

$$= \frac{\pi^2}{72} + \frac{\pi\sqrt{3}}{6} - 1 + \frac{5\pi\sqrt{3}}{6} - \frac{25\pi^2}{72} + \frac{\pi\sqrt{3}}{6} + \frac{\pi^2}{72}$$

$$= -\frac{23}{72}\pi^2 + \frac{7}{6}\pi\sqrt{3} - 1 \text{ units}^2$$

381 a If $\mathbf{r} = (-2t+2)\mathbf{i} + t\mathbf{j} + (3t+1)\mathbf{k}$ then

$$\mathbf{r} \bullet \begin{bmatrix} 2 \\ 1 \\ 1 \end{bmatrix} = \begin{bmatrix} -2t+2 \\ t \\ 3t+1 \end{bmatrix} \bullet \begin{bmatrix} 2 \\ 1 \\ 1 \end{bmatrix}$$

$$= (-4t+4) + t + (3t+1)$$
$$= 5 \qquad \text{and hence } l_1 \text{ lies in the plane.}$$

b If $\mathbf{r} \bullet \begin{bmatrix} 1 \\ k \\ 1 \end{bmatrix} = 3$, then $\begin{bmatrix} -2t+2 \\ t \\ 3t+1 \end{bmatrix} \bullet \begin{bmatrix} 1 \\ k \\ 1 \end{bmatrix} = 3$

$$\text{i.e.,} \quad (-2t+2) + kt + (3t+1) = 3$$
$$t(1+k) = 0$$
$$\text{i.e., } k = -1$$

c The line l_1 lies in the plane

$$-2x + py + 2z = q$$
if $-2(-2t+2) + p(t) + 2(3t+1) = q$
$$\Rightarrow \quad 4t - 4 + pt + 6t + 2 = q$$
$$\text{i.e., } (10 + p)t = q + 2$$

i.e., the line l_1 lies in the plane
$$-2x + py + 2z = q \quad \text{if} \quad p = -10 \quad \text{and} \quad q = -2$$
The system of equations
$$2x + y + z = 5$$
$$x - y + z = 3$$
$$-2x - 10y + 2z = -2$$

has an infinite number of solutions since the line
$l_1: (-2t+2)\mathbf{i} + t\mathbf{j} + (3t+1)\mathbf{k}$ lies in each of the 3 planes.

SOLUTIONS TO EXAMINATION PRACTICE SET 11

382 a
$$(a + 3i)(b - i) = 13 + i$$
$$\Rightarrow \quad [ab + 3] + [3b - a]i = 13 + i$$
$$\Rightarrow \quad ab + 3 = 13 \quad \text{and} \quad 3b - a = 1$$
$$\Rightarrow \quad ab = 10 \quad \text{and} \quad 3b - a = 1$$
$$\Rightarrow \quad 3b - \frac{10}{b} = 1$$
$$\Rightarrow \quad 3b^2 - 10 = b$$
$$\Rightarrow \quad 3b^2 - b - 10 = 0$$
$$\Rightarrow \quad (3b + 5)(b - 2) = 0$$
$$\Rightarrow \quad b = -\frac{5}{3} \text{ or } 2$$

But $b \in \mathbb{Z}$ $\therefore$ $b = 2$.
Consequently $a = 5$, thus $a = 5$, $b = 2$

b
$$|z + 1 + i| = 2|z - 2 - i|$$
$$\Rightarrow \quad |5 + ai + 1 + i| = 2|5 + ai - 2 - i|$$
$$\Rightarrow \quad |6 + (a+1)i| = 2|3 + (a-1)i|$$
$$\Rightarrow \quad \sqrt{36 + (a+1)^2} = 2\sqrt{9 + (a-1)^2}$$
$$\Rightarrow \quad 36 + (a+1)^2 = 4\left[9 + (a-1)^2\right]$$
$$\Rightarrow \quad 36 + a^2 + 2a + 1 = 36 + 4a^2 - 8a + 4$$
$$\Rightarrow \quad 3a^2 - 10a + 3 = 0$$
$$\Rightarrow \quad (3a - 1)(a - 3) = 0 \quad \text{and so} \quad a = \frac{1}{3} \text{ or } 3$$
But, $a \in \mathbb{Z}$, $\therefore$ $a = 3$.

383 a Let the arithmetic sequence have first term u, and common difference d.

Sum of even terms
$$= u_2 + u_4 + u_6 + u_8 + \ldots + u_{30}$$
$$= u_1 + d + u_3 + d + u_5 + d + \ldots + u_{29} + d$$
$$= \text{sum of odd terms} + 15d$$
i.e., sum of even terms $-$ sum of odd terms $= 15d$
$$\therefore \quad 15d = 8 \quad \Rightarrow \quad d = \frac{8}{15}$$

b
$$S_n = \frac{n}{2}[2u_1 + (n-1)d] = \frac{n}{2}\left[2u_1 + \frac{8(n-1)}{15}\right]$$
i.e., $S_n = n\left(u_1 + \frac{4(n-1)}{15}\right)$

384
$$\log_6 x + \log_x(2x - 1)\log_6 x = 1$$
$$\therefore \quad \frac{\log x}{\log 6} + \frac{\log(2x-1)}{\log x} \times \frac{\log x}{\log 6} = 1$$
$$\Rightarrow \quad \log x + \log(2x - 1) = \log 6$$
$$\Rightarrow \quad \log x(2x - 1) = \log 6$$
$$\Rightarrow \quad 2x^2 - x = 6$$
$$\Rightarrow \quad 2x^2 - x - 6 = 0$$
$$\Rightarrow \quad (2x + 3)(x - 2) = 0 \quad \text{and so} \quad x = -\frac{3}{2} \text{ or } 2$$
But $x > 0$ and $2x - 1 > 0$ $\Rightarrow$ $x > \frac{1}{2}$ $\therefore$ $x = 2$.

385 $f : x \mapsto \sqrt{x}$, $g : x \mapsto 1 - \sin x$
Domain of f is all $x \geqslant 0$
Domain of $f \circ g = f(g(x))$ is all x such that $g(x) \geqslant 0$
i.e., $1 - \sin x \geqslant 0$ i.e., $\sin x \leqslant 1$ which is true for all $x \in \mathbb{R}$.
$\therefore$ the domain of $f \circ g$ is $\{x : x \in \mathbb{R}\}$
As $f \circ g = \sqrt{1 - \sin x}$, range of $f \circ g$ is $\{y : 0 \leqslant y \leqslant \sqrt{2}\}$.

386 a Let $f(x) = e^{-\frac{1}{2}x}$ and $g(x) = \sin 3x$.
A graph of f and g is shown.

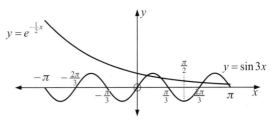

From the graph, there are exactly 4 roots in the interval from $-\pi$ to π.

b The solution closest to $\frac{\pi}{2}$ is the first root after 2. Using technology, $x \approx 2.207\,09$

387 The graphs meet where $2|x - 3| = |x + 7|$
$$\Rightarrow \quad 4(x-3)^2 - (x+7)^2 = 0$$
$$\Rightarrow \quad [2x - 6 + x + 7][2x - 6 - x - 7] = 0$$
$$\Rightarrow \quad [3x + 1][x - 13] = 0$$
$$\Rightarrow \quad x = -\frac{1}{3} \text{ or } 13$$
We sketch $y = 2|x - 3|$ and $y = |x + 7|$.

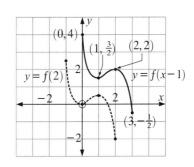

$2|x - 3| \leqslant |x + 7|$ when the graph of $y = 2|x - 3|$ is below the graph of $y = |x + 7|$.
This is between A and B, i.e., for $-\frac{1}{3} \leqslant x \leqslant 13$.

388 a

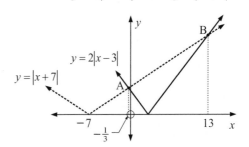

b Relative minimum of $y = f(x - 1) + \frac{3}{2}$ is $\left(1, \frac{3}{2}\right)$.
Relative maximum of $y = f(x - 1) + \frac{3}{2}$ is $(2, 2)$.

389 $\sin\left(\frac{\pi}{2} - \theta\right)\cos\left(\frac{\pi}{2} + \theta\right)\,\text{cosec}\,(\pi - 2\theta)$

$= \cos\theta \times (-\sin\theta) \times \dfrac{1}{\sin(\pi - 2\theta)}$

$= -\cos\theta\sin\theta \times \dfrac{1}{\sin 2\theta}$

$= -\sin\theta\cos\theta \times \dfrac{1}{2\sin\theta\cos\theta}$

$= -\frac{1}{2}$

390
$$\cos 2x = -\cos x, \quad 0 \leqslant x \leqslant 2\pi$$
$\Rightarrow \quad 2\cos^2 x - 1 + \cos x = 0$
$\Rightarrow \quad (2\cos x - 1)(\cos x + 1) = 0$
$\Rightarrow \quad \cos x = \frac{1}{2}$ or -1

$\Rightarrow \quad x = \frac{\pi}{3}, \pi, \frac{5\pi}{3}$

391 Graph is $y = a\sin bx + c$

$y(0) = c = 1$

period $= \dfrac{2\pi}{b} = \pi \Rightarrow b = 2$

amplitude $= |a| = 3 \Rightarrow a = 3$

a $a = 3$ **b** $b = 2$ **c** $c = 1$

392 $\mathbf{AB} = \begin{bmatrix} -7 & 11 & a+3 \\ -7 & 6 & -2a+1 \\ -12 & 16 & 4 \end{bmatrix}$ $\mathbf{BA} = \begin{bmatrix} 4 & 5+4a \\ -11 & -1 \end{bmatrix}$

393 Normal has vector $\begin{bmatrix} 2 \\ 2 \\ -1 \end{bmatrix}$ and line has vector $\begin{bmatrix} 1 \\ -2 \\ -1 \end{bmatrix}$

If θ is the angle between the normal and the line

$\cos\theta = \dfrac{\begin{bmatrix} 2 \\ 2 \\ -1 \end{bmatrix} \bullet \begin{bmatrix} 1 \\ -2 \\ -1 \end{bmatrix}}{\sqrt{4+4+1}\sqrt{1+4+1}} = \dfrac{-1}{3\sqrt{6}} \Rightarrow \theta = 97.8°$

The acute angle between the normal and the line is $82.2°$ and the angle between the plane and the line is $90° - 82.2° = 7.8°$.

394 $|\mathbf{a} \times \mathbf{b}| = |\mathbf{a}||\mathbf{b}|\sin\theta$

Hence $\sin\theta = \dfrac{|12\mathbf{j} - 5\mathbf{k}|}{4 \times 5} = \dfrac{\sqrt{12^2 + 5^2}}{20} = \dfrac{13}{20}$

and $\theta = 40.54°$ or $139.46°$

$\mathbf{a} \bullet \mathbf{b} = |\mathbf{a}||\mathbf{b}|\cos\theta$

$= 4 \times 5 \times \cos(40.54°) \approx 15.20$

or $\mathbf{a} \bullet \mathbf{b} = 4 \times 5 \times \cos(139.46°) \approx -15.20$

395 a There are 4 odd digits.

There are 4 odd digits to select from at the start leaving 3 odd digits to end.

This leaves 5 digits from which to select the remaining 3.

As order matters, this can be done in $P_3^5 = 5 \times 4 \times 3$ ways.

Total number is $4 \times 3 \times (5 \times 4 \times 3) = 720$ ways.

b Starting with an even digit the number of arrangements can be represented in the diagram

even	odd	even	odd	even
3	4	2	3	1

Total is 72.

Starting with an odd digit we have

odd	even	odd	even	odd
4	3	3	2	2

Total number of ways is 144.

Total number of ways of alternating is $72 + 144 = 216$

396
$$P(A \cup B) = P(A) + P(B) - P(A \cap B)$$
But $P(A \cap B) = P(A).P(B)$ {independent A and B}

So, $0.8 = 0.27 + P(B) - 0.27\,P(B)$

$0.53 = (1 - 0.27)\,P(B)$

$P(B) = \dfrac{0.53}{0.73} \approx 0.726$

397 Since 12 customers/hour arrive, 6 will arrive each $\frac{1}{2}$ hour.

Let $X =$ number of customers that arrive each $\frac{1}{2}$ hour

then $X \sim \text{Po}(6)$ and $P(X = 5) = \dfrac{6^5 e^{-6}}{5!} \approx 0.161$

398 a Using the midpoint of each time interval, the mean time,

$\overline{t} = \dfrac{\sum ft}{\sum f} \approx 50.25$ (f is the frequency)

and $s_n{}^2 = \dfrac{\sum f(t - \overline{t})^2}{\sum f} \approx 519.94$

Hence, $s_n = \sqrt{519.94} \approx 22.80$

b An unbiased estimate of σ is

$s_{n-1} = \sqrt{\dfrac{n}{n-1}}s_n = \sqrt{\dfrac{80}{79}} \times 22.8 \approx 22.95$

399 $y = x^2 \ln\left(\dfrac{1}{x^2}\right) = x^2 \ln x^{-2}$

$\therefore \quad y = -2x^2 \ln x$

So, $\dfrac{dy}{dx} = -4x \ln x - 2x^2\left(\dfrac{1}{x}\right)$

$= -4x \ln x - 2x$

and $\dfrac{d^2y}{dx^2} = -4\ln x - 4x\left(\dfrac{1}{x}\right) - 2$

$= -4\ln x - 6$

which is $0 \Leftrightarrow \ln x = -\dfrac{3}{2} \Leftrightarrow x = e^{-\frac{3}{2}}$

The sign diagram for $\dfrac{d^2y}{dx^2}$ is:

$$\xrightarrow[\qquad e^{-\frac{3}{2}} \qquad]{\quad + \quad | \quad - \quad}$$

and $y(e^{-\frac{3}{2}}) = \left(e^{-\frac{3}{2}}\right)^2 \ln\left(e^{-\frac{3}{2}}\right)^{-2} = e^{-3}\ln e^3 = 3e^{-3}$

$\therefore$ the point of inflection is at $\left(e^{-\frac{3}{2}}, 3e^{-3}\right)$

400 a When $x = -2$, $3(4) + 2(-2)y - y^2 = 7$

$\Rightarrow 12 - 4y - y^2 = 7$

$\Rightarrow y^2 + 4y - 5 = 0$

$\Rightarrow (y - 1)(y + 5) = 0$

$\Rightarrow y = 1$ or -5

$\therefore$ points are $(-2, 1)$ and $(-2, -5)$

b Now $6x + \left[2y + 2x\dfrac{dy}{dx}\right] - 2y\dfrac{dy}{dx} = 0$

$\Rightarrow 6x + 2y + (2x - 2y)\dfrac{dy}{dx} = 0$

and at $(-2, 1)$, $-12 + 2 + (-6)\dfrac{dy}{dx} = 0$

$\Rightarrow 6\dfrac{dy}{dx} = -10$

$\Rightarrow \dfrac{dy}{dx} = -\dfrac{5}{3}$

$\therefore$ tangent has slope $-\dfrac{5}{3} \Rightarrow$ normal has slope $\dfrac{3}{5}$

$\therefore$ equation is $y - 1 = \dfrac{3}{5}(x + 2)$ i.e., $5y - 5 = 3x + 6$

i.e., $3x - 5y = -11$

$\left[\begin{array}{l} \textbf{or} \quad \text{at } (-2, -5), \ \dfrac{dy}{dx} = -\dfrac{22}{6} = -\dfrac{11}{3} \\ \Rightarrow \quad \text{normal has slope } \dfrac{3}{11} \\ \Rightarrow \quad \text{normal is } \ y + 5 = \dfrac{3}{11}(x + 2) \\ \qquad \text{i.e., } \ 3x - 11y = 49 \end{array}\right]$

401 $\displaystyle\int \frac{\arctan x}{1+x^2}\,dx$

$\qquad u = \arctan x$

$\qquad \dfrac{du}{dx} = \dfrac{1}{1+x^2}$

$= \displaystyle\int u\frac{du}{dx}\,dx$

$= \int u\,du$

$= \dfrac{u^2}{2} + c$

$= \tfrac{1}{2}(\arctan x)^2 + c$

402 $x = 8y - 7 - y^2$ meets $x - 2y + 2 = 0$ where

$\qquad 8y - 7 - y^2 = 2y - 2$

i.e., $y^2 - 6y + 5 = 0$

$\qquad (y-1)(y-5) = 0$ and so $y = 1$ or 5

Where $y = 1$, $x = 2 - 2 = 0$

Where $y = 5$, $x = 10 - 2 = 8$ $\quad\therefore$ meet at $(0, 1)$ and at $(8, 5)$

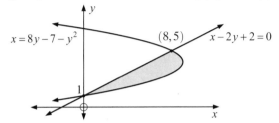

Area $= \displaystyle\int_1^5 (8y - 7 - y^2) - (2y - 2)\,dy$

$= \displaystyle\int_1^5 -y^2 + 6y - 5\,dy$

$= \left[\dfrac{-y^3}{3} + \dfrac{6y^2}{2} - 5y\right]_1^5$

$= \left(-\tfrac{125}{3} + 75 - 25\right) - \left(-\tfrac{1}{3} + 3 - 5\right)$

$= \dfrac{32}{3}$ units^2

403 $\displaystyle\int \arcsin x\,dx$

$= \int 1\arcsin x\,dx$

$\qquad\begin{bmatrix} u' = 1 & v = \arcsin x \\ u = x & v' = \dfrac{1}{\sqrt{1-x^2}} \end{bmatrix}$

$= x\arcsin x - \displaystyle\int \frac{x}{\sqrt{1-x^2}}\,dx$

$\qquad\begin{bmatrix} x = 1 - x^2 \\ \dfrac{dw}{dx} = -2x \end{bmatrix}$

$= x\arcsin x - \displaystyle\int w^{-\frac{1}{2}}\left(\frac{1}{-2}\frac{dw}{dx}\right)dw$

$= x\arcsin x + \tfrac{1}{2}\displaystyle\int w^{-\frac{1}{2}}\,dw$

$= x\arcsin x + \tfrac{1}{2}\dfrac{w^{\frac{1}{2}}}{\frac{1}{2}} + c$

$= x\arcsin x + \sqrt{1-x^2} + c$

404 $\displaystyle\int_0^a x\sqrt{1-x^2}\,dx = 0.2$

$\Rightarrow -\tfrac{1}{2}\displaystyle\int_0^a (1-x^2)^{\frac{1}{2}}(-2x)\,dx = 0.2$

$\Rightarrow -\tfrac{1}{2}\left[\dfrac{(1-x^2)^{\frac{3}{2}}}{\frac{3}{2}}\right]_0^a = 0.2$

$\Rightarrow -\tfrac{1}{3}\left[(1-x^2)^{\frac{3}{2}}\right]_0^a = 0.2$

$\Rightarrow (1-a^2)^{\frac{3}{2}} - 1 = -0.6$

$\Rightarrow (1-a^2)^{\frac{3}{2}} = 0.4$

$\Rightarrow 1 - a^2 = (0.4)^{\frac{2}{3}}$

$\Rightarrow a^2 = 1 - (0.4)^{\frac{2}{3}}$

$\Rightarrow a \approx 0.676$, as $a > 0$

405 a $|\mathbf{p} + \mathbf{q}| = \sqrt{(\mathbf{p}+\mathbf{q})\bullet(\mathbf{p}+\mathbf{q})} = \sqrt{25} = 5$

b $(\mathbf{p}+\mathbf{q})\bullet(\mathbf{p}+\mathbf{q}) = \mathbf{p}\bullet\mathbf{p} + \mathbf{p}\bullet\mathbf{q} + \mathbf{q}\bullet\mathbf{p} + \mathbf{q}\bullet\mathbf{q}$

$\qquad\qquad = |\mathbf{p}|^2 + 2(\mathbf{p}\bullet\mathbf{q}) + |\mathbf{q}|^2$

i.e., $25 = 25 + 2(\mathbf{p}\bullet\mathbf{q})$ (given)

and $\mathbf{p}\bullet\mathbf{q} = 0$

c

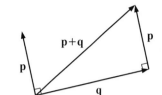

Note that since $\mathbf{p}\bullet\mathbf{q} = 0$

$\mathbf{p}$ and $\mathbf{q}$ are perpendicular.

406 a $\qquad z = re^{i\theta}$

$\therefore \quad z^n = (re^{i\theta})^n$

$\Rightarrow \quad z^n = r^n e^{in\theta}$

$\qquad\qquad = r^n(\cos(n\theta) + i\sin(n\theta))$

i.e., $z^n = r^n(\cos n\theta + i\sin n\theta)$

b i $1 + i$ has $|1+i| = \sqrt{1+1} = \sqrt{2}$

$\therefore \quad 1 + i = \sqrt{2}\left(\frac{1}{\sqrt{2}} + \frac{1}{\sqrt{2}}i\right)$

$\Rightarrow \quad 1 + i = \sqrt{2}\,\text{cis}\left(\frac{\pi}{4}\right)$

$1 - i$ has $|1-i| = \sqrt{1+1} = \sqrt{2}$

$\therefore \quad 1 - i = \sqrt{2}\left(\frac{1}{\sqrt{2}} - \frac{1}{\sqrt{2}}i\right)$

$\Rightarrow \quad 1 - i = \sqrt{2}\,\text{cis}\left(-\frac{\pi}{4}\right)$

ii $(1+i)^n + (1-i)^n$

$= \left[\sqrt{2}\,\text{cis}\left(\frac{\pi}{4}\right)\right]^n + \left[\sqrt{2}\,\text{cis}\left(-\frac{\pi}{4}\right)\right]^n$

$= 2^{\frac{n}{2}}\,\text{cis}\left(\frac{n\pi}{4}\right) + 2^{\frac{n}{2}}\,\text{cis}\left(\frac{-n\pi}{4}\right)$ {De Moivre}

$= 2^{\frac{n}{2}}\left(\cos\frac{n\pi}{4} + i\sin\frac{n\pi}{4} + \cos\frac{n\pi}{4} - i\sin\frac{n\pi}{4}\right)$

$= 2^{\frac{n}{2}} \times 2\cos\left(\frac{n\pi}{4}\right)$

$= 2^{\frac{n}{2}+1}\cos\left(\frac{n\pi}{4}\right)$

iii If $(1+i)^n + (1-i)^n = 64$

then $2^{\frac{n}{2}+1}\cos\frac{n\pi}{4} = 2^6$

$\Rightarrow \cos\frac{n\pi}{4} = 2^{6-1-\frac{n}{2}}$

$\Rightarrow \cos\frac{n\pi}{4} = 2^{5-\frac{n}{2}}$

But the LHS $= \pm\frac{1}{\sqrt{2}}, 0, \pm 1$

Also, $2^{5-\frac{n}{2}} > 0$ for all n

$\Rightarrow \cos\dfrac{n\pi}{4} > 0$

$\therefore \quad 2^{5-\frac{n}{2}} = 2^{-\frac{1}{2}}$ or 2^0

$\Rightarrow 5 - \dfrac{n}{2} = -\dfrac{1}{2}$ or $5 - \dfrac{n}{2} = 0$

$\Rightarrow \dfrac{n}{2} = \dfrac{11}{2}$ or $\dfrac{n}{2} = 5$

$\Rightarrow n = 10$ or 11

If $n = 10$, $\cos\frac{5\pi}{2} = 2^0$

$\Rightarrow \cos\frac{\pi}{2} = 1$

$\Rightarrow 0 = 1$ false

If $n = 11$, $\cos\frac{11\pi}{4} = 2^{-\frac{1}{2}}$

$\Rightarrow \cos\frac{3\pi}{4} = \frac{1}{\sqrt{2}}$

$\Rightarrow -\frac{1}{\sqrt{2}} = \frac{1}{\sqrt{2}}$ false

So, no integer solutions exist.

407 $f(x) = \dfrac{x^2 + 1}{e^x}$

a As $x \to \infty$, $e^x \to \infty$ more rapidly than $x^2 + 1 \to \infty$
$\therefore$ as $x \to \infty$, $f(x) \to 0$ (above).

b $f'(x) = \dfrac{2xe^x - (x^2 + 1)e^x}{e^{2x}} = \dfrac{2x - x^2 - 1}{e^x}$

$= \dfrac{-(x-1)^2}{e^x}$

c $f'(x) = 0$ when $(x-1)^2 = 0 \Rightarrow x = 1$
Sign diag of $f'(x)$:

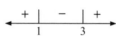

$\therefore$ stationary inflection at $(1, f(1))$ i.e., at $\left(1, \dfrac{2}{e}\right)$

d $f''(x) = \dfrac{(2 - 2x)e^x - (2x - x^2 - 1)e^x}{e^{2x}}$

$= \dfrac{2 - 2x - 2x + x^2 + 1}{e^x}$

$= \dfrac{x^2 - 4x + 3}{e^x}$

e $f''(x) = 0$ when $x^2 - 4x + 3 = 0$
$(x - 3)(x - 1) = 0$
$x = 3$ or 1

Sign diag. of $f''(x)$:

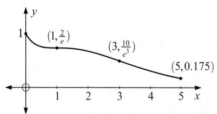

Changing signs $\Rightarrow$ non-stationary inflection at $\left(3, \dfrac{10}{e^3}\right)$

f $f(0) = 1$ and $f(5) = \dfrac{26}{e^5} \approx 0.175$

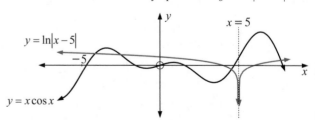

SOLUTIONS TO EXAMINATION PRACTICE SET 12

408 $1 + 2 + 3 + 4 + 5 + \ldots + 999 = \dfrac{999}{2}[1 + 999]$

$= \dfrac{999}{2} \times 1000$

$= 499\,500$

For multiples of 6

$6 + 12 + 18 + \ldots + 996$ $6\,\underline{|\,1000}$
$= \dfrac{166}{2}[6 + 996]$ $166\tfrac{4}{6}$
$= 83 \times 1002$
$= 83\,166$

For multiples of 8

$8 + 16 + 24 + \ldots + 992$ $8\,\underline{|\,1000}$
$= \dfrac{124}{2}(8 + 992)$ 125
$= 62 \times 1000$
$= 62\,000$

For multiples of 24   (counted twice)

$24 + 48 + 72 + \ldots + 984$ $24\,\underline{|\,1000}$
$= \dfrac{41}{2}(24 + 984)$ $41\tfrac{16}{24}$
$= \dfrac{41}{2} \times 1008$
$= 41 \times 504$
$= 20\,664$

$\therefore$ sum required
$= 499\,500 - 83\,166 - 62\,000 + 20\,664$
$= 374\,998$

---

409 a

$2^{x+1} = 5^{x-1}$

$\log 2^{x+1} = \log 5^{x-1}$

$\Rightarrow (x+1)\log 2 = (x-1)\log 5$

$\Rightarrow x + 1 = (x-1)\dfrac{\log 5}{\log 2}$

$\Rightarrow x + 1 = (x-1)\log_2 5$

$\Rightarrow x + 1 = x\log_2 5 - \log_2 5$

$\Rightarrow x(1 - \log_2 5) = -1 - \log_2 5$

$\Rightarrow x = \dfrac{1 + \log_2 5}{\log_2 5 - 1}$

b Using a gcalc, $x \approx 2.51$

410 $|w| = |z|$, $\arg w = \frac{\pi}{6}$, $\arg z = \frac{\pi}{3}$

a $\arg(wz) = \arg w + \arg z = \frac{\pi}{6} + \frac{\pi}{3} = \frac{\pi}{2}$

b $w + z = R\operatorname{cis}\left(\frac{\pi}{6}\right) + R\operatorname{cis}\left(\frac{\pi}{3}\right)$
$= R\left(\operatorname{cis}\left(\frac{\pi}{6}\right) + \operatorname{cis}\left(\frac{\pi}{3}\right)\right)$

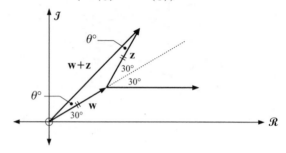

$\theta + \theta = 30° \Rightarrow \theta = 15°$
$\arg(w + z) = 30° + \theta° = 45° = \frac{\pi}{4}$

411 f is defined for all x i.e., domain is all $x \in \mathbb{R}$

If $x \geqslant 2$ $|x - 2| - 4|x + 1| = (x - 2) - 4(x + 1)$
                              $= -3x - 6$

If $-1 \leqslant x \leqslant 2$ $|x - 2| - 4|x + 1| = -(x - 2) - 4(x + 1)$
                                   $= -5x - 2$

If $x \leqslant -1$ $|x - 2| - 4|x + 1| = -(x - 2) - 4(-[x + 1])$
                                $= 3x + 6$

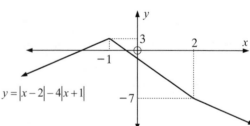

$y = |x - 2| - 4|x + 1|$

f has a maximum value of 3 (which occurs if $x = -1$)
Range of f is $y \leqslant 3$. (A gcd solution is easier.)

412 The graph of $y = \ln|x - 5|$ and $y = x\cos x$ is shown.
Note that $x = 5$ is an asymptote for $y = \ln|x - 5|$

$y = \ln|x - 5|$

$y = x\cos x$

From the graph there are exactly 3 roots in the interval.
Roots are $x = -4.1497$, -2.5056, 4.5404
Using the fact that $y = \ln|x - 5|$ (or $y = x\cos x$), the coordinates of the points of intersection are:
$(-4.1497, 2.2137)$, $(-2.5056, 2.0156)$, $(4.5404, -0.7774)$

413 Since $xy = 2$, i.e., $y = \dfrac{2}{x}$ providing $x \neq 0$, then the graphs meet where

$$x^3 + \left(\dfrac{2}{x}\right)^3 = 9$$

$$\Rightarrow \quad x^3 + \dfrac{8}{x^3} = 9$$

$$\Rightarrow \quad x^6 + 8 = 9x^3$$

$$\Rightarrow \quad x^6 - 9x^3 + 8 = 0$$

then $z^2 - 9z + 8 = 0$ $\{$letting $x^3 = z\}$

$$\Rightarrow \quad (z - 8)(z - 1) = 0$$

$$\text{i.e.,} \quad z = 8 \text{ or } 1$$

$$x^3 = 8 \text{ or } 1$$

$$x = 2 \text{ or } 1$$

So, $x = 2$, $y = 1$ or $x = 1$, $y = 2$.

414 $6x^2 + px + q = 6\left(x^2 + \dfrac{p}{6}x + \dfrac{q}{6}\right)$

$$= 6\left((x - 2)(x + \tfrac{1}{2})\right)$$

$$= 6\left(x^2 - 2x + \tfrac{1}{2}x - 1\right)$$

$$= 6\left(x^2 - \tfrac{3}{2}x - 1\right)$$

Hence,

a $\dfrac{p}{6} = -\dfrac{3}{2}$, $p = -9$ **b** $\dfrac{q}{6} = -1$, $q = -6$

415 $\tan\beta = \dfrac{2}{3}$, $\pi < \beta < \dfrac{3\pi}{2}$

Now $\tan\beta = \dfrac{2\tan\left(\frac{\beta}{2}\right)}{1 - \tan^2\left(\frac{\beta}{2}\right)}$

$$\therefore \quad \dfrac{2t}{1 - t^2} = \dfrac{2}{3} \quad \{\text{with } t = \tan(\tfrac{\beta}{2})\}$$

$$\Rightarrow \quad 3t = 1 - t^2$$

$$\Rightarrow \quad t^2 + 3t - 1 = 0$$

$$\Rightarrow \quad t = \dfrac{-3 \pm \sqrt{9 - 4(1)(-1)}}{2}$$

$$\Rightarrow \quad t = \dfrac{-3 \pm \sqrt{13}}{2}$$

But $\dfrac{\pi}{2} < \dfrac{\beta}{2} < \dfrac{3\pi}{4}$

$\therefore$ $\dfrac{\beta}{2}$ lies in quad 2 and so $\tan\left(\dfrac{\beta}{2}\right)$ is negative.

$$\Rightarrow \quad \tan\left(\dfrac{\beta}{2}\right) = \dfrac{-3 - \sqrt{13}}{2}$$

416 $2\sin^2 x - \sin x - 2\sin x \cos x + \cos x = 0$

$$\Rightarrow \quad \sin x(2\sin x - 1) - \cos x(2\sin x - 1) = 0$$

$$\Rightarrow \quad (2\sin x - 1)(\sin x - \cos x) = 0$$

$$\Rightarrow \quad \sin x = \tfrac{1}{2} \quad \text{or} \quad \sin x = \cos x$$

$$\Rightarrow \quad \sin x = \tfrac{1}{2} \quad \text{or} \quad \tan x = 1$$

$$\Rightarrow \quad x = \dfrac{\pi}{6}, \dfrac{\pi}{4}, \dfrac{5\pi}{6}$$

417 $f(x) = \cos 2x - \sin 2x$, $0 \leqslant x \leqslant \pi$

a $f(0) = 1$, $f(\pi) = 1$

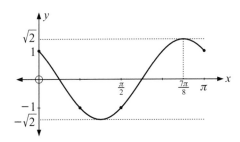

b max. value is $\sqrt{2}$ (when $x = \dfrac{7\pi}{8}$)

418 $\begin{bmatrix} y & 2 & -1 \\ 1 & y & 3 \\ 4 & -1 & 1 \end{bmatrix}$ is singular if $\begin{vmatrix} y & 2 & -1 \\ 1 & y & 3 \\ 4 & -1 & 1 \end{vmatrix} = 0$

$$\begin{vmatrix} y & 2 & -1 \\ 1 & y & 3 \\ 4 & -1 & 1 \end{vmatrix} = y\begin{vmatrix} y & 3 \\ -1 & 1 \end{vmatrix} + 2\begin{vmatrix} 3 & 1 \\ 1 & 4 \end{vmatrix} + (-1)\begin{vmatrix} 1 & y \\ 4 & -1 \end{vmatrix}$$

$$= y(y + 3) + 2(11) - 1(-1 - 4y)$$

$$= y^2 + 7y + 23$$

which is 0 if $y = \dfrac{-7 \pm \sqrt{49 - 92}}{2}$

i.e., if $y = -\dfrac{7}{2} \pm \dfrac{\sqrt{43}}{2}i$

419 a If $\mathbf{a}$ and $\mathbf{b}$ are perpendicular then $\mathbf{a} \bullet \mathbf{b} = 0$

$$\text{i.e.,} \quad -t + 2(1 + t) - 2(2t) = 0$$

$$\text{i.e.,} \quad -t + 2 + 2t - 4t = 0$$

$$-3t + 2 = 0 \quad \text{and so} \quad t = \tfrac{2}{3}$$

b The vectors are parallel if $\dfrac{-t}{1} = \dfrac{1 + t}{2} = \dfrac{2t}{-2}$

$$\text{i.e.,} \quad -2t = 1 + t$$

$$\text{i.e.,} \quad t = -\tfrac{1}{3}$$

420

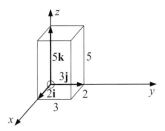

Diagonal from origin to $2\mathbf{i} + 3\mathbf{j} + 5\mathbf{k}$ has direction $\begin{bmatrix} 2 \\ 3 \\ 5 \end{bmatrix}$

Diagonal from $5\mathbf{k}$ to $2\mathbf{i} + 3\mathbf{j}$ has direction $\begin{bmatrix} 2 \\ 3 \\ -5 \end{bmatrix}$

If the angle between the diagonals is θ then

$$\begin{bmatrix} 2 \\ 3 \\ 5 \end{bmatrix} \bullet \begin{bmatrix} 2 \\ 3 \\ -5 \end{bmatrix} = \left|\begin{bmatrix} 2 \\ 3 \\ 5 \end{bmatrix}\right|\left|\begin{bmatrix} 2 \\ 3 \\ -5 \end{bmatrix}\right|\cos\theta = \sqrt{38}\sqrt{38}\cos\theta$$

$$\Rightarrow \quad 4 + 9 - 25 = 38\cos\theta$$

$$\Rightarrow \quad \cos\theta = \dfrac{-12}{38} \quad \text{and so} \quad \theta \approx 108.4°$$

The acute angle between the diagonals is $71.6°$

Note: This angle may depend on the diagonals you select.

421 a $\overrightarrow{AB} = \begin{bmatrix} -2 \\ 4 \\ 2 \end{bmatrix}$ $\overrightarrow{AC} = \begin{bmatrix} 1 \\ -2 \\ -1 \end{bmatrix}$

Hence $\overrightarrow{AB} = -2\overrightarrow{AC}$ and A, B and C are collinear.

b AC : CB $= -1 : 3$

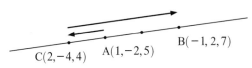

c P has position vector $\dfrac{1}{3}\begin{bmatrix} 1 \\ -2 \\ 5 \end{bmatrix} + \dfrac{2}{3}\begin{bmatrix} -1 \\ 2 \\ 7 \end{bmatrix} = \begin{bmatrix} -\frac{1}{3} \\ \frac{2}{3} \\ \frac{19}{3} \end{bmatrix}$

$$\Rightarrow \quad \text{P is at } \left(-\tfrac{1}{3}, \tfrac{2}{3}, \tfrac{19}{3}\right).$$

422 a Sample mean, $\overline{x} \approx 750.6$ and sample standard deviation, $s_n \approx 3.412$

b An unbiased estimate of σ is

$$s_{n-1} = \sqrt{\dfrac{n}{n-1}}s_n = \sqrt{\dfrac{10}{9}} \times 3.412 \approx 3.569$$

423 a Total number of ways of selecting 5 from 12 is $\binom{12}{5}$.

If no men are selected, there are $\binom{7}{5}$ of selecting 5 women.

The probability of selecting 5 women is $\dfrac{\binom{7}{5}}{\binom{12}{5}} \approx 0.265$

b Number of ways of selecting 3 women and 2 men is $\binom{7}{3}\binom{5}{2}$

So the probability of selecting 3 women and 2 men is

$\dfrac{\binom{7}{3}\binom{5}{2}}{\binom{12}{5}} \approx 0.442$

424 The tree diagram shows the situation:

$C \equiv$ owns a car

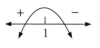

a Probability a student does not have a car is

$\frac{42}{100} \times \frac{13}{100} + \frac{58}{100} \times \frac{8}{100} = 0.101$

b Now, $P(M \mid C') = \dfrac{P(M \cap C')}{P(C')}$

$= \dfrac{0.58 \times 0.08}{0.42 \times 0.13 + 0.58 \times 0.08} \approx 0.459$

425 $X \sim N(90, \sigma^2)$.

Now $P(X < 88) = 0.289\,25$

$\Rightarrow P\left(\dfrac{X - 90}{\sigma} < \dfrac{88 - 90}{\sigma}\right) = 0.28925$

$\Rightarrow P\left(Z < \dfrac{-2}{\sigma}\right) = 0.289\,25$

$\Rightarrow -\dfrac{2}{\sigma} = \text{invNorm}(0.289\,25)$

$\Rightarrow \sigma = -2 \div \text{invNorm}(0.289\,25)$

$\Rightarrow \sigma \approx 3.60$

$P(90 < X < 92) = \text{normalcdf}\,(90, 92, 90, 3.60)$
≈ 0.212

i.e., about 21.2% of the scores lie between 90 and 92.

426 a $f(x) = 4xe^{-x}, \quad x \geqslant 0$

$\therefore \quad f'(x) = 4e^{-x} + 4xe^{-x}(-1)$
$= 4e^{-x}(1 - x)$

which is 0 $\Leftrightarrow x = 1 \quad$ {as $e^{-x} > 0$ for all x}

$f'(x)$ has sign diag.:

$\therefore$ a local max. at $\left(1, \dfrac{4}{e}\right)$

b $f''(x) = -4e^{-x}(1 - x) + 4e^{-x}(-1)$
$= 4e^{-x}(-1 + x - 1)$
$= 4e^{-x}(x - 2) \quad$ which is 0 $\Leftrightarrow x = 2$

$f''(x)$ has sign diag:

and as the signs alternate, point of inflection is $\left(2, \dfrac{8}{e^2}\right)$.

427

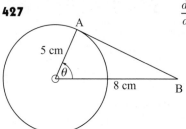

$\dfrac{d\theta}{dt} = \dfrac{1 \text{ rev}}{2 \text{ sec}} = \dfrac{2\pi^c}{2 \text{ sec}} = \pi^c/\text{sec}$

Area $\triangle OAB = \frac{1}{2}(5)(8)\sin\theta$

i.e., $A = 20\sin\theta$

$\dfrac{dA}{dt} = 20\cos\theta\dfrac{d\theta}{dt}$

Particular case: $\theta = \frac{\pi}{6}$

$\dfrac{dA}{dt} = 20\left(\dfrac{\sqrt{3}}{2}\right)(\pi)$

$= 10\sqrt{3}\pi \text{ cm/sec}$

i.e., area is increasing at $10\pi\sqrt{3}$ cm/sec

428 $\int \tan^5 x \, dx$

$= \int (\tan^3 x)(\tan^2 x) \, dx$

$= \int \tan^3 x(\sec^2 x - 1) \, dx$

$= \int [\tan x]^3 \sec^2 x \, dx - \int \tan^3 x \, dx$

$= \int u^3 \dfrac{du}{dx} \, dx - \int \tan x \tan^2 x \, dx \qquad \begin{array}{l} u = \tan x \\[4pt] \dfrac{du}{dx} = \sec^2 x \end{array}$

$= \dfrac{u^4}{4} - \int \tan x(\sec^2 x - 1) \, dx$

$= \frac{1}{4}\tan^4 x - \int \tan x \sec^2 x \, dx + \int \tan x \, dx$

$= \frac{1}{4}\tan^4 x - \int v\dfrac{dv}{dx} \, dx - \int \dfrac{-\sin x}{\cos x} \, dx$

$= \frac{1}{4}\tan^4 x - \dfrac{v^2}{2} - \ln|\cos x| + c$

$= \frac{1}{4}\tan^4 x - \frac{1}{2}\tan^2 x - \ln|\cos x| + c$

429 a $\displaystyle\int \dfrac{\sin x}{(1 + \cos x)^2} \, dx \qquad \left[\begin{array}{l} \text{Let } u = 1 + \cos x \\[4pt] \therefore \quad \dfrac{du}{dx} = -\sin x \end{array} \right]$

$= \int u^{-2}\left(-\dfrac{du}{dx}\right) \, dx$

$= \int -u^{-2} \, du$

$= \dfrac{-u^{-1}}{-1} + c$

$= \dfrac{1}{u} + c$

$= \dfrac{1}{1 + \cos x} + c$

b

Area

$= \displaystyle\int_{\frac{\pi}{3}}^{\frac{2\pi}{3}} \dfrac{\sin x}{(1 + \cos x)^2} \, dx$

$= \left[\dfrac{1}{1 + \cos x}\right]_{\frac{\pi}{3}}^{\frac{2\pi}{3}}$

$= \dfrac{1}{1 - \frac{1}{2}} - \dfrac{1}{1 + \frac{1}{2}}$

$= 2 - \dfrac{2}{3}$

$= \dfrac{4}{3}$ units^2

430 $\displaystyle\int \dfrac{1}{x^2}\ln x \, dx \qquad \left[\text{Let} \quad \begin{array}{ll} u' = x^{-2} & v = \ln x \\[4pt] u = \dfrac{x^{-1}}{-1} & v' = \dfrac{1}{x} \end{array} \right]$

$= -\dfrac{1}{x}\ln x - \int -\dfrac{1}{x}\left(\dfrac{1}{x}\right) \, dx$

$= -\dfrac{\ln x}{x} + \int x^{-2} \, dx$

$= -\dfrac{\ln x}{x} + \dfrac{x^{-1}}{-1} + c$

$= \dfrac{-\ln x}{x} - \dfrac{1}{x} + c$

431 $\displaystyle\int_{-a}^{a} 3x^2 - 8x + 2 \, dx = 12a$

$\Rightarrow \left[\dfrac{3x^3}{3} - \dfrac{8x^2}{2} + 2x\right]_{-a}^{a} = 12a$

$\Rightarrow \quad (a^3 - 4a^2 + 2a) - (-a^3 - 4a^2 - 2a) = 12a$
$$\Rightarrow \quad 2a^3 + 4a = 12a$$
$$\Rightarrow \quad 2a^3 - 8a = 0$$
$$\Rightarrow \quad 2a(a^2 - 4) = 0$$
$$\Rightarrow \quad 2a(a + 2)(a - 2) = 0$$
$$\Rightarrow \quad a = 0 \quad \text{or} \quad \pm 2$$
$$\Rightarrow \quad a = 2 \quad \{a > 0\}$$

432 $f(x) = \dfrac{\sin x}{\cos x + \sqrt{2}}, \quad 0 < x < 2\pi$

a i $f'(x) = \dfrac{\cos x(\cos x + \sqrt{2}) - \sin x(-\sin x)}{(\cos x + \sqrt{2})^2}$

$\qquad = \dfrac{\cos^2 x + \sqrt{2}\cos x + \sin^2 x}{(\cos x + \sqrt{2})^2}$

$\qquad = \dfrac{1 + \sqrt{2}\cos x}{(\cos x + \sqrt{2})^2}$

ii when $f'(x) = 0, \quad 1 + \sqrt{2}\cos x = 0$

$\Rightarrow \quad \cos x = -\dfrac{1}{\sqrt{2}}$ and so $x = \dfrac{3\pi}{4}, \dfrac{5\pi}{4}$

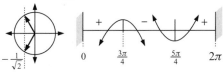

$\therefore$ local max. at $\left(\dfrac{3\pi}{4}, 1\right)$ local min. at $\left(\dfrac{5\pi}{4}, -1\right)$

b i $f''(x)$

$= \dfrac{\begin{array}{l}(-\sqrt{2}\sin x)(\cos x + \sqrt{2})^2 \\ \quad -(1 + \sqrt{2}\cos x)2(\cos x + \sqrt{2})(-\sin x)\end{array}}{(\cos x + \sqrt{2})^4}$

$= \dfrac{-\sqrt{2}\sin x \cos x - 2\sin x + 2\sin x + 2\sqrt{2}\sin x \cos x}{(\cos x + \sqrt{2})^3}$

$= \dfrac{\sqrt{2}\sin x \cos x}{(\cos x + \sqrt{2})^3}$

ii when $f''(x) = 0, \quad \sin x \cos x = 0$

$\Rightarrow \quad \sin x = 0 \quad \text{or} \quad \cos x = 0$

$\therefore \quad x = \dfrac{\pi}{2}, \pi, \dfrac{3\pi}{2}$

There are
changes in
signs of $f''(x)$:

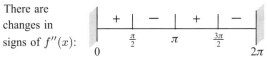

$\Rightarrow$ points of inflection at $\left(\dfrac{\pi}{2}, \dfrac{1}{\sqrt{2}}\right), (\pi, 0), \left(\dfrac{3\pi}{2}, \dfrac{-1}{\sqrt{2}}\right)$

c

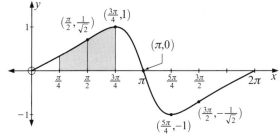

d Area $= \displaystyle\int_{\frac{\pi}{4}}^{\frac{3\pi}{4}} \dfrac{\sin x}{\cos x + \sqrt{2}} \, dx$

$= \left[-\ln\left|\cos x + \sqrt{2}\right|\right]_{\frac{\pi}{4}}^{\frac{3\pi}{4}}$

$= -\ln\left[\dfrac{-1}{\sqrt{2}} + \sqrt{2}\right] + \ln\left|\dfrac{1}{\sqrt{2}} + \sqrt{2}\right|$

$= -\ln\left|\sqrt{2} - \tfrac{1}{2}\sqrt{2}\right| + \ln\left|\sqrt{2} + \tfrac{1}{2}\sqrt{2}\right|$

$= -\ln(\tfrac{1}{2}\sqrt{2}) + \ln(\tfrac{3}{2}\sqrt{2})$

$= \ln\left(\dfrac{\frac{3}{2}\sqrt{2}}{\frac{1}{2}\sqrt{2}}\right)$

$= \ln 3 \quad \text{units}^2$

---

433 a $P(n)$ is $2^{n-1} \leqslant n!$ for all $n \in \mathbb{Z}^+$

Proof: (By the Principle of Math Induction)

(1) If $n = 1$, $2^{n-1} = 2^0 = 1$ and $1! = 1$
   as $1 \leqslant 1$ is a true statement, $P(1)$ is true.

(2) Suppose $P(k)$ is true, i.e., $2^{k-1} \leqslant k!$ or $k! \geqslant 2^{k-1}$
   Now $(k + 1)! - 2^k$
   $= (k + 1)k! - 2^k$
   $\geqslant (k + 1)2^{k-1} - 2^k$
   $= 2^{k-1}(k + 1 - 2)$
   $= 2^{k-1}(k - 1)$
   $\geqslant 0$ as $2^{k-1} > 0$ and $k \geqslant 1$
   This means $(k + 1)! \geqslant 2^k$ or $2^k \leqslant (k + 1)!$

Thus $P(k+1)$ is true whenever $P(k)$ it true and $P(1)$ is true. $\Rightarrow$ $P(n)$ is true {P of MI}

b Given $\dfrac{dA}{dt} \propto A$ $\quad \begin{cases} t = 5, \quad A = 32 \\ t = 10, \quad A = 40 \end{cases}$

i $\dfrac{dA}{dt} \propto A \qquad \Rightarrow \quad \dfrac{dA}{dt} = kA$

$\Rightarrow \quad \dfrac{1}{A}\dfrac{dA}{dt} = k$

$\Rightarrow \quad \displaystyle\int \dfrac{1}{A}\dfrac{dA}{dt} \, dt = \int k \, dt$

$\Rightarrow \quad \displaystyle\int \dfrac{1}{A} dA = \int k \, dt$

$\Rightarrow \quad \ln|A| = kt + c$

$\Rightarrow \quad |A| = e^{kt+c}$

$\Rightarrow \quad A = \pm e^c e^{kt}$ and so, $A = A_0 e^{kt}$

ii when $t = 5$, $A = 32$ $\therefore$ $32 = A_0 e^{5k}$ ...... (1)

when $t = 10$, $A = 40$ $\therefore$ $40 = A_0 e^{10k}$ ...... (2)

$(2) \div (1)$ gives $\dfrac{A_0 e^{10k}}{A_0 e^{5k}} = \dfrac{40}{32}$

i.e., $e^{10k-5k} = \dfrac{5}{4}$

or $e^{5k} = \dfrac{5}{4}$ ...... (3)

$\therefore \quad 5k = \ln(1.25)$

$\therefore \quad k = \tfrac{1}{5}\ln(1.25)$

$\therefore \quad k \approx 0.044\,63$

iii From (1) $\quad 32 = A_0 e^{5k}$

$\therefore \quad 32 = A_0\left(\dfrac{5}{4}\right)$ {from (3)}

$\therefore \quad A_0 = 32 \times \dfrac{4}{5} = 25.6$

i.e., original coverage $= 25.6$ km^2

iv When $A = 100$ km^2

$100 \approx 25.6 e^{0.044\,63t}$

$\Rightarrow \quad e^{0.044\,63t} \approx \dfrac{100}{25.6}$

$\Rightarrow \quad 0.044\,63t \approx \ln\left(\dfrac{100}{25.6}\right)$

$\Rightarrow \quad 0.044\,63t \approx 1.3626$

$\Rightarrow \quad t \approx 30.53.....$

So, it will take $30\tfrac{1}{2}$ years.

SOLUTIONS TO EXAMINATION PRACTICE SET 13

434 a $u_1 = 285$, $u_{10} = 213$

Now $u_{10} = u_1 + 9d \Rightarrow 213 = 285 + 9d$
$\Rightarrow 9d = -72$
$\Rightarrow d = -8$

Thus, $u_n = 285 + (n - 1)(-8)$
$= 285 - 8n + 8$

So, $u_n = 293 - 8n$

b $u_n > 0$ for $293 - 8n > 0$
$$\Rightarrow \quad 8n < 293$$
$$\Rightarrow \quad n < 36\tfrac{5}{8}$$
i.e., 36 terms are positive.

435 a $\dfrac{1}{u_1} + \dfrac{1}{u_2} + \dfrac{1}{u_3} + \ldots\ldots + \dfrac{1}{u_n}$

$= \dfrac{1}{u_1} + \dfrac{1}{u_1 r} + \dfrac{1}{u_1 r^2} + \ldots\ldots + \dfrac{1}{u_1 r^{n-1}}$ which is geometric

with first term $\dfrac{1}{u_1}$ and common ratio $\dfrac{1}{r}$

$= \dfrac{1}{u_1} \left(\dfrac{(\frac{1}{r})^n - 1}{\frac{1}{r} - 1} \right)$

$= \dfrac{1}{u_1} \left(\dfrac{1 - r^n}{r^n(\frac{1}{r} - 1)} \right)$

$= \dfrac{1}{u_1} \left(\dfrac{1 - r^n}{r^{n-1} - r^n} \right)$

b $\tfrac{1}{3} + \tfrac{1}{6} + \tfrac{1}{12} + \ldots\ldots + \tfrac{1}{3072}$

is the sum of the reciprocals of   3, 6, 12, ..., 3072

which is geometric with $u_1 = 3$, $r = 2$

$$u_n = u_1 r^{n-1} \quad \Rightarrow \quad 3072 = 3 \times 2^{n-1}$$
$$\Rightarrow \quad 2^{n-1} = 1024$$
$$\Rightarrow \quad 2^{n-1} = 2^{10} \quad \text{and so} \quad n = 11$$

$\therefore \quad S_{11} = \tfrac{1}{3} \left(\dfrac{1 - 2^{11}}{2^{10} - 2^{11}} \right)$

$= \tfrac{1}{3} \left(\dfrac{-2047}{1024 - 2048} \right)$

$= \dfrac{-2047}{-3072}$

$= \dfrac{2047}{3072}$

436 $\qquad 3\binom{n}{2} = \binom{n}{3}$

$\Rightarrow \quad 3\dfrac{n(n-1)}{2 \times 1} = \dfrac{n(n-1)(n-2)}{3 \times 2 \times 1}$

$\Rightarrow \quad 9n(n-1) = n(n-1)(n-2)$

where $n \geqslant 2$ and $n \geqslant 3$

So, n and $n - 1$ cannot be 0

Thus $9 = n - 2$ and so $n = 11$.

437 $\cos\theta + i\sin\theta = \operatorname{cis}\theta$
$\cos\theta - i\sin\theta = \operatorname{cis}(-\theta)$

$\therefore \quad \dfrac{\left(\cos\frac{\pi}{3} - i\sin\frac{\pi}{3}\right)^5 \left(\cos\frac{\pi}{4} + i\sin\frac{\pi}{4}\right)^3}{\left(\cos\frac{\pi}{12} - i\sin\frac{\pi}{12}\right)^7}$

$= \dfrac{\left[\operatorname{cis}\left(-\frac{\pi}{3}\right)\right]^5 \times \left[\operatorname{cis}\frac{\pi}{4}\right]^3}{\left[\operatorname{cis}\left(-\frac{\pi}{12}\right)\right]^7}$

$= \dfrac{\operatorname{cis}\left(-\frac{5\pi}{3}\right) \operatorname{cis}\left(\frac{3\pi}{4}\right)}{\operatorname{cis}\left(-\frac{7\pi}{12}\right)}$ {De Moivre}

$= \operatorname{cis}\left(\dfrac{-5\pi}{3} + \dfrac{3\pi}{4} + \dfrac{7\pi}{12} \right)$

$= \operatorname{cis}\left(-\tfrac{\pi}{3} \right)$

$= \tfrac{1}{2} - \tfrac{\sqrt{3}}{2}i$

438 a $(f \circ g)(-4)$
$= f(g(-4))$
$= f(3(2 - (-4)))$
$= f(18)$
$= 2(18) - 3$
$= 33$

b f is $y = 2x - 3$
so f^{-1} is $x = 2y - 3$
i.e., $x + 3 = 2y$
$$y = \dfrac{x+3}{2}$$
$$f^{-1}(2) = \left(\dfrac{2+3}{2}\right) = \tfrac{5}{2}$$

439 a $(f \circ g)(x) = 2x - 1$ i.e., $(g(x))^{\frac{1}{3}} = 2x - 1$
$$\text{i.e.,} \quad g(x) = (2x - 1)^3$$

b $(g \circ f)(x) = 2x - 1$ i.e., $g(x^{\frac{1}{3}}) = 2x - 1$
$$= 2\left(x^{\frac{1}{3}}\right)^3 - 1$$
$$\text{so} \quad g(x) = 2x^3 - 1$$

440 $\qquad P(n) = 1000 + ae^{kn}$ and $P(0) = 2000$
But $P(0) = 1000 + ae^{k0} = 1000 + a$
$\therefore \quad a = 1000$

After 1 year, $n = 12$ and $P(12) = 1000 + ae^{k(12)}$
$$= 1000 + 1000e^{12k}$$
$$= 4000 \quad \text{(given)}$$

So, $1000e^{12k} = 3000$ i.e., $e^{12k} = 3$
$$12k = \ln 3$$
$$k = \tfrac{1}{12}\ln 3$$

If $P(n) = 10\,000$, $1000 + ae^{kn} = 10\,000$
$$\text{i.e.,} \quad 1000e^{kn} = 9000$$
$$\text{i.e.,} \quad e^{kn} = 9$$
$$3^{\frac{n}{12}} = 3^2 \quad \{\text{as } e^k = 3^{\frac{1}{12}}\}$$
Hence, $n = 24$ months.

After 2 years the population will reach $10\,000$.

441

$\therefore \quad \tan A = \tfrac{3}{4}$

Now $\tan(A + B) = \dfrac{\tan A + \tan B}{1 - \tan A \tan B}$

$\therefore \quad \dfrac{-63}{16} = \dfrac{\frac{3}{4} + t}{1 - \frac{3}{4}t}$ {for $t = \tan B$}

$\Rightarrow \quad \dfrac{-63}{16} = \dfrac{3 + 4t}{4 - 3t}$

$\Rightarrow \quad -252 + 189t = 48 + 64t$

$\Rightarrow \quad 125t = 300$

$\Rightarrow \quad t = \dfrac{300}{125} = \tfrac{12}{5}$ $\therefore \quad \cos B = \tfrac{5}{13}$

442 $2\sin x \cos x + 1 = 0$, $0 \leqslant x \leqslant 2\pi$

$\Rightarrow \quad \sin 2x = -1$

$\Rightarrow \quad 2x = \tfrac{3\pi}{2} + k2\pi$

$\Rightarrow \quad x = \tfrac{3\pi}{4} + k\pi, \quad k \in \mathbb{Z}$

$\Rightarrow \quad x = \tfrac{3\pi}{4}, \ \tfrac{7\pi}{4}$

443 $y = 2\sin\left(x - \tfrac{\pi}{3}\right) + 1$, $-\pi \leqslant x \leqslant \pi$.

has max. value 3 when

$\sin\left(x - \tfrac{\pi}{3}\right) = 1 \Rightarrow \quad x - \tfrac{\pi}{3} = \tfrac{\pi}{2} + k2\pi$

$\Rightarrow \quad x = \tfrac{5\pi}{6} + k2\pi$

period is 2π

$$y(0) = 2\sin\left(-\tfrac{\pi}{3}\right) + 1$$
$$= 2\left(-\tfrac{\sqrt{3}}{2}\right) + 1$$
$$= 1 - \sqrt{3} \approx -0.73$$

min. value $= 2(-1) + 1 = -1$ when $x = -\tfrac{\pi}{6}$

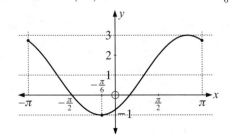

444 a

$$\begin{bmatrix} 2 & 1 & k \\ 3 & 0 & -2 \end{bmatrix} \begin{bmatrix} 0 & k \\ 5 & 1 \\ 6 & 2 \end{bmatrix} = \begin{bmatrix} 5+6k & 1+4k \\ -12 & -4+3k \end{bmatrix}$$

b $\mathbf{AB} - \mathbf{C} = 0$ if $5 + 6k - 23 = 0$ ...... (1)
$\qquad\qquad\qquad\qquad 1 + 4k - 13 = 0$ ...... (2)
$\qquad\qquad\qquad\qquad -4 + 3k - 5 = 0$ ...... (3)

i.e., $k = 3$ checks in the three equations.

445 a $\mathbf{b} \times \mathbf{c} = \begin{vmatrix} \mathbf{i} & \mathbf{j} & \mathbf{k} \\ 1 & -3 & -1 \\ 2 & -1 & 1 \end{vmatrix}$

$\qquad\qquad = \mathbf{i}(-3-1) + \mathbf{j}(-2-1) + \mathbf{k}(-1+6)$
$\qquad\qquad = -4\mathbf{i} - 3\mathbf{j} + 5\mathbf{k}$

b $\mathbf{a} \times (\mathbf{b} \times \mathbf{c}) = \begin{vmatrix} \mathbf{i} & \mathbf{j} & \mathbf{k} \\ 2 & -1 & 3 \\ -4 & -3 & 5 \end{vmatrix}$

$\qquad\qquad = \mathbf{i}(-5+9) + \mathbf{j}(-12-10) + \mathbf{k}(-6-4)$
$\qquad\qquad = 4\mathbf{i} - 22\mathbf{j} - 10\mathbf{k}$

$\mathbf{b}(\mathbf{a} \bullet \mathbf{c}) = (\mathbf{i} - 3\mathbf{j} - \mathbf{k})(4 + 1 + 3)$
$\qquad\qquad = 8\mathbf{i} - 24\mathbf{j} - 8\mathbf{k}$

$\mathbf{c}(\mathbf{a} \bullet \mathbf{b}) = (2\mathbf{i} - \mathbf{j} + \mathbf{k})(2 + 3 - 3)$
$\qquad\qquad = 4\mathbf{i} - 2\mathbf{j} + 2\mathbf{k}$

and $\mathbf{b}(\mathbf{a} \bullet \mathbf{c}) - \mathbf{c}(\mathbf{a} \bullet \mathbf{b}) = 4\mathbf{i} - 22\mathbf{j} - 10\mathbf{k}$
$\qquad\qquad\qquad\qquad\qquad = \mathbf{a} \times (\mathbf{b} \times \mathbf{c})$

446

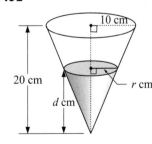

B(2, 0, −3)
A(3, −1, 5)
C(1, 3, −3)
θ

$\overrightarrow{AB} = \begin{bmatrix} 2-3 \\ 0--1 \\ -3-5 \end{bmatrix} = \begin{bmatrix} -1 \\ 1 \\ -8 \end{bmatrix},$

$\overrightarrow{AC} = \begin{bmatrix} 1-3 \\ 3--1 \\ -3-5 \end{bmatrix} = \begin{bmatrix} -2 \\ 4 \\ -8 \end{bmatrix}$

$\overrightarrow{AB} \bullet \overrightarrow{AC} = |\overrightarrow{AB}||\overrightarrow{AC}| \cos\theta$

i.e., $2 + 4 + 64 = \sqrt{1 + 1 + 64}\sqrt{4 + 16 + 64} \cos\theta$

$\Rightarrow \cos\theta = \dfrac{70}{\sqrt{66}\sqrt{84}}$

$\Rightarrow \theta \approx 19.9°$

447 a $\mathbf{r} \times (\mathbf{s} \times \mathbf{t}) = \mathbf{s}(\mathbf{r} \bullet \mathbf{t}) - \mathbf{t}(\mathbf{r} \bullet \mathbf{s})$

b $\mathbf{r} \times (\mathbf{s} \times \mathbf{t}) + \mathbf{s} \times (\mathbf{t} \times \mathbf{r}) + \mathbf{t} \times (\mathbf{r} \times \mathbf{s})$
$= [\mathbf{s}(\mathbf{r} \bullet \mathbf{t}) - \mathbf{t}(\mathbf{r} \bullet \mathbf{s})] + [\mathbf{t}(\mathbf{s} \bullet \mathbf{r}) - \mathbf{r}(\mathbf{s} \bullet \mathbf{t})]$
$\quad + [\mathbf{r}(\mathbf{t} \bullet \mathbf{s}) - \mathbf{s}(\mathbf{t} \bullet \mathbf{r})]$
$= \mathbf{0}$

448 a Number plates are of the type

letter	letter	letter	number	number	number
26	26	26	9	10	10

Total $(26)^3 \times 9 \times 10^2 = 15\,818\,00$

b Number plates beginning with AB and ending in 0 are of the type

		letter	number	number	
A	B	26	9	10	0

Total $26 \times 9 \times 10$

Probability of this number plate is $\dfrac{26 \times 9 \times 10}{(26)^3 \times 9 \times 10^2}$

$\qquad\qquad = \dfrac{2340}{15\,818\,00}$

$\qquad\qquad \doteqdot 0.001\,48$

449 Using a tree diagram

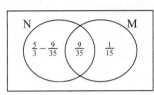

$\frac{4}{13}$ — R $<$ $\frac{3}{12}$ — R, $\frac{9}{12}$ — B

$\frac{9}{13}$ — B $<$ $\frac{4}{12}$ — R, $\frac{8}{12}$ — B

Probability of one of each colour is $\dfrac{4}{13} \times \dfrac{9}{12} + \dfrac{9}{13} \times \dfrac{4}{12}$

$\qquad\qquad = \dfrac{72}{156}$

$\qquad\qquad \approx 0.462$

450 a Since $P(N) = \frac{3}{5}$, $P(N') = 1 - \frac{3}{5} = \frac{2}{5}$

b

N		M
$\frac{3}{5} - \frac{9}{35}$	$\frac{9}{35}$	$\frac{1}{15}$

Since $P(M \mid N) = \dfrac{P(M \cap N)}{P(N)} = \dfrac{3}{7}$

and $P(N) = \frac{3}{5}$, $P(M \cap N) = \frac{3}{5} \times \frac{3}{7} = \frac{9}{35}$

Since $P(M \mid N') = \dfrac{P(M \cap N')}{P(N')} = \dfrac{1}{6}$

and $P(N') = \frac{2}{5}$, then $P(M \cap N') = \frac{2}{5} \times \frac{1}{6} = \frac{1}{15}$

$P(M \cup N) = \frac{3}{5} + \frac{1}{15} = \frac{2}{3}$

and $P[(M \cup N)'] = P(M' \cap N') = 1 - \frac{2}{3} = \frac{1}{3}$

451 $y = \dfrac{\ln x}{x^2}$ has $\dfrac{dy}{dx} = \dfrac{\frac{1}{x}(x^2) - \ln x(2x)}{x^4} = \dfrac{x - 2x\ln x}{x^4}$

$\qquad\qquad\qquad\qquad\qquad = \dfrac{1 - 2\ln x}{x^3}$

and $\dfrac{d^2y}{dx^2} = \dfrac{\left(-\frac{2}{x}\right)x^3 - (1 - 2\ln x)3x^2}{x^6}$

$\qquad\qquad = \dfrac{-2x^2 - 3x^2 + 6x^2\ln x}{x^6}$

$\qquad\qquad = \dfrac{-5 + 6\ln x}{x^4}$

which is $0 \iff -5 + 6\ln x = 0$

$\qquad\qquad \iff 6\ln x = 5 \Rightarrow \ln x = \frac{5}{6} \Rightarrow x = e^{\frac{5}{6}}$

$f''(x)$ has sign diag: (− then + at $e^{\frac{5}{6}}$)

as signs change we have a point of inflection at $\left(e^{\frac{5}{6}}, \dfrac{\ln e^{\frac{5}{6}}}{e^{\frac{5}{3}}}\right)$

i.e., $\left(e^{\frac{5}{6}}, \dfrac{5}{6e^{\frac{5}{3}}}\right)$.

452

20 cm, 10 cm, d cm, r cm

If the depth of water is d cm

$\dfrac{r}{d} = \dfrac{10}{20} = \dfrac{1}{2}$

$\Rightarrow r = \frac{1}{2}d$

Let the volume of water be V cm³

$\therefore V = \frac{1}{3}\pi r^2 d$

$\Rightarrow V = \frac{1}{3}\pi\left(\dfrac{d^2}{4}\right)d = \dfrac{\pi}{12}d^3$

Thus $\dfrac{dV}{dt} = \dfrac{\pi}{12} \times 3d^2 \dfrac{dd}{dt}$

Particular case: $d = 15$, $\dfrac{dV}{dt} = 30$ cm³s⁻¹

$\therefore 30 = \dfrac{\pi}{12} \times 3 \times 15^2 \dfrac{dd}{dt}$

$\Rightarrow \dfrac{dd}{dt} = \dfrac{8}{15\pi}$ cms⁻¹ i.e., depth is increasing at $\dfrac{8}{15\pi}$ cm/s.

453 $\displaystyle\int \frac{\sin^3 x}{\cos^2 x}\,dx$

$= \displaystyle\int \frac{\sin^2 x \sin x}{\cos^2 x}\,dx$

$= \displaystyle\int \frac{(1 - \cos^2 x)\sin x}{\cos^2 x}\,dx$

$= \displaystyle\int [\cos x]^{-2}\sin x - \sin x\,dx$
$\qquad\qquad\qquad u = \cos x$

$= \displaystyle\int u^{-2}\left(-\frac{du}{dx}\right)dx - (-\cos x) + c$
$\qquad\qquad \dfrac{du}{dx} = -\sin x$

$= -\dfrac{u^{-1}}{-1} + \cos x + c$

$= \dfrac{1}{u} + \cos x + c$

$= \sec x + \cos x + c$

454 From a gcalc

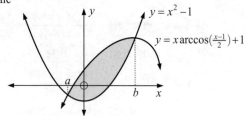

Area $= \displaystyle\int_a^b x\arccos\left(\frac{x-1}{2}\right) + 1 - x^2 + 1\,dx$

where $a \approx -0.6330....., \quad b \approx 2.0227.....$

$\therefore$ area ≈ 4.84 units^2

455 $\displaystyle\int x^2 \sin x\,dx$
$\qquad\left[\text{Let } \begin{array}{ll} u' = \sin x & v = x^2 \\ u = -\cos x & v' = 2x \end{array}\right]$

$= -x^2\cos x - \displaystyle\int -2x\cos x\,dx$

$= -x^2\cos x + 2\displaystyle\int x\cos x\,dx$
$\qquad\left[\text{Let } \begin{array}{ll} u' = \cos x & v = x \\ u = \sin x & v' = 1 \end{array}\right]$

$= -x^2\cos x + 2\left\{x\sin x - \displaystyle\int \sin x\,dx\right\}$

$= -x^2\cos x + 2x\sin x - 2(-\cos x) + c$

$= -x^2\cos x + 2x\sin x + 2\cos x + c$

456 $\displaystyle\int_0^2 \frac{1}{1+ux}\,dx = \frac{1}{u}$

$\Rightarrow \left[\dfrac{1}{u}\ln|1+ux|\right]_0^2 = \dfrac{1}{u}$

$\Rightarrow \dfrac{1}{u}\ln|1+2u| - \dfrac{1}{u}\ln 1 = \dfrac{1}{u}$

$\Rightarrow \ln|1+2u| = 1$

$\Rightarrow |1+2u| = e$

$\Rightarrow 1+2u = \pm e$

$\Rightarrow 2u = \pm e - 1$

$\Rightarrow u = \dfrac{e-1}{2} \quad$ or $\quad \dfrac{-e-1}{2}$

If $u = -\left(\dfrac{e+1}{2}\right)$ the function

$\dfrac{1}{1+ux} = \dfrac{1}{1 - \left(\frac{e+1}{2}\right)x}$ is not defined if $x = \dfrac{2}{e+1}$

Since $0 < \dfrac{2}{e+1} < 2$, the definite integral

$\displaystyle\int_0^2 \frac{1}{1 - \left(\frac{e+1}{2}\right)x}\,dx$ is not defined.

Hence, the only value is $u = \dfrac{e-1}{2}$.

457 a i
$w^6 = 64 = 64\,\text{cis}\,(0 + k2\pi), \quad k \in \mathbb{Z}$

$\Rightarrow \quad w^6 = 2^6\,\text{cis}\,(k2\pi), \quad k \in \mathbb{Z}$

$\Rightarrow \quad w = 2\,\text{cis}\left(\frac{k2\pi}{6}\right), \quad k \in \mathbb{Z}$

$\Rightarrow \quad w = 2\,\text{cis}\,0, \ 2\,\text{cis}\left(\frac{\pi}{3}\right), \ 2\,\text{cis}\left(\frac{2\pi}{3}\right),$
$\qquad\qquad 2\,\text{cis}\left(\frac{3\pi}{3}\right), \ 2\,\text{cis}\left(\frac{4\pi}{3}\right), \ 2\,\text{cis}\left(\frac{5\pi}{3}\right)$

$\Rightarrow \quad z = \pm 2, \ 2\left(\frac{1}{2} \pm \frac{\sqrt{3}}{2}i\right), \ 2\left(-\frac{1}{2} \pm \frac{\sqrt{3}}{2}i\right)$

$\Rightarrow \quad z = \pm 2, \ 1 \pm i\sqrt{3}, \ -1 \pm i\sqrt{3}$

ii If $(z+1)^6 = 64(z-2)^6$, then $\left(\dfrac{z+1}{z-2}\right)^6 = 64$

$\dfrac{z+1}{z-2} = \pm 2, \quad \dfrac{z+1}{z-2} = 1 \pm i\sqrt{3}, \quad \dfrac{z+1}{z-2} = -1 \pm i\sqrt{3}$

All of these have form $\dfrac{z+1}{z-2} = w, \quad$ say

$\Rightarrow z + 1 = wz - 2w \quad \Rightarrow z(1-w) = -2w - 1$

$\qquad\qquad\qquad\qquad \Rightarrow z = \dfrac{2w+1}{w-1}$

If $\dfrac{z+1}{z-2} = 2, \quad z = \dfrac{5}{1} = 5$

If $\dfrac{z+1}{z-2} = -2, \quad z = \dfrac{-3}{-3} = 1$

If $\dfrac{z+1}{z-2} = 1 + i\sqrt{3}, \quad z = \dfrac{2 + 2i\sqrt{3} + 1}{i\sqrt{3}}$
which simplifies to $2 - i\sqrt{3}$

If $\dfrac{z+1}{z-2} = 1 - i\sqrt{3}, \quad z = \dfrac{2 - 2\sqrt{3}i + 1}{-i\sqrt{3}}$
which simplifies to $2 + i\sqrt{3}$

If $\dfrac{z+1}{z-2} = -1 + i\sqrt{3}, \quad z = \dfrac{-2 + 2\sqrt{3}i + 1}{i\sqrt{3} - 2}$

i.e., $z = \dfrac{-2 + 2\sqrt{3}i + 1}{i\sqrt{3} - 2} \quad$ which simplifies to $\quad \frac{1}{7}(8 - 3\sqrt{3}i)$

Likewise, if $\dfrac{z+1}{z-2} = -1 - i\sqrt{3}, \quad z = \frac{1}{7}(8 + 3\sqrt{3}i)$

$\therefore \quad z = 5, 1, 2 \pm i\sqrt{3}, \frac{1}{7}(8 \pm 3\sqrt{3}i)$.

b $P(n)$ is

"If $u_{n+2} = u_n + u_{n+1}, \quad u_1 = u_2 = 1, \quad n \in \mathbb{Z}^+$

then $u_n = \dfrac{\left(\frac{1+\sqrt{5}}{2}\right)^n - \left(\frac{1-\sqrt{5}}{2}\right)^n}{\sqrt{5}}$".

Proof (By the Principle of Math Induction)

(1) If $n = 1$, $u_1 = \dfrac{\frac{1+\sqrt{5}}{2} - \frac{1-\sqrt{5}}{2}}{\sqrt{5}} = \dfrac{1+\sqrt{5}-1+\sqrt{5}}{2\sqrt{5}}$

$= \dfrac{2\sqrt{5}}{2\sqrt{5}} = 1$ which is true $\Rightarrow P(1)$ is true.

If $n = 2$, $u_2 = \dfrac{\left(\frac{1+\sqrt{5}}{2}\right)^2 - \left(\frac{1-\sqrt{5}}{2}\right)^2}{\sqrt{5}}$

$= \dfrac{(1+2\sqrt{5}+5) - (1-2\sqrt{5}+5)}{4\sqrt{5}} = \dfrac{4\sqrt{5}}{4\sqrt{5}} = 1$

which is true $\Rightarrow P(2)$ is true.

(2) Now suppose $P(k)$ and $P(k+1)$ are true.

i.e., $u_k = \dfrac{\left(\frac{1+\sqrt{5}}{2}\right)^k - \left(\frac{1-\sqrt{5}}{2}\right)^k}{\sqrt{5}} \quad$ and

$u_{k+1} = \dfrac{\left(\frac{1+\sqrt{5}}{2}\right)^{k+1} - \left(\frac{1-\sqrt{5}}{2}\right)^{k+1}}{\sqrt{5}}$

Now u_{k+2}

$= u_{k+1} + u_k$

$$= \frac{\left(\frac{1+\sqrt{5}}{2}\right)^{k+1} - \left(\frac{1-\sqrt{5}}{2}\right)^{k+1}}{\sqrt{5}} + \frac{\left(\frac{1+\sqrt{5}}{2}\right)^{k} - \left(\frac{1-\sqrt{5}}{2}\right)^{k}}{\sqrt{5}}$$

$$= \frac{\left(\frac{1+\sqrt{5}}{2}\right)^{k}\left[\frac{1+\sqrt{5}}{2}+1\right] - \left(\frac{1-\sqrt{5}}{2}\right)^{k}\left[\frac{1-\sqrt{5}}{2}+1\right]}{\sqrt{5}}$$

$$= \frac{\left(\frac{1+\sqrt{5}}{2}\right)^{k}\left(\frac{3+\sqrt{5}}{2}\right) - \left(\frac{1-\sqrt{5}}{2}\right)^{k}\left(\frac{3-\sqrt{5}}{2}\right)}{\sqrt{5}}$$

and we notice that $\left(\frac{1+\sqrt{5}}{2}\right)^2 = \frac{1+2\sqrt{5}+5}{4} = \frac{6+2\sqrt{5}}{4} = \frac{3+\sqrt{5}}{2}$

and $\left(\frac{1-\sqrt{5}}{2}\right)^2 = \frac{3-\sqrt{5}}{2}$ likewise

So, $u_{k+2} = \dfrac{\left(\frac{1+\sqrt{5}}{2}\right)^{k}\left(\frac{1+\sqrt{5}}{2}\right)^2 - \left(\frac{1-\sqrt{5}}{2}\right)^{k}\left(\frac{1-\sqrt{5}}{2}\right)^2}{\sqrt{5}}$

$$= \frac{\left(\frac{1+\sqrt{5}}{2}\right)^{k+2} - \left(\frac{1-\sqrt{5}}{2}\right)^{k+2}}{\sqrt{5}}$$

Thus $P(k+2)$ is true whenever $P(k)$ and $P(k+1)$ are true and as $P(1)$ and $P(2)$ are true.

$\Rightarrow \quad P(n)$ is true $\{$P of MI$\}$

458 a $P(n)$ is: $\dfrac{d^n}{dx^n}(xe^x) = (x+n)e^x, \quad n \in Z^+$

Proof: By the Principle of Math Induction

(1) If $n = 1$, $\dfrac{d}{dx}(xe^x) = 1e^x + xe^x$
$= e^x(x+1)$
$= (x+1)e^x$ $\therefore$ $P(1)$ is true.

(2) If $P(k)$ is true, $\dfrac{d^k}{dx^k}(xe^x) = (x+k)e^x$

$\therefore \dfrac{d^{k+1}}{dx^{k+1}}(xe^x) = \dfrac{d}{dx}(x+k)e^x = 1e^x + (x+k)e^x$
$= e^x(x+k+1)$
$= e^x(x+[k+1])$

Thus $P(k+1)$ is true whenever $P(k)$ is true and $P(1)$ is true $\Rightarrow$ $P(n)$ is true $\{$P of MI$\}$

b

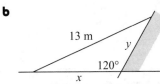

13 m
y
$120°$
x
$\dfrac{dx}{dt} = 2$ m/min

By the Cosine Rule,

$13^2 = x^2 + y^2 - 2xy\cos(120°)$
$\Rightarrow 169 = x^2 + y^2 + xy \quad \{\cos 120° = -\frac{1}{2}\}$
$\Rightarrow 2x\dfrac{dx}{dt} + 2y\dfrac{dy}{dt} + \dfrac{dx}{dt}y + x\dfrac{dy}{dt} = 0$
$\Rightarrow (2x+y)\dfrac{dx}{dt} + (x+2y)\dfrac{dy}{dt} = 0$

Particular case $x = 7$

$\therefore 169 = 7^2 + y^2 + 7y$
$\Rightarrow y^2 + 7y - 120 = 0$
$\Rightarrow (y-8)(y+15) = 0$
$\Rightarrow y = 8$ or -15
$\Rightarrow y = 8 \quad \{y > 0\}$

$\therefore 22(2) + 23\dfrac{dy}{dt} = 0$ and so $\dfrac{dy}{dt} = -\dfrac{44}{23}$

$\therefore$ ladder moves down the wall at $\frac{44}{23}$ m/min at that instant.

459 a

	A				B			
-3	-2	-1	0	1	2	3	Z
22	29	36	43	50	57	64	X

b Let the a be the greatest age at death in region A

then, $P(X \leqslant a) = 0.09$

$\Rightarrow P(Z \leqslant \dfrac{a - 43}{7}) = 0.09$

$\Rightarrow \dfrac{a - 43}{7} = \text{invNorm}(0.09)$

$\Rightarrow a = 43 + 7 \times \text{invNorm}(0.09)$

$\Rightarrow a \approx 33.6$

The greatest age is about 33 years and 7 months.

c Let b be the lowest age at death in region B

then $P(X \geqslant b) = 0.11 \Rightarrow P(X \leqslant b) = 0.89$

$\Rightarrow P(Z \leqslant \dfrac{b - 43}{7}) = 0.89$

$\Rightarrow \dfrac{b - 43}{7} = \text{invNorm}(0.89)$

$\Rightarrow b = 43 + 7 \times \text{invNorm}(0.89)$

$\Rightarrow b \approx 51.6$

i.e., lowest age is about 51 years and 7 months.

d Since the total area is 1, the shaded region has area
$1 - (0.09 + 0.11) = 0.80$

SOLUTIONS TO EXAMINATION PRACTICE SET 14

460 a $-8 = 8(-1) = 8 \text{ cis } \pi$

b If $z^3 = -8$

$\therefore z^3 = 8 \text{ cis } (\pi + k2\pi) \quad k = 0, 1, 2$

$\therefore z = 2 \text{ cis } \left(\dfrac{\pi + k2\pi}{3}\right) \quad \{$De Moivre$\}$

$\Rightarrow z = 2 \text{ cis } \frac{\pi}{3}, \quad 2 \text{ cis } (\pi), \quad 2 \text{ cis } \left(\frac{5\pi}{3}\right)$

$\Rightarrow z = 2\left(\frac{1}{2} + \frac{\sqrt{3}}{2}i\right), \quad 2(-1), \quad 2\left(\frac{1}{2} - \frac{\sqrt{3}}{2}i\right)$

$\Rightarrow z = 1 + i\sqrt{3}, \quad -2, \quad 1 - i\sqrt{3}$

461 For $(2-x)^8$, $T_{r+1} = \binom{8}{r}2^{8-r}(-x)^r = \binom{8}{r}2^{8-r}(-1)^r x^r$

For $(1 + 2x)(2 - x)^8$, the coefficient of x^7

$= 1 \times \binom{8}{7}2^{8-7}(-1)^7 + 2\binom{8}{6}2^{8-6}(-1)^6$

$= 8 \times 2 \times -1 + 2 \times 28 \times 4$

$= 208$

462 Sequence is geometric, $u_1 = 100$, $r = 1.1$

a $u_n = u_1 r^{n-1} \Rightarrow u_n = 100 \times (1.1)^{n-1}$

b $S_n = \dfrac{a(r^n - 1)}{r - 1} = \dfrac{100((1.1)^n - 1)}{0.1}$

$\therefore S_n = 1000((1.1)^n - 1)$

c We want n such that $S_n > 4000$

i.e., $1000((1.1)^n - 1) > 4000$

$\Rightarrow (1.1)^n - 1 > 4$

$\Rightarrow (1.1)^n > 5$

$\Rightarrow \log(1.1)^n > \log 5$

$\Rightarrow n\log(1.1) > \log 5$

$\Rightarrow n > \dfrac{\log 5}{\log 1.1}$

$\Rightarrow n > 16.88......$

$\Rightarrow n = 17, 18, 19, 20, ...$

i.e., first exceeded \$4000 on 17th birthday.

463 a $6 \times 6 \times 6 = 216$ numbers **b** $6 \times 5 \times 4 = 120$ numbers

c The first digit is 4, 5, 6 or 7

- if the first digit is 4 or 6

2	4	2	$= 16$

4 or 6 — other 2 evens

- if the first digit is 5 or 7

2	4	3	$= 24$

3 possible evens

$\therefore$ total number is 40

d We can choose 3 from 6 in $C_3^6 = 20$ possible ways and there is one order (ascending) for each way.

∴ total number of ways = 20

464 f is $y = \sqrt{5 - 2x}$

so f^{-1} is $x = \sqrt{5 - 2y}$

i.e., $x^2 = 5 - 2y \Rightarrow y = \dfrac{5 - x^2}{2}$

so $f^{-1}(5) = \dfrac{5 - (5^2)}{2} = -10$

465 a Stretch $f(x)$ vertically by a factor of 2 gives $2f(x)$

Stretch $2f(x)$ horizontally by a factor of $\frac{1}{2}$ gives

$$2f\left(\frac{x}{\frac{1}{2}}\right) = 2f(2x)$$

A translation of $\frac{1}{2}$ horizontally gives $\quad 2f\left(2\left(x - \frac{1}{2}\right)\right)$
$$= 2f(2x - 1)$$

A translation of -3 vertically gives $2f(2x - 1) - 3$ and as $f(x) = x + 2$, $\quad 2f(2x - 1) - 3$
$$= 2(2x - 1 + 2) - 3$$
$$= 2(2x + 1) - 3$$
$$= 4x - 1$$

b

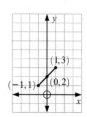

Stretch vertically by a factor of 2.

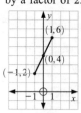

Stretch horizontally by a factor of $\frac{1}{2}$.

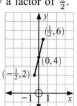

A translation of $\frac{1}{2}$ horizontally.

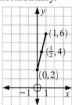

A translation -3 vertically.

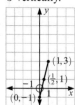

466 a $f(x) = 2x^3 - 9x^2 + 30x - 13$

$f\left(\frac{1}{2}\right) = 2\left(\frac{1}{2}\right)^3 - 9\left(\frac{1}{2}\right)^2 + 30\left(\frac{1}{2}\right) - 13 = 0$

b So, $x - \frac{1}{2}$ is a factor of $f(x)$

using synthetic division:

$$\begin{array}{c|cccc} \frac{1}{2} & 2 & -9 & 30 & -13 \\ & 0 & 1 & -4 & 13 \\ \hline & 2 & -8 & 26 & 0 \end{array}$$

so $f(x) = (x - \frac{1}{2})(2x^2 - 8x + 26)$
$$= (2x - 1)(x^2 - 4x + 13)$$

$x^2 - 4x + 13 = 0$ if $x = \dfrac{4 \pm \sqrt{16 - 52}}{2} = \dfrac{4 \pm 6i}{2}$

$x = 2 + 3i$ or $2 - 3i$

∴ $2x^3 - 9x^2 + 30x - 13$
$$= (2x - 1)(x - (2 + 3i))(x - (2 - 3i))$$

467 $\tan\left(A + \frac{\pi}{4}\right) = 3 \quad \Rightarrow \quad \dfrac{\tan A + \tan\frac{\pi}{4}}{1 - \tan A \tan\frac{\pi}{4}} = 3$

$$\Rightarrow \quad \frac{\tan A + 1}{1 - \tan A} = 3$$

$$\Rightarrow \quad \tan A + 1 = 3 - 3\tan A$$

$$\Rightarrow \quad 4\tan A = 2$$

$$\Rightarrow \quad \tan A = \tfrac{1}{2}$$

468

$$\cos 2x + \sqrt{3}\sin 2x = 1, \quad -\pi \leqslant x \leqslant \pi$$

$$\Rightarrow \quad 1 - 2\sin^2 x + 2\sqrt{3}\sin x \cos x = 1$$

$$\Rightarrow \quad -2\sin^2 x + 2\sqrt{3}\sin x \cos x = 0$$

$$\Rightarrow \quad \sin x(\sqrt{3}\cos x - \sin x) = 0$$

$$\Rightarrow \quad \sin x = 0 \quad \text{or} \quad \sqrt{3}\cos x = \sin x$$

$$\Rightarrow \quad \sin x = 0 \quad \text{or} \quad \tan x = \sqrt{3}$$

$$\Rightarrow \quad x = -\pi, \tfrac{-2\pi}{3}, 0, \tfrac{\pi}{3}, \pi$$

469 $\sin(x + y) = 0 \quad \Rightarrow \quad x + y = k\pi, \quad k \in Z$

which is a family of straight lines of slope -1.

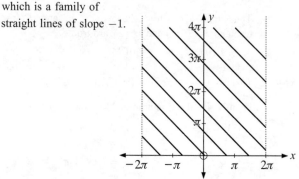

470 Order of $\mathbf{W}$ must agree with order of $\mathbf{V}$, i.e., $\mathbf{W}$ is $n \times r$.
$\mathbf{D}$ is the result of the product of $m \times n$ matrix, with an $n \times r$ matrix. i.e., $\mathbf{D}$ is an $m \times r$ matrix.

471 a If $\qquad \overrightarrow{y} = -2\overrightarrow{x}$

then $|\overrightarrow{x} + 2\overrightarrow{y}| = |\overrightarrow{x} - 4\overrightarrow{x}| = |-3\overrightarrow{x}| = 3|\overrightarrow{x}| = 6$

b

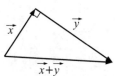

Since $\overrightarrow{x}$ and $\overrightarrow{y}$ are perpendicular then $\overrightarrow{x}$ and $2\overrightarrow{y}$ are perpendicular. Using Pythagoras' theorem,

$$|\overrightarrow{x} + 2\overrightarrow{y}| = \left(|\overrightarrow{x}|^2 + |2\overrightarrow{y}|^2\right)^{\frac{1}{2}}$$
$$= \left(|\overrightarrow{x}|^2 + 4|\overrightarrow{y}|^2\right)^{\frac{1}{2}}$$
$$= \left(|\overrightarrow{x}|^2 + 4(3|\overrightarrow{x}|)^2\right)^{\frac{1}{2}}$$
$$= (37|\overrightarrow{x}|^2)^{\frac{1}{2}}$$
$$= 2\sqrt{37}$$

472 The three vectors are coplanar if the normal to $\mathbf{u}$ and $\mathbf{v}$ is parallel to the normal to $\mathbf{u}$ and $\mathbf{w}$ (or $\mathbf{v}$ and $\mathbf{w}$)

$$\mathbf{u} \times \mathbf{v} = \begin{vmatrix} \mathbf{i} & \mathbf{j} & \mathbf{k} \\ 2 & 2 & 3 \\ 1 & 2 & -3 \end{vmatrix} \begin{array}{l} = \mathbf{i}(-6 - 6) - \mathbf{j}(-6 - 3) + \mathbf{k}(4 - 2) \\ = -12\mathbf{i} + 9\mathbf{j} + 2\mathbf{k} \end{array}$$

and $\mathbf{u} \times \mathbf{w} = \begin{vmatrix} \mathbf{i} & \mathbf{j} & \mathbf{k} \\ 2 & 2 & 3 \\ 1 & 2 - \lambda & \lambda + 1 \end{vmatrix}$

$= \mathbf{i}((2\lambda + 2) - (6 - 3\lambda)) - \mathbf{j}((2\lambda + 2) - 3) + \mathbf{k}((4 - 2\lambda) - 2$
$= (5\lambda - 4)\mathbf{i} + (1 - 2\lambda)\mathbf{j} + (2 - 2\lambda)\mathbf{k}$

The vectors are parallel if $\dfrac{5\lambda - 4}{-12} = \dfrac{1 - 2\lambda}{9} = \dfrac{2 - 2\lambda}{2}$

Using $\dfrac{1 - 2\lambda}{9} = \dfrac{2 - 2\lambda}{2} = 1 - \lambda$

then $1 - 2\lambda = 9 - 9\lambda \quad \Rightarrow \quad \lambda = \frac{8}{7}$

and $\lambda = \frac{8}{7}$ checks in the other equation.

473

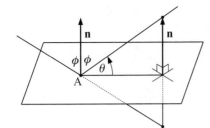

The plane has 2 direction vectors $\begin{bmatrix} 1 \\ -1 \\ 1 \end{bmatrix}$ and $\begin{bmatrix} 0 \\ -1 \\ 2 \end{bmatrix}$

Hence, $\mathbf{n} = \begin{bmatrix} 1 \\ -1 \\ 1 \end{bmatrix} \times \begin{bmatrix} 0 \\ -1 \\ 2 \end{bmatrix} = \begin{vmatrix} \mathbf{i} & \mathbf{j} & \mathbf{k} \\ 1 & -1 & 1 \\ 0 & -1 & 2 \end{vmatrix}$

$\qquad = \mathbf{i}\,(-2+1) - \mathbf{j}(2-0) + \mathbf{k}(-1-0)$

$\qquad = -\mathbf{i} - 2\mathbf{j} - \mathbf{k}$

$\qquad = -\begin{bmatrix} 1 \\ 2 \\ 1 \end{bmatrix}$ is a normal to the plane.

The line has direction vector $\begin{bmatrix} 1 \\ 2 \\ 2 \end{bmatrix}$.

An angle ϕ between the normal and the line is given by (see diagram)

$\begin{bmatrix} 1 \\ 2 \\ 1 \end{bmatrix} \bullet \begin{bmatrix} 1 \\ 2 \\ 2 \end{bmatrix} = \sqrt{1+4+1}\sqrt{1+4+4}\cos\phi$

$\Rightarrow \quad 7 = \sqrt{6}\sqrt{9}\cos\phi$

and so $\quad \cos\phi = \dfrac{7}{\sqrt{54}}$ and $\phi = 0.309^c$

Hence the angle between the line and its reflection is $2 \times \phi = 0.618^c$.

474 Since P is a probability function,

$$\sum P(X = x) = \sum_{x=0}^{\infty} a(\tfrac{1}{7})^x = 1$$

But $\displaystyle\sum_{x=0}^{\infty} (\tfrac{1}{7})^x = \dfrac{u_1}{1-r} = \dfrac{1}{1-\frac{1}{7}} = \dfrac{7}{6}$

Hence, as $\displaystyle\sum_{x=0}^{\infty} a(\tfrac{1}{7})^x = 1$, $a \times \tfrac{7}{6} = 1$ and so, $a = \tfrac{6}{7}$.

475 Probability of not obtaining a score of 35 is $\tfrac{1}{5}$.

If X is the number out of 9 who do not obtain a score of 35, $X \sim \text{Bin}\,(9, \tfrac{1}{5})$

$\text{P}(X = 3) = \binom{9}{3}\left(\tfrac{1}{5}\right)^3\left(\tfrac{4}{5}\right)^6 = \text{binompdf}(9, 0.2, 3)$

$\qquad\qquad\qquad \approx 0.176$

476 We start by putting Mrs Smith in her place first. There are 8 ways of doing this. Now we put Mr Jones in a chair.

As Mr Jones is not to sit next to Mrs Smith, there are only 5 chairs for him to sit on. The remaining 6 members can sit anywhere in 6! different ways.

So, the total number of ways is $8 \times 5 \times 6! = 28\,800$.

477 a Let $y = x^{\frac{1}{x}}$, $\therefore \ln y = \dfrac{1}{x}\ln x = \dfrac{\ln x}{x}$

$\Rightarrow \dfrac{1}{y}\dfrac{dy}{dx} = \dfrac{\left(\frac{1}{x}\right)x - \ln x(1)}{x^2} = \dfrac{1 - \ln x}{x^2}$

$\Rightarrow \dfrac{dy}{dx} = \left(\dfrac{1 - \ln x}{x^2}\right)x^{\frac{1}{x}}$

b A stationary point exists when $\dfrac{dy}{dx} = 0$

$\qquad$ i.e., $\ln x = 1 \ \Rightarrow \ x = e$

$\qquad$ and when $x = e$, $y = e^{\frac{1}{e}}$

$\qquad \therefore \ (e, e^{\frac{1}{e}})$ is a stationary point.

478 $\qquad f(x) = 2xe^x - 6e^x - 3x^2 + 12x + 5$

So, $f'(x) = 2e^x + 2xe^x - 6e^x - 6x + 12$

$\qquad\qquad = e^x(2x - 4) - 6x + 12$

$\qquad\qquad = 2e^x(x - 2) - 6(x - 2)$

$\qquad\qquad = 2(x - 2)[e^x - 3]$

which is $0 \ \Leftrightarrow \ x = 2$ or $e^x = 3 \ \Leftrightarrow \ x = 2$ or $\ln 3$

479 $\displaystyle\int \dfrac{dx}{x^2 + 2x + 10}$

$= \displaystyle\int \dfrac{1}{x^2 + 2x + 1 + 9}\,dx$

$= \displaystyle\int \dfrac{1}{(x + 1)^2 + 9}\,dx \qquad\qquad u = x + 1$

$= \displaystyle\int \dfrac{1}{u^2 + 9}\,du \qquad\qquad\qquad \dfrac{du}{dx} = 1$

$= \tfrac{1}{3}\arctan\left(\dfrac{u}{3}\right) + c$

$= \tfrac{1}{3}\arctan\left(\dfrac{x + 1}{3}\right)$

480

$\qquad\qquad \text{Volume} = \pi\displaystyle\int_0^{\pi} y^2\,dx$

$\qquad\qquad\qquad\qquad = \pi\displaystyle\int_0^{\pi} \sin^2 x\,dx$

$\qquad\qquad\qquad\qquad = \pi\displaystyle\int_0^{\pi} \left(\tfrac{1}{2} - \tfrac{1}{2}\cos 2x\right)dx$

$\qquad\qquad\qquad\qquad = \pi\left[\tfrac{1}{2}x - \tfrac{1}{4}\cos 2x\right]_0^{\pi}$

$\qquad\qquad\qquad\qquad = \pi(\tfrac{\pi}{2} - \tfrac{1}{4} - 0 + \tfrac{1}{4})$

$\qquad\qquad\qquad\qquad = \dfrac{\pi^2}{2}\ \text{units}^3$

$y = \sin x$

481 $\int x\tan^2 x\,dx$

$= \int x(\sec^2 x - 1)\,dx$

$= \int x\sec^2 x - x\,dx$

$= \dfrac{-x^2}{2} + \int x\sec^2 x\,dx \quad \left[\text{Let} \begin{array}{cc} u' = \sec^2 x & v = x \\ u = \tan x & v' = 1 \end{array}\right]$

$= \dfrac{-x^2}{2} + \left\{x\tan x - \int \tan x\,dx\right\}$

$= \dfrac{-x^2}{2} + x\tan x + \int -\dfrac{\sin x}{\cos x}\,dx$

$= \dfrac{-x^2}{2} + x\tan x + \ln|\cos x| + c$

482 $\displaystyle\int_0^a \dfrac{x^2}{x^3 + 1}\,dx = 2$

$\Rightarrow \tfrac{1}{3}\displaystyle\int_0^a \dfrac{3x^2}{x^3 + 1} = 2$

$\Rightarrow \displaystyle\int_0^a \dfrac{3x^2}{x^3 + 1} = 6$

$\Rightarrow \left[\ln|x^3 + 1|\right]_0^a = 6$

$\Rightarrow \ln|a^3 + 1| - \ln 1 = 6$

$\Rightarrow \ln|a^3 + 1| = 6$

$\Rightarrow a^3 + 1 = e^6$

$\Rightarrow a^3 = e^6 - 1$ and so $a = \sqrt[3]{e^6 - 1}$

483 a i $1 - i\sqrt{3}$ has $\left|1 - i\sqrt{3}\right| = \sqrt{1 + 3} = 2$

$$\Rightarrow \quad 1 - i\sqrt{3} = 2\left(\tfrac{1}{2} - \tfrac{i\sqrt{3}}{2}\right)$$
$$= 2 \operatorname{cis}\left(\tfrac{-\pi}{3}\right)$$
$$= 2\left[\left(\cos(\tfrac{-\pi}{3}) + i\sin(\tfrac{-\pi}{3})\right)\right]$$

$1 - i$ has $|1 - i| = \sqrt{1 + 1} = \sqrt{2}$

$$\Rightarrow \quad 1 - i = \sqrt{2}\left(\tfrac{1}{\sqrt{2}} - \tfrac{1}{\sqrt{2}}i\right)$$
$$= \sqrt{2} \operatorname{cis}\left(-\tfrac{\pi}{4}\right)$$
$$= \sqrt{2}\left[\cos\left(\tfrac{-\pi}{4}\right) + i\sin\left(\tfrac{-\pi}{4}\right)\right]$$

ii
$$\frac{(1 - i\sqrt{3})^{11}}{(1 - i)^{18}} = \frac{\left[2 \operatorname{cis}\left(\tfrac{-\pi}{3}\right)\right]^{11}}{\left[\sqrt{2} \operatorname{cis}\left(\tfrac{-\pi}{4}\right)\right]^{18}}$$
$$= \frac{2^{11} \operatorname{cis}\left(\tfrac{-11\pi}{3}\right)}{2^9 \operatorname{cis}\left(\tfrac{-9\pi}{2}\right)}$$
$$= 2^2 \operatorname{cis}\left(\tfrac{-11\pi}{3} - \tfrac{-9\pi}{2}\right)$$
$$= 4 \operatorname{cis}\left(\tfrac{9\pi}{2} - \tfrac{11\pi}{3}\right)$$
$$= 4 \operatorname{cis}\left(\tfrac{5\pi}{6}\right)$$
$$= 4\cos\left(\tfrac{5\pi}{6}\right) + 4\sin\left(\tfrac{5\pi}{6}\right)i$$
$$= 4\left(\tfrac{-\sqrt{3}}{2}\right) + 4\left(\tfrac{1}{2}\right)i$$
$$= -2\sqrt{3} + 2i$$

b $\quad z^5 = \sqrt{3} - i$ has $\left|\sqrt{3} - i\right| = \sqrt{3 + 1} = \sqrt{4} = 2$

$$\therefore \quad z^5 = 2\left(\tfrac{\sqrt{3}}{2} - \tfrac{1}{2}i\right)$$
$$= 2 \operatorname{cis}\left(\tfrac{-\pi}{6}\right)$$
$$= 2 \operatorname{cis}\left(-\tfrac{\pi}{6} + 2k\pi\right), \quad k \in \mathbb{Z}$$
$$\therefore \quad z = 2^{\frac{1}{5}} \operatorname{cis}\left(\frac{-\tfrac{\pi}{6} + k2\pi}{5}\right), \quad k \in \mathbb{Z} \quad \{\text{De Moivre}\}$$
$$\therefore \quad z = \sqrt[5]{2} \operatorname{cis}\left(\tfrac{-\pi}{30}\right), \quad \sqrt[5]{2} \operatorname{cis}\left(\tfrac{11\pi}{30}\right), \quad \sqrt[5]{2} \operatorname{cis}\left(\tfrac{23\pi}{30}\right),$$
$$\sqrt[5]{2} \operatorname{cis}\left(\tfrac{-13\pi}{30}\right), \quad \sqrt[5]{2} \operatorname{cis}\left(\tfrac{-25\pi}{30}\right).$$

484 a $\quad f'(x)$
$$= \lim_{h \to 0} \frac{f(x + h) - f(x)}{h}$$
$$= \lim_{h \to 0} \frac{3(x + h)^2 + 5(x + h) - 2 - (3x^2 + 5x - 2)}{h}$$
$$= \lim_{h \to 0} \frac{3x^2 + 6xh + 3h^2 + 5x + 5h - 2 - 3x^2 - 5x + 2}{h}$$
$$= \lim_{h \to 0} \frac{6xh + 3h^2 + 5h}{h}$$
$$= \lim_{h \to 0} 6x + 5 + 3h$$
$$= 6x + 5$$

b $\quad f(x) = \dfrac{e^x - e^{-x}}{e^x + e^{-x}}$

i $\quad f'(x)$
$$= \frac{(e^x + e^{-x})(e^x + e^{-x}) - (e^x - e^{-x})(e^x - e^{-x})}{(e^x + e^{-x})^2}$$
$$= \frac{(e^x + e^{-x})^2 - (e^x - e^{-x})^2}{(e^x + e^{-x})^2}$$
$$= \frac{(e^x + e^{-x} + e^x - e^{-x})(e^x + e^{-x} - e^x + e^{-x})}{(e^x + e^{-x})^2}$$
$$= \frac{(2e^x)(2e^{-x})}{(e^x + e^{-x})^2}$$
$$= \frac{4}{(e^x + e^{-x})^2} \quad \text{which is never zero.}$$

So, no stationary points exist.

ii
$$f'(x) = 4(e^x + e^{-x})^{-2}$$
$$\therefore \quad f''(x) = -8(e^x + e^{-x})^{-3}(e^x - e^{-x})$$
$$= \frac{-8(e^x - e^{-x})}{(e^x + e^{-x})^3}$$

iii
$$\int_0^{\ln 3} \frac{e^x - e^{-x}}{e^x + e^{-x}}\,dx \quad \begin{matrix} \leftarrow f'(x) \\ \leftarrow f(x) \end{matrix}$$
$$= \left[\ln\left|e^x + e^{-x}\right|\right]_0^{\ln 3}$$
$$= \ln\left(3 + \tfrac{1}{3}\right) - \ln(1 + 1)$$
$$= \ln\left(\tfrac{10}{3}\right) - \ln 2$$
$$= \ln\left(\tfrac{5}{3}\right)$$

485 a Let T_a be the maximum temperature in Adelaide then
$T_a \sim N(33, 3.5^2)$

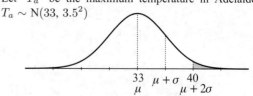

$P(T_a \geqslant 40) = \text{normalcdf}(40, E99, 33, 3.5) \approx 0.0228$

About 2.28% of January days in Adelaide will have temperatures above $40°$.

b Since the maximum temperature in Adelaide was $40°$, the minimum in Prague was $-12°$.

c Let T_p be the minimum temperature in Prague then
$T_p \sim N(-3.2, (4.9)^2)$ and
$$P(T_p < -12) = \text{normalcdf}(-E99, -12, -3.2, 4.9)$$
$$\approx 0.0363$$

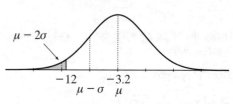

d Adelaide was 2 standard deviations above the mean while Prague was about 1.80 standard deviations below the mean. Hence the temperature in Adelaide was more extreme.

e $P(T_a \geqslant 46.4) = \text{normalcdf}(46.4, E99, 33, 33.5)$
$$\approx 6.444 \times 10^{-5}$$
Let b be the corresponding extreme temperature in Prague, then
$$P(T_p \leqslant b) = 6.444 \times 10^{-5}$$
$$P\left(Z \leqslant \frac{b - -3.2}{4.9}\right) = 6.444 \times 10^{-5}$$
$$\Rightarrow \quad \frac{b - -3.2}{4.9} = \text{invNorm}(6.444 \times 10^5)$$
$$\Rightarrow \quad b = -3.2 + 4.9 \times \text{invNorm}(6.444 \times 10^5)$$
$$\Rightarrow \quad b = -22.0$$
i.e., it would have to be $-22.0°$ in Prague.

SOLUTIONS TO EXAMINATION PRACTICE SET 15

486 $1 - \tan^2 x + \tan^4 x - \dots\dots$ is geometric with
$$u_1 = 1 \quad \text{and} \quad r = -\tan^2 x$$

a It converges when $-1 < r < 1$
$$\Rightarrow \quad -1 < -\tan^2 x < 1$$
$$\Rightarrow \quad -1 < \tan^2 x < 1$$
$$\Rightarrow \quad 0 \leqslant \tan^2 x < 1 \quad \{\text{as } a^2 \geqslant 0 \text{ for all } a\}$$
$$\Rightarrow \quad -1 < \tan x < 1$$
$$\Rightarrow \quad x \in \left]0, \tfrac{\pi}{4}\right[\text{ or } \left]\tfrac{3\pi}{4}, \pi\right[\text{ or } \left]\pi, \tfrac{5\pi}{4}\right[\text{ or } \left]\tfrac{7\pi}{4}, 2\pi\right[.$$

b $S_\infty = \dfrac{u_1}{1 - r} = \dfrac{1}{1 + \tan^2 x}$

$\Rightarrow \quad S_\infty = \dfrac{1}{\sec^2 x} = \cos^2 x$

c When $S_\infty = \frac{1}{2}, \quad \cos^2 x = \frac{1}{2}$

$\Rightarrow \quad \cos x = \pm \dfrac{1}{\sqrt{2}}$

$\Rightarrow \quad x = \frac{\pi}{4}, \frac{3\pi}{4}, \frac{5\pi}{4}, \frac{7\pi}{4}$

487 $a + \dfrac{a}{b^2} + \dfrac{a}{b^4} + \ldots\ldots$ is geometric with $u_1 = a$ and $r = \dfrac{1}{b^2}$

a It converges where $-1 < r < 1$ i.e., $-1 < \dfrac{1}{b^2} < 1$

But $b^2 > 0$ for all b $\Rightarrow \quad 0 < \dfrac{1}{b^2} < 1$

$\Rightarrow \quad b^2 > 1$

$\Rightarrow \quad b < -1$ or $b > 1$

or $b \in \,]-\infty, -1[\, \cup \,]-1, \infty[$

b $S_\infty = \dfrac{u_1}{1-r} = \left(\dfrac{a}{1 - \frac{1}{b^2}}\right) \times \dfrac{b^2}{b^2}$ i.e., $S_\infty = \dfrac{ab^2}{b^2 - 1}$

c $0.\overline{32} = \dfrac{32}{10^2} + \dfrac{32}{10^4} + \dfrac{32}{10^6} + \ldots\ldots$

$= \dfrac{32}{10^2}\left(1 + \dfrac{1}{10^2} + \dfrac{1}{10^4} + \ldots\ldots\right)$

$= \dfrac{32}{100}\left(\dfrac{1 \times 10^2}{100 - 1}\right)$

$= \dfrac{32}{99}$

488 a The 7 letters are all different.

$\therefore \quad 7! = 5040$ different words.

b

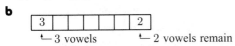

So, there are $3 \times 2 \times 5! = 720$ ways

c These 3 vowels can be ordered in 3! ways.

Considering the vowels as one block, this block plus the other 4 can be ordered in 5! ways.

$\therefore$ total numbers $= 3! \times 5! = 720$

489 If $z = R\,\text{cis}\,\theta, \quad 1 < R < 2$

a $-z = -R\,\text{cis}\,\theta = R\,\text{cis}\,(\theta + \pi)$

b $\overline{z} = R\,\text{cis}\,(-\theta)$

c $iz = R\,\text{cis}\,(\theta + \frac{\pi}{2})$

d $z^2 = R^2\,\text{cis}\,(2\theta),$
$\quad 2 < R^2 < 4$

e $\sqrt{z} = \sqrt{R}\,\text{cis}\,\left(\frac{\theta}{2}\right),$
$\quad 1 < \sqrt{R} < \sqrt{2}$

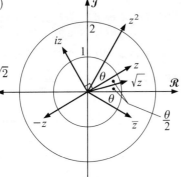

490 $(f \circ g)(x) = f(g(x))$

$= f(2x^3)$

$= 2(2x^3) - 1$

$= 4x^3 - 1$

So the function $(f \circ g)^{-1}$ is $x = 4y^3 - 1$

i.e., $4y^3 = x + 1$

$y^3 = \dfrac{x+1}{4}$

$y = \left(\dfrac{x+1}{4}\right)^{\frac{1}{3}}$

So, $(f \circ g)^{-1} : x \mapsto \left(\dfrac{x+1}{4}\right)^{\frac{1}{3}}$

491 a Graphs of $y = f(x)$ and $y = |\,f(x)\,|$.

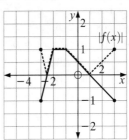

b The y-intercept of $y = f(x)$ is $f(0) = 2$, hence the y-intercept of $y = \dfrac{1}{f(x)}$ is $\dfrac{1}{f(0)} = \frac{1}{2}$.

c

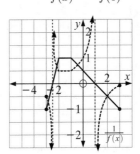

Graph of $y = f(x)$ and $y = \dfrac{1}{f(x)}$.

492 a Since the graph is concave down, $a < 0$.

b Since the y-intercept is negative $c < 0$.

c $ax^2 + bx = -c \Leftrightarrow ax^2 + bx + c = 0$
From the graph this has exactly one solution.

d $b^2 - 4ac = 0$ since the equation $ax^2 + bx + c = 0$ has a single solution.

e $y = ax^2 + bx + c = a\left[x^2 + \dfrac{b}{a}x\right] + c$

$= a\left[\left(x + \dfrac{b}{2a}\right)^2 - \dfrac{b^2}{4a^2}\right] + c$

$= a\left(x + \dfrac{b}{2a}\right)^2 - \dfrac{b^2}{4a} + c$

$= a\left(x + \dfrac{b}{2a}\right)^2 + \dfrac{-b^2 + 4ac}{4a}$

$\Rightarrow h = -\dfrac{b}{2a}$ and $k = \dfrac{-b^2 + 4ac}{4a}$ where (h, k) is the vertex $\therefore$ axis of symmetry is $x = -\dfrac{b}{2a}$

For the points $x_1 = -\dfrac{b}{2a} + k$ and

$x_2 = -\dfrac{b}{2a} - k$

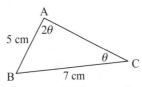

we have $\left(x_1 + \dfrac{b}{2a}\right)^2 = \left(x_2 + \dfrac{b}{2a}\right)^2 = k^2$

and hence y is symmetric about $x = -\dfrac{b}{2a}$

493

By the Sine Rule, $\dfrac{\sin 2\theta}{7} = \dfrac{\sin \theta}{5}$

$\therefore \quad 5\sin 2\theta = 7\sin\theta$

$\therefore \quad 10\sin\theta\cos\theta - 7\sin\theta = 0$

$\therefore \quad \sin\theta(10\cos\theta - 7) = 0$

$\therefore \quad \cos\theta = \frac{7}{10}$ as $\sin\theta \neq 0$

$\therefore \quad \theta = \arccos(0.7) \approx 45.6°$

494
$$\sin 2x + \cos 2x = 1, \quad 0 \leqslant x \leqslant 2\pi$$
$$\Rightarrow \quad 2\sin x \cos x + 1 - 2\sin^2 x = 1$$
$$\Rightarrow \quad 2\sin x \cos x - 2\sin^2 x = 0$$
$$\Rightarrow \quad 2\sin x(\cos x - \sin x) = 0$$
$$\Rightarrow \quad \sin x = 0 \quad \text{or} \quad \cos x = \sin x$$
$$\Rightarrow \quad \sin x = 0 \quad \text{or} \quad \tan x = 1$$
$$\Rightarrow \quad x = 0, \tfrac{\pi}{4}, \pi, \tfrac{5\pi}{4}, 2\pi$$

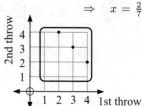

495 $y = x \arcsin\left(\tfrac{x}{3} - 0.5\right), \quad -1 \leqslant x \leqslant 3$

$y(-1) = -1 \arcsin\left(-\tfrac{5}{6}\right) \approx 0.985$

$y(3) = 3 \arcsin(0.5) = \tfrac{\pi}{2}$

from gcalc $y_{\min} = -0.190$, where $x = 0.742$

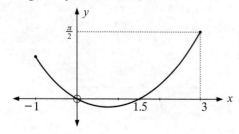

496 In augmented form, we use row reduction:
$$\begin{bmatrix} 1 & -1 & -1 & | & 1 \\ 2 & 1 & 1 & | & 2 \\ 4 & -1 & -1 & | & k \end{bmatrix}$$
$$\sim \begin{bmatrix} 1 & -1 & -1 & | & 1 \\ 0 & 3 & 3 & | & 0 \\ 0 & 3 & 3 & | & k-4 \end{bmatrix} \quad \begin{matrix} \\ R_2 \to R_2 - 2R_1 \\ R_3 \to R_3 - 4R_1 \end{matrix}$$
$$\sim \begin{bmatrix} 1 & -1 & -1 & | & 1 \\ 0 & 3 & 3 & | & 0 \\ 0 & 0 & 0 & | & k-4 \end{bmatrix} \quad \begin{matrix} \\ \\ R_3 \to R_3 - R_2 \end{matrix}$$

a   The system has an infinite number of solutions if $k = 4$.
b   The system has no solutions if $k \neq 4$.

497 Area of the parallelogram is $|\mathbf{a} \times \mathbf{b}|$ where $\mathbf{a} \times \mathbf{b}$
$$= \begin{vmatrix} \mathbf{i} & \mathbf{j} & \mathbf{k} \\ 3 & -4 & 1 \\ 2 & 1 & -5 \end{vmatrix} = \mathbf{i}(20-1) - \mathbf{j}(-15-2) + \mathbf{k}(3--8)$$
$$= 19\mathbf{i} - 17\mathbf{j} + 11\mathbf{k}$$

Area of parallelogram is $\sqrt{19^2 + 17^2 + 11^2} \approx 27.8 \text{ units}^2$

498 If R is perpendicular to both P and Q, the normal $\mathbf{n}$ of R is perpendicular to the normal of P and Q.

i.e., $\mathbf{n}$ is parallel to $\begin{bmatrix} 6 \\ -2 \\ 3 \end{bmatrix} \times \begin{bmatrix} 1 \\ -3 \\ 5 \end{bmatrix} = \begin{vmatrix} \mathbf{i} & \mathbf{j} & \mathbf{k} \\ 6 & -2 & 3 \\ 1 & -3 & 5 \end{vmatrix}$
$$= \mathbf{i}(-10+9) - \mathbf{j}(30-3) + \mathbf{k}(-18+2)$$
$$= -\mathbf{i} - 27\mathbf{j} - 16\mathbf{k}$$

An equation of R is $\begin{bmatrix} x \\ y \\ z \end{bmatrix} \cdot \begin{bmatrix} -1 \\ -27 \\ -16 \end{bmatrix} = \begin{bmatrix} -1 \\ -27 \\ -16 \end{bmatrix} \cdot \begin{bmatrix} 2 \\ 2 \\ 3 \end{bmatrix}$

i.e., $-x - 27y - 16z = -104$
i.e., $x + 27y + 16z = 104$

499 a The line has direction $\begin{bmatrix} 1 \\ 2 \\ -2 \end{bmatrix}$

A point on the line, say A, is $(-1, 1, 1)$.
Let B be the point $(1, 3, -2)$ on the plane.

Then $\overrightarrow{AB} = \begin{bmatrix} 2 \\ 2 \\ -3 \end{bmatrix}$ and a normal to the plane is

$$\begin{bmatrix} 1 \\ 2 \\ -2 \end{bmatrix} \times \begin{bmatrix} 2 \\ 2 \\ -3 \end{bmatrix} = \begin{vmatrix} \mathbf{i} & \mathbf{j} & \mathbf{k} \\ 1 & 2 & -2 \\ 2 & 2 & -3 \end{vmatrix}$$

$$= \mathbf{i}(-6+4) - \mathbf{j}(-3--4+) + \mathbf{k}(2-4)$$
$$= -2\mathbf{i} - \mathbf{j} - 2\mathbf{k}$$

An equation of the plane is
$$\begin{bmatrix} -2 \\ -1 \\ -2 \end{bmatrix} \cdot \begin{bmatrix} x \\ y \\ z \end{bmatrix} = \begin{bmatrix} -2 \\ -1 \\ -2 \end{bmatrix} \cdot \begin{bmatrix} 1 \\ 3 \\ -2 \end{bmatrix}$$
i.e., $-2x - y - 2z = -1$
i.e., $2x + y + 2z = 1$

b Distance of plane to $(0, 0, 0)$ is
$$\frac{|2(0) + 1(0) + 2(0) - 1|}{\sqrt{2^2 + 1^2 + 2^2}} = \tfrac{1}{3} \text{ unit}$$

500 As the probabilities add to 1, $\tfrac{2}{7} + \tfrac{1}{3} + x + \tfrac{2}{21} = 1$
$$\Rightarrow \quad 6 + 7 + 21x + 2 = 21$$
$$\Rightarrow \quad 21x = 6$$
$$\Rightarrow \quad x = \tfrac{2}{7}$$

A total of 6 after two rolls can only occur if we get
4 and 2   or   3 and 3
or   2 and 4
with probability of occuring
$$= \tfrac{2}{21} \times \tfrac{1}{3} + \tfrac{2}{7} \times \tfrac{2}{7} + \tfrac{1}{3} \times \tfrac{2}{21} = \tfrac{64}{441}.$$

501 a Total number of students is 16.
We can select 7 from 16 in $\binom{16}{7} = 11\,440$ ways.

b The number of ways of selecting a committee with **both** Haakon and Josefine is $\binom{14}{5} = 2002$.
So if they cannot be both on the committee the number of ways is $\binom{16}{7} - \binom{14}{5} = 9438$

c If there are more boys than girls, the committee must be one of the following:
For 4 boys 3 girls,   number is $\binom{9}{4}\binom{7}{3}$
For 5 boys 2 girls,   number is $\binom{9}{5}\binom{7}{2}$
For 6 boys 1 girl,   number is $\binom{9}{6}\binom{7}{1}$
For 7 boys 0 girls,   number is $\binom{9}{7}$

Total is $\binom{9}{4}\binom{7}{3} + \binom{9}{5}\binom{7}{2} + \binom{9}{6}\binom{7}{1} + \binom{9}{7} = 7680$

502 Let X be the score on a mathematics test then
$X \sim N(64, (8.352)^2)$
$P(X \geqslant 80) = \text{normcdf}(80, E99, 64, 8.352) \approx 0.0277$

503 a   Let $y = \dfrac{x}{\sqrt{x-6}} = \dfrac{x}{(x-6)^{\frac{1}{2}}}$

$$\therefore \quad \frac{dy}{dx} = \frac{1(x-6)^{\frac{1}{2}} - x\left(\frac{1}{2}\right)(x-6)^{-\frac{1}{2}}}{(x-6)^1}$$
$$= \frac{\dfrac{\sqrt{x-6}}{1} - \dfrac{x}{2\sqrt{x-6}}}{(x-6)}$$
$$= \frac{2(x-6) - x}{2(x-6)^{\frac{3}{2}}}$$
$$= \frac{x-12}{2(x-6)^{\frac{3}{2}}}$$

b $\dfrac{dy}{dx} = 0 \iff x - 12 = 0 \iff x = 12$

Sign diag. of $\dfrac{dy}{dx}$ is:

$\therefore$ x-coordinate of minimum turning point is 12.

504 $y = 10 - xe^x$

Let P be at $(u, 10 - ue^u)$

and let A be the area of OABP.

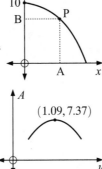

$$\therefore \quad A = u(10 - ue^u) = 10u - u^2e^u$$
$$\therefore \quad \frac{dA}{du} = 10 - \left[2ue^u + u^2e^u\right]$$
$$= 10 - ue^u(u + 2)$$

From a gcalc the graph
of A against u is:

$(1.09, 7.37)$

$\Rightarrow \quad$ maximum area ≈ 7.37 units^2

505
$$\int_0^{\frac{\pi}{2}} \frac{\sin x}{1 + \cos x}\, dx$$

$\left\{ \begin{array}{l} u = 1 + \cos x \\[4pt] \dfrac{du}{dx} = -\sin x \\[4pt] u(0) = 2 \\[4pt] u\left(\frac{\pi}{2}\right) = 1 \end{array} \right.$

$$= \int_0^{\frac{\pi}{2}} \frac{1}{u}\left(-\frac{du}{dx}\right) dx$$
$$= -\int_2^1 \frac{1}{u}\, du$$
$$= \int_1^2 \frac{1}{u}\, du$$
$$= \left[\ln |u|\right]_1^2$$
$$= \ln 2 - \ln 1$$
$$= \ln 2$$

506

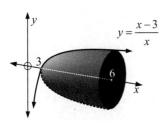

$y = \dfrac{x-3}{x}$

Volume $= \pi \int_3^6 y^2\, dx$

$$= \pi \int_3^6 \left(1 - \frac{3}{x}\right)^2 dx$$
$$= \pi \int_3^6 1 - \frac{6}{x} + 9x^{-2}\, dx$$
$$= \pi \left[x - 6\ln|x| + \frac{9x^{-1}}{-1}\right]_3^6$$
$$= \pi \left\{\left(6 - 6\ln 6 - \tfrac{3}{2}\right) - \left(3 - 6\ln 3 - 3\right)\right\}$$
$$= \pi \left\{\tfrac{9}{2} - 6\ln 6 + 6\ln 3\right\}$$
$$= \pi \left(\tfrac{9}{2} + 6\ln(\tfrac{1}{2})\right)$$
$$= \pi \left(\tfrac{9}{2} - 6\ln 2\right) \text{ units}^3$$

507
$$\int \sqrt{4 - x^2}\, dx \qquad\qquad x = 2\sin\theta$$

$\qquad\qquad\qquad\qquad\qquad\qquad \dfrac{dx}{d\theta} = 2\cos\theta$

$$= \int \sqrt{4 - 4\sin^2\theta}\, 2\cos\theta\, d\theta$$
$$= \int 2\sqrt{1 - \sin^2\theta}\, 2\cos\theta\, d\theta$$
$$= 4 \int \cos^2\theta\, d\theta$$
$$= 4 \int \tfrac{1}{2} + \tfrac{1}{2}\cos 2\theta\, d\theta$$
$$= 4 \left\{\tfrac{1}{2}\theta + \tfrac{1}{4}\sin 2\theta\right\} + c$$
$$= 2\theta + \sin 2\theta + c$$
$$= 2\theta + 2\sin\theta\cos\theta + c$$
$$= 2\arcsin\left(\tfrac{x}{2}\right) + 2\left(\tfrac{x}{2}\right)\left(\frac{\sqrt{4 - x^2}}{2}\right) + c$$
$$= 2\arcsin\left(\tfrac{x}{2}\right) + \tfrac{1}{2}x\sqrt{4 - x^2} + c$$

(right triangle with hypotenuse 2, side x, angle θ, and base $\sqrt{4 - x^2}$)

508
$$\int_0^a \frac{x}{x^2 + 1}\, dx = 1$$
$$\therefore \quad \frac{1}{2}\int_0^a \frac{2x}{x^2 + 1}\, dx = 1$$
$$\Rightarrow \quad \int_0^a \frac{2x}{x^2 + 1}\, dx = 2$$
$$\Rightarrow \quad \ln\left|a^2 + 1\right| = 2$$
$$\Rightarrow \quad a^2 + 1 = \pm e^2$$
$$\Rightarrow \quad a^2 = \pm e^2 - 1$$
$$\Rightarrow \quad a = \pm\sqrt{\pm e^2 - 1}$$
$$\Rightarrow \quad a = \sqrt{e^2 - 1}, \quad a > 0$$

509 $f(x) = x^n$

a i
$$f(x + h)$$
$$= (x + h)^n$$
$$= x^n + \binom{n}{1}x^{n-1}h + \binom{n}{2}x^{n-2}h^2 + \ldots\ldots$$
$$\ldots\ldots + \binom{n}{n-2}x^2h^{n-2} + \binom{n}{n-1}xh^{n-1} + h^n$$

ii
$$f'(x)$$
$$= \lim_{h \to 0} \frac{f(x + h) - f(x)}{h}$$
$$= \lim_{h \to 0} \frac{x^n + \binom{n}{1}x^{n-1}h + \binom{n}{2}x^{n-2}h^2 + \ldots\ldots + nxh^{n-1} + h^n - x^n}{h}$$
$$= \lim_{h \to 0} \binom{n}{1}x^{n-1} + \binom{n}{2}x^{n-2}h + \ldots\ldots + h^{n-1}$$
$$= nx^{n-1} + 0 + 0 + \ldots\ldots + 0$$
$$= nx^{n-1}$$

b i
$$v = 4t^3 - 9t^2 + 2, \quad t \geqslant 0$$
$$\therefore \quad a = 12t^2 - 18t \text{ ms}^{-2}$$

ii $a = 6t(2t - 3)$ with sign diag.:

(sign diagram: $-$ then $+$, zeros at 0 and $\frac{3}{2}$)

v is a min. where $\dfrac{dv}{dt} = 0$

i.e., $a = 0, \quad t = \tfrac{3}{2}$

$$\therefore \quad v_{min} = 4\left(\tfrac{27}{8}\right) - 9\left(\tfrac{9}{4}\right) + 2$$
$$= \tfrac{27}{2} - \tfrac{81}{4} + 2$$
$$= -\tfrac{19}{4} \text{ ms}^{-1}$$

iii $s = \int v\, dt = \dfrac{4t^4}{4} - \dfrac{9t^3}{3} + 2t + c$
$$= t^4 - 3t^3 + 2t + c$$

But $s(0) = -6 \quad \Rightarrow \quad c = -6$

$\therefore \quad s = t^4 - 3t^3 + 2t - 6$ metres

and $s = 0$ when

$$\Rightarrow \quad t^3(t - 3) + 2(t - 3) = 0$$
$$\Rightarrow \quad (t - 3)(t^3 + 2) = 0$$
$$\Rightarrow \quad t = 3 \quad \text{or} \quad -\sqrt[3]{2}$$
$$\Rightarrow \quad t = 3 \quad \{\text{as } t > 0\}$$

$\therefore$ first passes through O when $t = 3$ sec.

iv Total distance travelled in $[0, 5]$

$$= \int_0^5 |v|\, dt$$
$$= \int_0^5 \left|4t^3 - 9t^2 + 2\right| dt$$
$$\approx 2140 \text{ m} \quad \{\text{gcalc}\}$$

510 Let X be the score in the Biology exam then
$X \sim N(56, 30.512^2)$

a $P(X \geqslant 72)$ = normalcdf(72, E99, 56, 30.512)
$= 0.3$
About 30% gained a score of "6" or better.

b $P(X \geqslant 40)$ = normalcdf(40, E99, 56, 30.512)
$\doteqdot 0.70$
About 70% passed the exam.

c $P(X \geqslant 94)$ = normalcdf(94, E99, 56, 30.512)
$= 0.1065$
So 10.65% of students would gain a mark of 94% or more, and poor Micah would just miss out on a score of 7, but he would get a score of 6.

d Let E be the score in English then $E \sim N(63, 18.31)$
and $P(E \geqslant 87)$ = normalcdf(87, E99, 63, 18.31)
$= 0.0950$

and Micah scored better in English than in Biology.
30% of students received a 6 in Biology.

If 30% receive a 6 or better in English, if the mark is b then $P(E \geqslant b) = 0.30$

i.e., $P(E \leqslant b) = 0.70$ and b = invNorm(0.7, 63, 18.31)
$= 72.6\%$

Only 10% of the students receive a 7 in Biology.
Let s be the mark required to get a 7 in English then
$P(E \geqslant s) = 0.1$ i.e., $P(E \leqslant s) = 0.9$
and s = invNorm(0.9, 63, 18.31) $\doteqdot 86.5$
A grade of 86.5% of better would get a 7 in English.

From **a** 30% of the students receive a 6 (or better) in Biology. Let t be the mark required to get a 6 (or better) in English, then $P(E \geqslant t) = 0.30$ or $P(E \leqslant t) = 0.70$
i.e., t = invNorm(0.7, 63, 18.31) ≈ 72.6

i.e., students must get 72.6% or better to get a 6 in English.

511 a $x = 6 + 2\cos\left(\frac{4\pi}{25}t + \frac{\pi}{3}\right)$

  i Tide is highest when $\cos\left(\frac{4\pi}{25}t + \frac{\pi}{3}\right) = 1$

    $\Rightarrow \quad \frac{4\pi}{25}t + \frac{\pi}{3} = k2\pi$

    $\Rightarrow \quad \frac{4\pi}{25}t = -\frac{\pi}{3} + k2\pi$

    $\Rightarrow \quad 4\pi t = -\frac{25\pi}{3} + k50\pi$

    $\Rightarrow \quad t = -\frac{25}{12} + k\frac{25}{2}, \quad k = 0, 1, 2, 3, 4, ...$

    when $k = 1$, $t = -\frac{25}{12} + \frac{25}{2} = \frac{125}{12}$
           $t \approx 10.41666......$
           $t = 10$ hours 25 minutes
    $\therefore$ first high tide at 10:25 pm Sept 1

  ii period $= \frac{25}{2}$ {coefficient of k}
          $= 12\frac{1}{2}$
    i.e., $12\frac{1}{2}$ hours between high tides.

  iii If $x = 5.5$,
    $6 + 2\cos\left(\frac{4\pi}{25}t + \frac{\pi}{3}\right) = 5.5$

    $\Rightarrow \quad 2\cos\left(\frac{4\pi}{25}t + \frac{\pi}{3}\right) = -0.5$

    $\Rightarrow \quad \cos\left(\frac{4\pi}{25}t + \frac{\pi}{3}\right) = -0.25$

    3:00 pm on Sept 2 is $t = 27$
    So we seek the solution when t is first > 27.
    From a gcalc, $t \approx 31.788...$
    So, first time is 31 h 47 min after 12:00 midday Sept 1
    i.e., 7:47 pm September 2.

b i By the Cosine Rule:

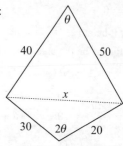

$$x^2 = 40^2 + 50^2 - 2 \times 40 \times 50\cos\theta$$
$$\text{and} \quad x^2 = 30^2 + 20^2 - 2 \times 30 \times 20\cos 2\theta$$

$\Rightarrow \quad 1600 + 2500 - 4000\cos\theta = 900 + 400 - 1200\cos 2\theta$
$\Rightarrow \quad 4100 - 4000\cos\theta = 1300 - 1200\cos 2\theta$
$\Rightarrow \quad 41 - 40\cos\theta = 13 - 12\cos 2\theta$
$\Rightarrow \quad 3\cos 2\theta - 10\cos\theta + 7 = 0$
$\Rightarrow \quad 3(2\cos^2\theta - 1) - 10\cos\theta + 7 = 0$
$\Rightarrow \quad 6\cos^2\theta - 3 - 10\cos\theta + 7 = 0$
$\Rightarrow \quad 6\cos^2\theta - 10\cos\theta + 4 = 0$
$\Rightarrow \quad 3\cos^2\theta - 5\cos\theta + 2 = 0$
$\Rightarrow \quad (3\cos\theta - 2)(\cos\theta - 1) = 0$
$\Rightarrow \quad \cos\theta = \frac{2}{3}$ or 1
where $\cos\theta = 1$ is impossible
Thus $\cos\theta = \frac{2}{3}$
$\Rightarrow \quad \theta = \arccos\left(\frac{2}{3}\right) \quad (\approx 48.2°)$

ii As $\cos\theta = \frac{2}{3}$
$\sin\theta = \frac{\sqrt{5}}{3}$

and $\sin 2\theta = 2\sin\theta\cos\theta = 2\left(\frac{\sqrt{5}}{3}\right)\left(\frac{2}{3}\right) = \frac{4\sqrt{5}}{9}$

Area $= \frac{1}{2}(40 \times 50 \times \sin\theta) + \frac{1}{2}(30 \times 20 \times \sin 2\theta)$
$= 1000\sin\theta + 300\sin 2\theta$
$= 1000\left(\frac{\sqrt{5}}{3}\right) + 300\left(\frac{4\sqrt{5}}{9}\right)$
$= 1000\left(\frac{\sqrt{5}}{3}\right) + 100\left(\frac{4\sqrt{5}}{3}\right)$
$= \frac{\sqrt{5}}{3}(1000 + 400)$
$= \frac{1400}{3}\sqrt{5}$ m^2

NOTES

NOTES

NOTES

NOTES

NOTES

NOTES